$$R_1 = \frac{R_a R_b + R_b R_c + R_c R_a}{R_a}$$

$$R_a \quad \frac{R_1 R_2}{R_1 + R_2 + R_3}$$

$$R_\Delta = \frac{\text{sum of all possible Products}}{\text{opposite}}$$

$$R_Y = \frac{\text{Product of adjacents}}{\text{sum}}$$

TRANSIENTS
IN
ELECTRICAL CIRCUITS

GLADWYN V. LAGO

ASSOCIATE PROFESSOR OF ELECTRICAL ENGINEERING
UNIVERSITY OF MISSOURI

and

DONALD L. WAIDELICH

PROFESSOR OF ELECTRICAL ENGINEERING
UNIVERSITY OF MISSOURI

THE RONALD PRESS COMPANY · NEW YORK

To Our Juniors

PREFACE

The increasing use of pulses in electronic circuitry, automatic control devices, and analog and digital computers during the last few years has made the study of transients every bit as important as the standard a.c. circuit theory. This book on electrical transients has been written for junior and senior electrical engineering students. It assumes that these students have had courses in differential and integral calculus and at least one introductory course in electrical circuit theory. Aside from these assumptions, the book has been designed to be adaptable to variously organized curricula.

In the first four chapters, attention has been paid to the classical method of solving ordinary linear differential equations by using electrical circuits as examples. Circuits containing current sources as well as voltage sources are analyzed. The concept of duality is introduced in these chapters and is used throughout the book.

After the classical method is explained, the Laplace transform method of solving integro-differential equations is presented. A short table of transform pairs is developed in the text and a much longer table is contained in an appendix. These tables are used in such a manner that only a minimum knowledge of functions of a complex variable is necessary. The operational impedance concept is developed, and the poles and zeros of the impedance function are used to show the correlation between transient response and a.c. steady-state response. Various methods of factoring high-degree polynomials are set forth in such a manner as to familiarize the student with methods normally used in advanced servomechanism texts.

A number of applications is presented. One such application is concerned with the steady-state response to nonsinusoidal wave shapes by use of recurrent transient methods. Another application extends circuit theory methods to mechanical and electromechanical systems. The concept of electrical analogues of these systems is explained and used extensively. A third application is concerned with the transient analysis of servomechanisms.

The book concludes with three chapters devoted to the theory and application of Fourier series, integrals, and transforms in the solution of various circuit problems. The similarities and differences of Fourier and Laplace transforms are pointed out. No work on the solution of partial differential equations such as those of transmission lines and field theory has been included because it is felt that this properly belongs to a second course in the subject.

It is a pleasure for the authors to acknowledge the helpful suggestions and encouragement received from many students and colleagues at the University of Missouri and elsewhere. The authors wish to acknowledge particularly the help of their former colleagues, Bert Gastineau and Dr. John N. Warfield. The authors are also especially indebted to Hugh Kessinger, Charles Kost, Miller Cravens, E. C. Hausman, and Paul Klock for their help in preparing classroom notes and original drawings for the illustrations, and to Mrs. Eldred Holcomb and Mrs. Laverne Wiggs, who so painstakingly did the typing.

G. V. LAGO
D. L. WAIDELICH

Columbia, Missouri
   January, 1958

CONTENTS

TRANSIENTS
IN
ELECTRICAL CIRCUITS

CHAPTER 1

CIRCUITS WITH ONE TYPE OF ELEMENT

1–1. Introduction. A circuit containing elements of only one type, such as resistance, for example, is an idealized version of an actual circuit. All resistors have some inductance and capacitance associated with them; all capacitors have some resistance and inductance; and all inductors have some resistance and capacitance. Therefore the equivalent circuit of the most simple circuit would be a combination of R, C, and L. Most circuit elements, however, are made with two of the three characteristics carefully minimized so that the element is predominantly the third. In a similar manner, the voltage source is idealized in assuming that it is a constant-voltage source of E volts and zero internal resistance. Thus, before analyzing circuits with complicated combinations of R, C, and L, simpler circuits containing only one type of element should be analyzed.

In the following investigation of the circuit elements, a known voltage is applied to the element; a known current is passed through the element; a switch is closed, placing the element across a constant-voltage source of E volts, or a switch is opened, placing the element in series with a constant-current source of I amperes.

1–2. The R Circuit. The relationship between voltage and current in a circuit containing only resistance is the well-known one given by Ohm's law:

$$e_R = iR \qquad (1\text{-}2\text{-}1)$$

Fig. 1–2–1 shows the reference direction for the current i and the reference direction for the voltage e_R. The reference direction for the current i is taken to mean that, if at some instant the current is positive, it exists in

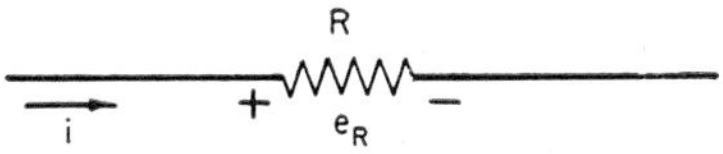

FIG. 1–2–1

the direction shown by the arrow; if, however, the instantaneous i is negative, the current exists in the opposite direction. In a similar fashion the $+$ and $-$ marks for the voltage e_R indicate the direction of e_R when e_R is positive, whereas when e_R is negative the positive end of e_R is that marked by the $-$ sign.

As the current is directly proportional to the voltage, the polarity of e_R can be reversed only if the current is reversed. If some arbitrary current function is passed through R, the voltage e_R will have exactly the same shape as the current. This is shown in Fig. 1-2-2. Conversely, if some

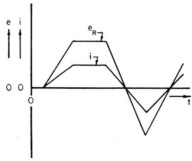

Fig. 1-2-2

arbitrary voltage function is placed across R, the current will have exactly the same shape as the voltage. Fig. 1-2-2 again demonstrates this situation.

If a switch is closed connecting R across a voltage source at $t = 0$ as shown in Fig. 1-2-3a, the current will jump to the value E/R instantaneously, as indicated in Fig. 1-2-3b. The steady-state value is reached

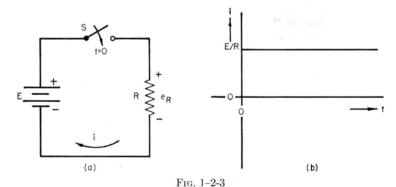

(a)

(b)

Fig. 1-2-3

instantly with no transient period. The power dissipated in a resistor R is

$$p = e_R i = i^2 R \tag{1-2-2}$$

while the energy dissipated is

$$W = \int_0^t p \, dt = \int_0^t i^2 R \, dt \tag{1-2-3}$$

In this book it is assumed that the resistance R is constant. Such a resistance is termed a linear type of element. If the resistance varies markedly with the current i, the voltage e, the time t, or perhaps some other variable such as temperature or pressure, it is usually called a nonlinear resistance. An example of a nonlinear resistor is an ordinary incandescent light bulb. Special methods of analysis are needed for most problems involving nonlinear resistors. Most resistors which are assumed to be linear may exhibit very definite nonlinear characteristics if the usual operating range is greatly exceeded, as, for example, when the current is many times the rated current.

1–3. Meaning of $t = 0$. In circuit analysis it is common to speak of conditions at the time $t = 0$ or, more exactly, at the time $t = 0+$. What is meant by this is the limit of the function of t as t approaches zero through positive values. If, for example, the function of time being considered is the current shown in Fig. 1–3-1, the current is zero up to $t = 0$; at $t = 0$

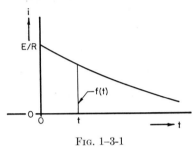

FIG. 1–3-1

it jumps to a value of E/R and then decreases. The curve at $t = 0$ is discontinuous, but by the current at $t = 0+$ is meant the value E/R which is the limit of $f(t)$ as t approaches zero through positive values.

1–4. The C Circuit. The relationship between voltage and charge on a capacitor is given by

$$e_c = \frac{q}{C} \tag{1–4-1}$$

where both the charge q and the voltage e_c are of the same polarity on the capacitor. If there is an initial charge $q(0)$ on the capacitor, which in turn

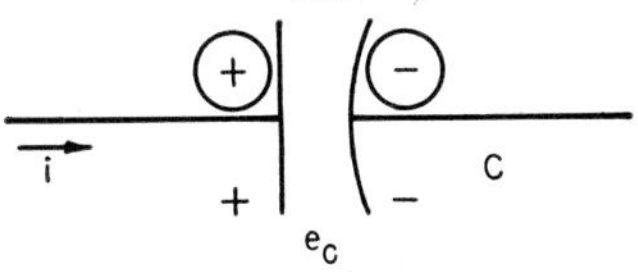

FIG. 1–4-1

implies an initial voltage $e(0) = q(0)/C$ and if $e(0)$ is of the polarity shown by the circled polarity marks $\oplus$, $\ominus$ in Fig. 1–4-1, then

$$q = \int_0^t i \, dt + q(0) \tag{1–4-2}$$

giving

$$e_c = \frac{1}{C} \int_0^t i \, dt + \frac{q(0)}{C} = \frac{1}{C} \int_0^t i \, dt + e(0) \tag{1–4-3}$$

The reference direction for current and the polarity reference for e_c are shown in Fig. 1–4-1.

The polarities of $q(0)$ and q may be the same, as indicated in Fig. 1–4-1, or they may be opposite. This permits solution of the problems without need of remembering which polarity for $q(0)$ is positive. If, for example, $q(0)$ is on C with the reverse polarity to that shown in Fig. 1–4-1, the analogous equation to Eq. 1–4-3 is

$$e_c = \frac{1}{C}\int_0^t i\,dt - \frac{q(0)}{C} = \frac{1}{C}\int_0^t i\,dt - e(0) \qquad (1\text{--}4\text{--}4)$$

Let it be assumed that a current as in Fig. 1–4-2a exists in a 50-μf capacitor, that the initial charge on C is zero, and that the voltage e_c is

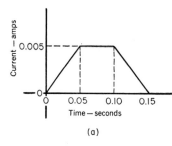

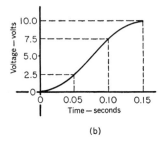

(a)   (b)

Fig. 1–4-2

desired. The problem can best be solved by working in the intervals of time in which an equation for the current can be easily written. Between $t = 0$ and $t = 0.05$, i has the equation $i = (0.005/0.05)t = 0.1\,t$. The equation for the voltage in this interval is

$$e_c = \frac{1}{C}\int_0^t i\,dt = \frac{1}{50\times 10^{-6}}\int_0^t 0.1\,t\,dt = \left[\frac{0.1\,t^2}{2}\times\frac{1}{50\times 10^{-6}}\right]_0^t = 10^3 t^2 \quad (1\text{--}4\text{--}5)$$

At $t = 0.05$ the value of e_c, as found by substituting in Eq. 1–4-5, is $e_c = 10^3(0.05)^2 = 2.5$ volts. This value of e_c becomes the $e(0)$ for the next interval of time.

For convenience in the next step the $t = 0$ axis is shifted over to the original $t = 0.05$ sec point. The equation for i in the interval between the new $t = 0$ and $t = 0.05$ is $i = 0.005$. The equation for the voltage in this interval is

$$e_c = \frac{1}{50\times 10^{-6}}\int_0^t 0.005\,dt + 2.5 = \left[\frac{0.005\,t}{50\times 10^{-6}}\right]_0^t + 2.5 = 10^2\,t + 2.5 \quad (1\text{--}4\text{--}6)$$

In order to find the voltage at the original $t = 0.1$ sec, $t = 0.05$ is substituted in Eq. 1–4-6, giving $e_c = 10^2(0.05) + 2.5 = 5 + 2.5 = 7.5$ volts, and this e_c becomes $e(0)$ for the third period of time.

Again for convenience the $t = 0$ axis is shifted to the original $t = 0.1$ sec point. The equation for i in the interval between the new $t = 0$ and $t = 0.05$ is $i = 0.005 - 0.1\,t$. The equation for the voltage in this interval is

$$e_c = \frac{\displaystyle\int_0^t [0.005 - 0.1\,t]\,dt}{50 \times 10^{-6}} + 7.5 = \left[\frac{0.005\,t - 0.1\,t^2/2}{50 \times 10^{-6}}\right]_0^t + 7.5$$
$$= 10^2\,t - 10^3\,t^2 + 7.5 \qquad\qquad (1\text{-}4\text{-}7)$$

In order to find the voltage at the original $t = 0.15$ sec point, $t = 0.05$ is substituted in Eq. 1-4-7, giving $e_c = 10^2(0.05) - 10^3(0.05)^2 + 7.5 = 10$ volts.

The voltage e_c is plotted in Fig. 1-4-2b with the original $t = 0$ as time reference.

If, instead of the current wave being known as in the preceding example, a known voltage wave such as that shown in Fig. 1-4-3a is placed across

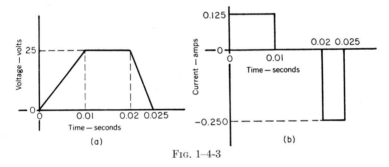

Fig. 1-4-3

the 50-μf capacitor, the current can be found by the following procedure. Eq. 1-4-3 is differentiated to put it into a more usable form for this example; thus

$$\frac{de_c}{dt} = \frac{i}{C} \quad \text{or} \quad i = C\frac{de_c}{dt} \qquad\qquad (1\text{-}4\text{-}8)$$

Again the time is divided into intervals. Between $t = 0$ and $t = 0.01$, $de_c/dt = 25/0.01 = 2500$, which yields the current

$$i = C\frac{de_c}{dt} = 50 \times 10^{-6} \times 2500 = 0.125 \text{ amp} \qquad (1\text{-}4\text{-}9)$$

Between $t = 0.01$ and 0.02, $de_c/dt = 0$; therefore the current is

$$i = 0 \qquad\qquad (1\text{-}4\text{-}10)$$

Between $t = 0.02$ and 0.025, $de_c/dt = -25/0.005 = -5000$ and the current is found to be

$$i = C\frac{de}{dt} = 50 \times 10^{-6}(-5000) = -0.25 \text{ amp} \qquad (1\text{-}4\text{-}11)$$

The current i is plotted in Fig. 1-4-3b.

If a voltage e such as that of Fig. 1–4–4a is applied to a capacitor C, the resulting current $i = C(de/dt)$ is zero until $t = 0$ and is zero for $t > T$. In the interval between $t = 0$ and $t = T$ the current $i = I = (CE/T)$ amperes. The wave shape of this current is termed a pulse or, more

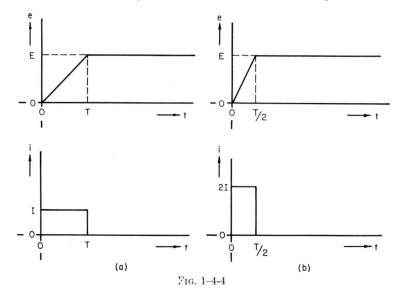

(a)   (b)

Fɪɢ. 1–4–4

specifically, a square pulse. The charge transferred is $q = IT = CE$ coulombs. If now the rise in the voltage e occurs in half the time, as shown in Fig. 1–4–4b, the resulting square pulse of current is of height $2I$ but is only of $(T/2)$ seconds duration. The charge transferred to the capacitor

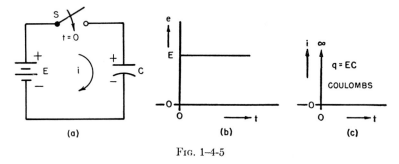

(a)   (b)   (c)

Fɪɢ. 1–4–5

C remains the same. Since charge is found by integrating current with respect to time, the area under the current curve is numerically equal to the charge; therefore the area under the two current curves remains the same. As the duration of the pulse approaches zero, the height of the current pulse approaches infinity and the pulse is said to become an impulse with the area under the curve still equal to q. Thus, in Fig. 1–4–5a, on closing the switch S at $t = 0$ the voltage across the capacitor jumps from zero to E volts; therefore the current flowing into the capacitor is zero for $t < 0$ and for $t > 0$, but at $t = 0$ there is an impulse of current which stems from instantaneous transferral of the charge $q = CE$ to the capacitor. Obviously, some sort of pictorial convention is needed to indicate an impulse of current (or voltage) on a figure, as it is impossible to depict the infinite height and zero width implied by the concept of an impulse. Fig. 1-4-5c indicates one such convention; the vertical arrow with the infinity sign over it indicates the infinite height, and the number immediately beside the arrow indicates the value of the impulse. A negative impulse would be indicated by a similar arrow pointing in the negative direction.

The resistance and inductance of an actual circuit prevent actual occurrence of a current impulse, but there is a finite pulse of current charging the capacitor in a relatively short length of time.

The rate at which energy is being stored (thus the power input to the capacitor) is

$$P = e_c i = C e_c \frac{de_c}{dt} \tag{1-4-12}$$

The energy stored in a capacitor is

$$W = \int_0^t P \, dt = \int_0^t e_c i \, dt = C \int_0^{e_c} e_c \, de_c = \left[\frac{c e_c^2}{2} \right]_0^{e_c} = \frac{c e_c^2}{2} \tag{1-4-13}$$

A linear capacitor is defined as one which has a constant capacitance C independent of variations of the voltage, current, or other variables. An example of a nonlinear capacitance is a capacitor made of ferroelectric materials such as barium titanate.

1-5. The L Circuit. The relationship between the voltage and the current in a circuit containing only inductance is given by

$$e_L = L \frac{di}{dt} \tag{1-5-1}$$

The polarity reference for this voltage with respect to the current direction is shown in Fig. 1-5-1a. It should be noted that e_L is proportional to

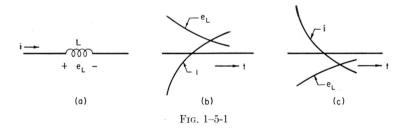

(a)   (b)   (c)

FIG. 1-5-1

the rate of change of the current. This is a simple relationship, yet it is the source of much confusion in setting up the Kirchhoff voltage equations in more complicated circuits. If, as noted in Fig. 1–5-1b, the current i is increasing, $e_L = L(di/dt)$ is positive and the voltage appears across L with the polarity of the polarity reference. If, as in Fig. 1–5-1c, the current i is decreasing, $e_L = L(di/dt)$ is negative and the voltage appears across L with polarity opposite to that of the polarity reference. Lenz's law yields that the induced voltage in an inductor is in such direction as to oppose a change in the current. If the current increases, the voltage will oppose the increase. If the current decreases, the voltage will oppose the decrease. The sign of di/dt and the polarity reference as shown take care of both cases.

Let it be assumed that an arbitrary current function such as that shown in Fig. 1–5-2a exists in an inductor of 0.050 henry and that the voltage e_L is desired. Again this problem can best be solved by using intervals of time for which an equation for the current can easily be written. Between $t = 0$ and $t = 0.05$ the current has the slope $di/dt = 5/0.05 = 100$ and the voltage e_L is

$$e_L = L\frac{di}{dt} = 0.05 \times 100 = 5 \text{ volts} \qquad (1\text{–}5\text{-}2)$$

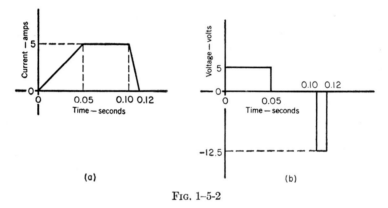

(a)　　　　　　　　　　　　　　　　　　(b)

Fig. 1–5-2

Between $t = 0.05$ and $t = 0.1$ the rate of change of current and the voltage are

$$\frac{di}{dt} = 0 \qquad e_L = 0 \qquad (1\text{–}5\text{-}3)$$

Between $t = 0.1$ and $t = 0.12$ these quantities are

$$\frac{di}{dt} = -\frac{5}{0.02} = -250 \qquad e_L = (0.05)(-250) = -12.5 \text{ volts} \qquad (1\text{–}5\text{-}4)$$

The wave shape of the voltage is shown in Fig. 1–5-2b.

If a current i as in Fig. 1–5-3a exists in an inductor L, the resulting voltage $e = L(di/dt)$ is zero until $t = 0$ and is zero for $t > T$. In the interval

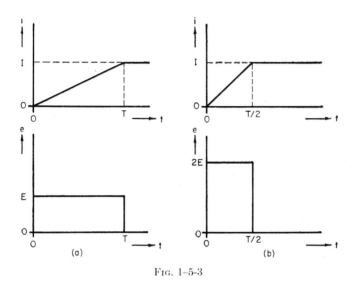

Fig. 1–5-3

between $t = 0$ and $t = T$ the voltage is $e = E = LI/T$ volts. The wave shape of this voltage is that of a square pulse. The area under the voltage curve is ET volt-seconds. If the rise of the current i occurs in half the time, as shown in Fig. 1–5-3b, the resulting square pulse of voltage has the height $2E$ and a duration of $T/2$ seconds. The area under the voltage curve remains $(2E)(T/2) = ET$ volt-seconds as before. If, as in Fig. 1–5-4a,

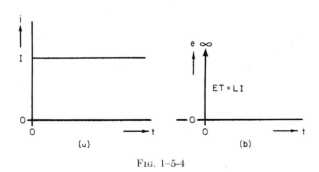

Fig. 1–5-4

the current jumps from zero to I amperes, an impulse of voltage is produced across the inductor, and the value of the impulse equals ET volt-seconds. It is to be noted that, when $E = LI/T$ is substituted for E in ET, this product also equals LI.

If instead of a current wave being given a known voltage such as that in Fig. 1–5-5a is placed across an inductor of $L = 0.2$ henry, the current can

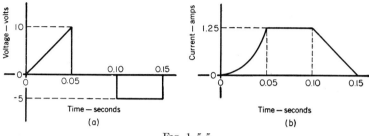

Fig. 1–5-5

be found as follows. Before this voltage is applied, the current is assumed to equal zero.

Eq. 1-5-1 can be put in a more usable form as

$$i = \frac{1}{L} \int e_L \, dt = \frac{1}{L} \int_0^t e_L \, dt + i(0) \qquad (1\text{--}5\text{-}5)$$

where $i(0)$ is the current at $t = 0$ in the direction of the current reference.

Again the time is considered in intervals. Between $t = 0$ and $t = 0.05$, $e_L = (10/0.05)t = 200 \, t$, and the current is

$$i = \frac{1}{0.2} \int_0^t 200 \, t \, dt + 0 = \left[\frac{1}{0.2} \frac{200 \, t^2}{2} \right]_0^t = 500 \, t^2 \qquad (1\text{--}5\text{-}6)$$

The current at $t = 0.05$, as found by substituting in Eq. 1–5-6, is $500(0.05)^2 = 1.25$ amp, which becomes $i(0)$ for the next interval of time. For convenience in the next step the $t = 0$ axis is shifted to the old $t = 0.05$ sec. The equation for the voltage in the interval between the new $t = 0$ and $t = 0.05$ is $e_L = 0$, and the current is

$$i = \frac{1}{0.2} \int_0^t 0 \, dt + 1.25 = 1.25 \text{ amp} \qquad (1\text{--}5\text{-}7)$$

which is $i(0)$ for the next interval of time.

Again the $t = 0$ axis is shifted to the original $t = 0.1$ point; the equation for the voltage is $e_L = -5$ and the current is

$$i = \frac{1}{0.2} \int_0^t (-5) \, dt + 1.25 = \left[\frac{-5 \, t}{0.2} \right]_0^t + 1.25 = -25 \, t + 1.25 \qquad (1\text{--}5\text{-}8)$$

The wave shape of the current is shown in Fig. 1–5-5b.

Now let it be supposed that an inductor in which no initial current exists is connected across the terminals of a battery of E volts at $t = 0$. The voltage across the inductor is $e_L = E = L(di/dt)$, so that the slope of the current is $di/dt = E/L$. The current starts at zero, and in this idealized version it increases without end at a constant rate, as shown in Fig. 1–5-6b.

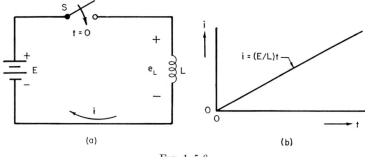

(a)　　　　　　　　　　　　(b)

Fɪɢ. 1–5-6

The power delivered to the inductor is

$$P = e_L i = Li\frac{di}{dt} \tag{1-5-9}$$

The energy in the inductor is

$$W = \int_0^t P\,dt = \int_0^t e_L i\,dt = L\int_0^i i\,di = \frac{Li^2}{2} \tag{1-5-10}$$

A linear inductor is one in which L is a constant, independent of voltage, current, or other variables. An example of a nonlinear inductor is a solenoid with a closed core of some ferromagnetic material.

1–6. Current Generators. In the preceding paragraphs, when a battery of E volts is used, the sources are considered constant-voltage sources with zero internal resistance. Another type of source which should be considered is the constant-current source of I amperes with zero internal conductance. Such a source may be approximated by the use of high resistance in series with a high-voltage battery.

If a constant-current generator is connected to a resistor R as shown in Fig. 1–6-1a, on opening the switch S at $t = 0$ the voltage across the resistor jumps to the value IR, as indicated in Fig. 1–6-1b.

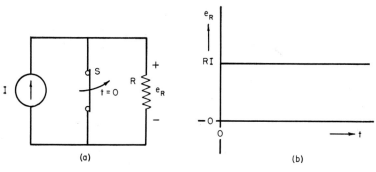

(a)　　　　　　　　　　　　(b)

Fɪɢ. 1–6-1

When the generator is connected to a capacitor C as shown in Fig. 1–6-2a and the switch S is opened at $t = 0$, the constant-current I existing in the

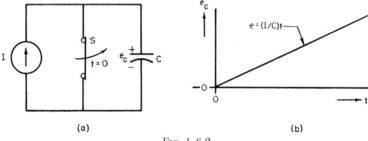

(a)   (b)

FIG. 1–6-2

capacitor charges the capacitor at a uniform rate. The resulting plot of voltage is a straight-line equation, $e_c = (I/C)t$, as in Fig. 1–6-2b.

When the constant-current generator is connected to an inductor L as shown in Fig. 1–6-3, the current in the inductor jumps from zero to I

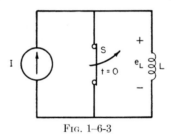

FIG. 1–6-3

amperes when the switch is opened. This is essentially the situation discussed in Art. 1–5; the impulse of voltage that is produced across the inductor due to the jump of current is as in Fig. 1–5-4b.

1–7. Comparison of the C and L Circuits. If the equations for the C and L circuits are compared as in Table 1–7, it is seen that e in one circuit equation appears where i does in the other corresponding circuit equation and vice versa.

TABLE 1–7

	The C Circuit	The L Circuit
Current	$i = C\dfrac{de}{dt}$	$i = \dfrac{1}{L}\displaystyle\int_0^t e\,dt + i(0)$
Voltage	$e = \dfrac{1}{C}\displaystyle\int_0^t i\,dt + e(0)$	$e = L\dfrac{di}{dt}$
Close switch on constant E generator	Impulse function of current	Ramp function of current
Open switch on constant I generator	Ramp function of voltage	Impulse function of voltage

The comparisons of the table evidence a very interesting concept known as duality. If the current in one circuit behaves in exactly the same manner as the voltage in another circuit, the two circuits are said to be duals. Mathematically, the solutions to these two circuits are of exactly the same form. Since every circuit (with certain exceptions) has a dual, this means that of all the possible circuits that exist approximately half are duals of the other half. In addition to the saving of labor in analysis implied by this fact, the concept of duality leads to a better understanding of the manner of response of a circuit.

If this chapter is reviewed in the light of the concept of duality, it is seen that the procedure for determining the voltage on a capacitor with a given wave shape of current is exactly the same as that for determining the current in an inductor when a wave shape of voltage is given. In addition, because of the concept of duality, the words current and voltage in the above statement can be interchanged and the statement will still be true.

Another fact may be stated concerning voltage and current sources. For a voltage source to be able to maintain a constant voltage E regardless of the current existing in the source, the internal resistance of the source must be zero. This zero resistance source is, of course, an idealized version of an actual voltage source and leads to results such as an impulse of current in closing a switch on an idealized capacitor. For a current source to be able to maintain a constant current I regardless of the magnitude of the conductance in which the current exists, the internal resistance of the source must be infinite or it must have a zero internal conductance. This zero conductance is also an idealized version of an actual constant-current source and leads to an impulse of voltage on opening a switch on an idealized inductor.

If the internal resistance of a voltage source is such that it cannot be neglected, the actual voltage source can be represented as an ideal voltage source in series with a resistor as shown in Fig. 1-7-1a. If this circuit is connected to a capacitor by closing a switch at $t = 0$, as shown in Fig. 1-7-1b, no impulse of current is possible, for an impulse of voltage across

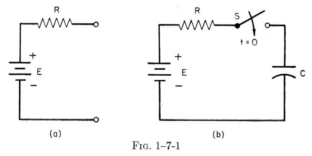

(a)   (b)

Fig. 1-7-1

the resistor R would be required, whereas only finite voltages are present in the circuit.

If the internal conductance of a current source is such that it cannot be neglected, the actual current source can be represented by an ideal current source in parallel with a conductance as shown in Fig. 1–7-2a. If this

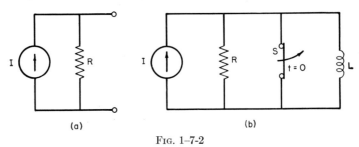

(a)   (b)

Fig. 1–7-2

circuit is connected to an inductor by opening a switch at $t = 0$, as in Fig. 1–7-2b, no impulse of voltage across the circuit is possible, for an impulse of current through R would be required; this is not possible because only finite currents are present in the circuit. The circuits of Figs. 1–7-1b and 1–7-2b will be analyzed in Chapter 2.

The concepts just discussed can be stated in a slightly different way. For the voltage (or charge) on a capacitor to jump from one value to another, an impulse of current is required. If a circuit is such that it is impossible for an impulse of current to occur, the voltage on the capacitor cannot jump. Similarly, for the current in an inductor to jump from one value to another, an impulse of voltage is required. If a circuit is such that it is impossible for an impulse of voltage to occur, the current in an inductor cannot jump.

By using the concept of duality it is seen that the voltage source and current source are duals. Also, the zero resistance of an idealized voltage source and the zero conductance of an idealized current source are duals; and the closing of a switch on a voltage source and the opening of a switch on a current source are dual operations. The concept of duality is further explored and utilized at appropriate points throughout the remainder of this book.

PROBLEMS

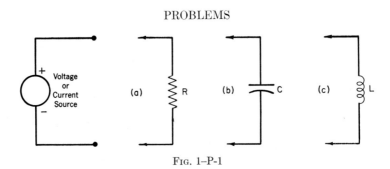

Fig. 1–P-1

1–1. The current i in Fig. 1–P-1 has the wave shape shown in Fig. 1–P-2. In part (a) of Fig. 1–P-1, $R = 17$ ohms; in (b), $C = 15\ \mu\mathrm{f}$; in (c), $L = 0.06$ henry.

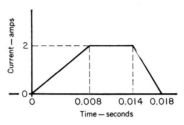

FIG. 1–P-2

Sketch the wave shape of voltage across the elements in (a), (b), and (c) when that element has the current i in it.

1–2. The voltage e in Fig. 1–P-1 has the wave shape shown in Fig. 1–P-3. In part (a) of Fig. 1–P-1, $R = 100$ ohms; in (b), $C = 5\ \mu\mathrm{f}$; in (c), $L = 0.25$ henry.

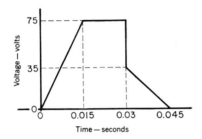

FIG. 1–P-3

Sketch the wave shape of current in the elements in (a), (b), and (c) when that element has the voltage e across it.

1–3. In the example accompanying Fig. 1–4-2 let it be assumed that the capacitor has an initial voltage of $e(0) = 5$ volts, of polarity opposite to the polarity reference for e_c. Sketch a plot of the voltage e_c.

1–4. In the example accompanying Fig. 1–4-2 let it be assumed that there is an initial current $i(0) = 0.01$ amp in a direction opposite to the reference current. In other words, the entire i curve shown in Fig. 1–4-2a is shifted downward by a value of 0.01 amp. Find the equations for e_c and sketch a plot of the voltage.

1–5. In the example accompanying Fig. 1–5-5 let it be assumed that the inductor has an initial current of $i(0) = 1$ amp in a direction opposite to the current reference. Sketch a plot of the current.

1–6. In the example accompanying Fig. 1–5-5 let it be assumed that there is an initial voltage of $e(0) = 5$ volts in the same polarity as the voltage reference. In other words, the entire voltage curve shown in Fig. 1–5-5a is shifted upward by a value of 5 volts. Find the equation for i and sketch a plot of the resulting curve.

1–7. At $t = 0$ a voltage $e = 0.06\,\epsilon^{-0.04t}$ is impressed across an inductor $L = 0.5$ henry in which no initial current exists. Find the equations for and sketch plots of current, power, and energy.

1–8. At $t = 0$ a voltage $0.06[1 - \epsilon^{-0.04t}]$ is impressed across an inductor $L = 0.5$ henry in which $i(0) = 2$ amp in the same direction as the reference current. Find the equations for and sketch plots of current, power, and energy.

1–9. At $t = 0$ a current $0.7[1 - \epsilon^{-0.14t}]$ exists in an inductor $L = 0.5$ henry Find the equations for and sketch plots of voltage, power, and energy.

1–10. Same as Prob. 1–8 except that $C = 25$ μf is substituted for L and $e(0) = 0$ volts.

1–11. Same as Prob 1–9 except that $C = 25$ μf is substituted for the L and $e(0) = 250$ volts with polarity opposite to the reference polarity.

1–12. The current of Fig. 1–P-4a exists in the 5-μf capacitor as in Fig. 1–P-4b,

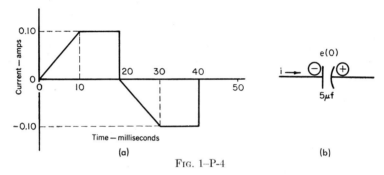

FIG. 1–P-4

and the initial voltage is 150 volts. Plot the voltage across the 5-μf capacitor for 50 msec.

1–13. If the current of Prob. 1–12 exists in a 7500-ohm resistor, plot: the voltage across the resistor; the instantaneous power, in watts, absorbed by the resistor. How many joules of energy are absorbed by the resistor during 50 msec?

1–14. The voltage e shown in Fig. 1–P-5 is that across a 0.025-μf capacitor. Plot the current that exists in the capacitor versus time.

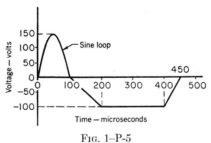

FIG. 1–P-5

1–15. The current shown in Fig. 1–P-6 exists in a 3-μf capacitor. The first part of the current is 90 degrees of a 60-cycle sinusoidal alternating current. If the voltage across the capacitor at $t = T$ is to be the same as at $t = 0$, find: (a) m, if $T = 1/100$ sec; (b) T, if $m = 100$ amp/sec.

1–16. The current passing through a 60-μh inductance has the shape and the scales of the voltage of Fig. 1–P-5 (the positive maximum of the current is 150 amp at $t = 50$ μsec). Plot the voltage across the inductance and the instantaneous power curve.

1–17. The voltage across a 0.35-mh inductance has the shape and the scales of the current of Fig. 1–P-4a (the positive maximum of the voltage is 0.1 kv). If the initial current is 1000 amp in the direction opposite to the reference current plot the current i and the instantaneous power.

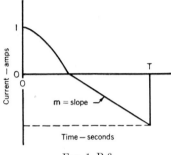

FIG. 1–P-6

1–18. A constant current of 5 ma exists in a capacitor. When the voltage reaches 175 volts, a gas tube fires and the capacitor voltage immediately drops to 60 volts, whereupon the gas tube stops conducting. The capacitor then again charges to 175 volts. What is the frequency of this sawtooth oscillator?

CHAPTER 2

CIRCUITS CONTAINING ONE STORAGE ELEMENT

2–1. Introduction. Circuits may be divided into classes according to the number of storage elements, inductors and capacitors, they contain. In this chapter circuits containing either one capacitor or one inductor are considered.

Certain transient problems involving circuits of one storage element may be solved very easily by using the principles of Chapter 1. As an example,

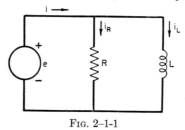

FIG. 2–1-1

if the voltage e is known, the total current i for the parallel resistor-inductor circuit of Fig. 2–1-1 is the sum of the current flowing in the resistor $i_R = (e/R)$ and the current flowing in the inductor

$$i_L = \frac{1}{L} \int_0^t e \, dt + i_L(0)$$

Another example would be that of obtaining the voltage e in the series

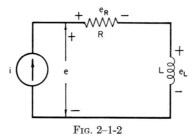

FIG. 2–1-2

resistor-inductor circuit of Fig. 2–1-2 when the current i is known. In this case $e = e_R + e_L$ and

$$e = iR + L \frac{di}{dt} \tag{2-1-1}$$

Transient problems involving more complicated circuits containing a single storage element are taken up in the remainder of this chapter.

18

2–2. The E-R-C Circuit. Fig. 2–2-1a is an idealized version of an actual circuit containing battery, resistor, and capacitor. The actual resistance

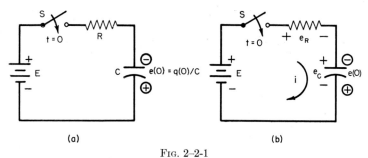

(a)   (b)

FIG. 2–2-1

associated with the battery and capacitor can be lumped with the resistance of the resistor to make up the total resistance R. It is assumed that the capacitor has an initial charge $q(0)$ of polarity shown by the circled $\oplus$, $\ominus$ marks in Fig. 2–2-1. The direction of the current i is chosen as shown in Fig. 2–2-1b. The polarity reference for the voltages e_R and e_c are those shown for this assumed direction of the current. Kirchhoff's voltage equation $E = e_R + e_c$ around the loop can be written

$$E = iR + \frac{1}{C}\int_0^t i\,dt - \frac{q(0)}{C}$$

or   (2-2-1)

$$E + e(0) = iR + \frac{1}{C}\int_0^t i\,dt$$

Before this equation is solved, an examination of what may be expected to happen is worth while. At $t = 0$ when the switch S is closed, there are $e(0)$ volts on the capacitor C and the battery has a voltage E. The $E + e(0)$ volts appear across the resistor R at time $t = 0$, thus establishing the initial current as

$$i(0) = \frac{E + e(0)}{R}$$

The capacitor voltage

$$e_c = \frac{1}{C}\int_0^t i\,dt - e(0)$$

starts at a negative voltage $e(0)$ with respect to the voltage reference for e_c. As current i begins to exist, however, the $(1/C)\int_0^t i\,dt$ component increases until at some time it equals $e(0)$. At this time the voltage of the capacitor C is zero, and the current is $i = E/R$. After this time, e_c builds up in the positive direction and approaches the battery voltage E as a limit or as its steady-state value. The current i starts at a value

$$i(0) = \frac{E + e(0)}{R}$$

but decreases with time t as the $(1/C) \int_0^t i \, dt$ component of voltage on the capacitor C increases. As the voltage on the capacitor C approaches E as the steady-state value, the voltage across the resistor R approaches zero and the current i approaches zero as its steady-state value.

Eq. 2–2-1 is first differentiated to put it into the differential equation form:

$$0 = R\frac{di}{dt} + \frac{i}{C} \tag{2–2-2}$$

The variables are separated:

$$\frac{di}{i} = -\frac{1}{RC} \, dt \tag{2–2-3}$$

and this equation is integrated to give

$$\ln i = -\frac{t}{RC} + K_1 \tag{2–2-4}$$

Eq. 2–2-4 can be written

$$\epsilon^{\ln i} = \epsilon \exp\left(-\frac{t}{RC} + K_1\right) = \epsilon^{-t/RC}\epsilon^{K_1} = A\epsilon^{-t/RC} \tag{2–2-5}$$

where

$$A = \epsilon^{K_1} \tag{2–2-6}$$

or

$$i = A\epsilon^{-t/RC} \tag{2–2-7}$$

The constant A can be determined if at any time t_1 the value i_1 of the current is known. Substituting these values in Eq. 2–2-7 gives

$$i_1 = A\epsilon^{-t_1/RC} \tag{2–2-8}$$

in which A is the only unknown. Quite often the most convenient time to choose for t_1 is $t = 0$, because the conditions at this time can be easily found. The conditions at $t = 0$ are commonly referred to as initial conditions. In this example the initial current is

$$i(0) = \frac{E + e(0)}{R}$$

and A, as found by applying these conditions to Eq. 2–2-7, is

$$\frac{E + e(0)}{R} = A\epsilon^{-0} = A \tag{2–2-9}$$

Substituting gives the final solution:

$$i = \frac{E + e(0)}{R}\epsilon^{-t/RC} \tag{2–2-10}$$

An alternative method of determining A is to solve for the voltage e_c across the capacitor; thus

$$e_c = \frac{1}{C}\int_0^t i \, dt - e(0) = \frac{1}{C}\int_0^t A\epsilon^{-t/RC} \, dt - e(0)$$
$$= AR(1 - \epsilon^{-t/RC}) - e(0) \tag{2–2-11}$$

Now, as $t \to \infty$, it is known that $e_c \to E$; therefore A can be found:

$$E = AR(1 - \epsilon^{-\infty}) - e(0) \quad \text{or} \quad A = \frac{E + e(0)}{R} \qquad (2\text{-}2\text{-}12)$$

If the polarity of $e(0)$ on the capacitor is that of the reference polarity,

$$i = \frac{E - e(0)}{R} \epsilon^{-t/RC} \qquad (2\text{-}2\text{-}13)$$

The steady-state value for i is zero, but an examination of Eqs. 2–2–10 and 2–2–13 indicates that i never actually reaches zero. However, when the exponent reaches 4, the term ϵ^{-4} is equal to 0.018. When the exponent reaches 6, the term ϵ^{-6} is equal to 0.0025. Therefore the current can be considered essentially zero when the exponent reaches a value of approximately 5 or 6.

This method of solution is termed a solution by the separation of variables. The form of the current $i = A\epsilon^{st}$ suggests another method of solving Eq. 2–2–2. Thus, for a current i to be a solution of Eq. 2–2–2, it is only necessary that, when i is substituted into the equation, the equation is satisfied. Thus a person might attempt to solve an equation by assuming a form for the current i, and if this current satisfies the differential equation it is the solution of the equation. Perhaps, if nothing were known about the equation at all, this method would not be very satisfactory. However, because of the known results obtained by using the separation of variables method, it is a reasonable conjecture that the form $i = A\epsilon^{st}$ should satisfy Eq. 2–2–2. From the form for i, di/dt is found to be

$$\frac{di}{dt} = As\epsilon^{st}$$

Substitution accordingly in Eq. 2–2–2 gives

$$R\frac{di}{dt} + \frac{i}{C} = RAs\epsilon^{st} + \frac{A\epsilon^{st}}{C} = A\epsilon^{st}\left[Rs + \frac{1}{C}\right] = 0 \qquad (2\text{-}2\text{-}14)$$

For the last equation to equal zero, either $A\epsilon^{st}$ must equal zero or the terms inside the bracket must; thus

$$Rs + \frac{1}{C} = 0 \qquad (2\text{-}2\text{-}15)$$

The term $A\epsilon^{st}$ cannot equal zero (except in very special cases) because this is the desired solution i. Therefore $Rs + 1/C$ must equal zero, and this leads to the evaluation of s as

$$s = -\frac{1}{RC} \qquad (2\text{-}2\text{-}16)$$

and substituting accordingly gives

$$i = A\epsilon^{st} = A\epsilon^{-t/RC} \qquad (2\text{-}2\text{-}17)$$

The constant A may be evaluated as before.

The method of solution just outlined is that to be found in the usual treatment of differential equations and is used for solutions of many of the problems in this book.

After the solution for the current is found, the unknown voltages can be found easily. For example, the voltage across the resistor R is

$$e_R = iR = [E + e(0)]\epsilon^{-t/RC} \qquad (2\text{-}2\text{-}18)$$

The voltage across the capacitor C is

$$e_c = \frac{1}{C}\int_0^t i\,dt - e(0) = \frac{1}{C}\int_0^t \frac{E + e(0)}{R}\,\epsilon^{-t/RC}\,dt - e(0)$$
$$= E - [E + e(0)]\epsilon^{-t/RC} \qquad (2\text{-}2\text{-}19)$$

A partial check on the correctness of this solution can be made by checking at $t = 0$, which gives $e_c = -e(0)$, and at $t = \infty$, which gives $e_c = E$; both are correct.

The charge q on the capacitor may be obtained by multiplying the e_c of Eq. 2-2-19 by C. Fig. 2-2-2 shows a plot of i, e_R, and e_c.

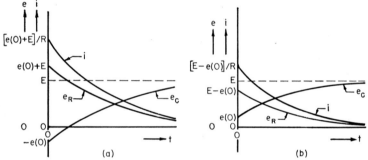

(a)	(b)
$e(0)$ has polarity opposite to the polarity reference.	$e(0)$ has the same polarity as the polarity reference.

Fig. 2-2-2

2-3. Time Constant. An examination of Eqs. 2-2-10 and 2-2-13 shows that the value of the product RC determines the time required for the current (or voltage) to reach any stated value. This is indicated in Fig. 2-3-1, which shows that the current drops sensibly to zero in a short time

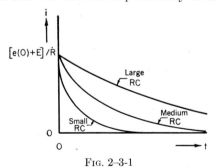

Fig. 2-3-1

if the product RC is small. On the other hand, if the product RC is large, the current requires a much longer time to attain the same small value. Since the exponent (t/RC) is a pure number, the product RC has the units of time. For these reasons the product RC is referred to as the "time constant" of the circuit and is designated by $t_c = RC$.

In many problems it is desirable to have a quick method of determining the time constant involved; this may be done by a number of methods, three of which will be explained. The first method might be called the 63.2 percent method and is quite useful in quick oscillographic measurements. All single-energy transients of a d-c nature start at one value and end at another value. There is an $\epsilon^{-t/RC}$ term multiplying the magnitude of the change. When the time t is equal to the time constant t_c, such as the $t_c = RC$ of an R-C circuit, the exponent is equal to -1 and $\epsilon^{-1} = 0.368$. Thus the circuit has gone through $1 - 0.368 = 0.632$ or 63.2 percent of its total change. If then in Fig. 2–2-2 the current or voltage has gone through 63.2 percent of its total change, the corresponding time as read from the curve is the time constant t_c. This method is not very accurate because it depends mainly on the shape of the curve in the vicinity of the 63.2 percent point.

A second quick method for obtaining the time constant is termed the initial-slope method. It consists in determining the initial slope of a quantity and extending the initial slope until it crosses the line representing the steady-state value of the quantity being observed. The time corresponding to this point of intersection is the time constant t_c. For example, if the current i is chosen for examination, its initial slope can be easily determined and extended until it crosses the $i = 0$ axis, as shown in Fig. 2–3-2, thus determining the time constant t_c. To demonstrate the validity

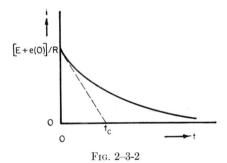

Fig. 2–3-2

of this procedure when the current i is used, the initial slope of the current curve can be found by differentiating Eq. 2–2-10 and substituting $t = 0$ into the result; thus

$$\left.\frac{di}{dt}\right|_{t=0} = \left[-\left(\frac{E + e(0)}{R^2 C}\right)\epsilon^{-t/RC}\right]_{t=0} = -\left(\frac{E + e(0)}{R^2 C}\right) \qquad (2\text{–}3\text{-}1)$$

The intersection on the time axis then is

$$\left(\frac{E + e(0)}{R}\right)\left(\frac{R^2C}{E + e(0)}\right) = RC = t_c \qquad (2\text{-}3\text{-}2)$$

which is the time constant. The accuracy of the initial-slope method is limited because the results depend mainly on the shape of the curve near $t = 0$.

Another method of obtaining the time constant involves the plotting of logarithms and may be termed the log-plot method. When the logarithm of the ϵ^{-t/t_c} term is plotted versus time t, the result is a straight line of slope $-1/t_c$. This has the advantage that when all the experimental points are plotted a straight line can be drawn which averages the experimental variations and usually gives a better value for t_c than use of any one point alone can do. The justification of this method can be shown as follows. Eq. 2-2-10 can be written

$$i = i(0)\epsilon^{-t/t_c} \quad \text{or} \quad \frac{i}{i(0)} = \epsilon^{-t/t_c} \qquad (2\text{-}3\text{-}3)$$

If the logarithm of this equation to the base 10 is taken, the result is

$$\log_{10}\left(\frac{i}{i(0)}\right) = t\left(\frac{-\log_{10}\epsilon}{t_c}\right) \qquad (2\text{-}3\text{-}4)$$

which plots as a straight line and the slope of the straight line is $-(\log_{10}\epsilon)/t_c$, from which t_c may be determined. Thus in the following example for a certain $E\text{-}R\text{-}C$ circuit the value of $i(0)$ is 10 amp and the following data apply:

t (milliseconds)	0	1	2	3	4	5	6
i (amperes)	10	7.5	5.6	4.2	3.2	2.4	1.8
$\log_{10}\dfrac{i}{i(0)}$	0	-0.1245	-0.2514	-0.3762	-0.4943	-0.6194	-0.7440

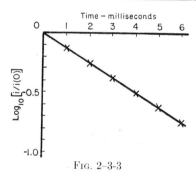

Fig. 2-3-3

The points plot as shown in Fig. 2-3-3, and a straight line drawn through the points has the slope

$$\frac{-0.750}{6 \times 10^{-3}} = -\frac{\log_{10}\epsilon}{t_c}$$

from which t_c can be found to be

$$t_c = 3.47 \times 10^{-3} \text{ sec}$$

2-4. Power and Energy in the E-R-C Circuit. The equations for power and energy in the various elements can be found once the equation for current is known. For the circuit of Fig. 2-2-1a the equation for the power delivered by the battery is

$$P = Ei = \frac{E[E + e(0)]}{R} \epsilon^{-t/RC} \qquad (2\text{-}4\text{-}1)$$

The energy delivered by the battery is

$$W = \int_0^t P \, dt = \int_0^t \frac{E^2 + e(0)E}{R} \epsilon^{-t/RC} \, dt$$
$$= E^2C + e(0)EC - [E^2C + e(0)EC]\epsilon^{-t/RC} \qquad (2\text{-}4\text{-}2)$$

In the steady state $(t \to \infty)$, the total energy delivered by the battery is

$$W = E^2C + e(0)EC \qquad (2\text{-}4\text{-}3)$$

The power dissipated in the resistor is

$$P = i^2R = \frac{[E + e(0)]^2}{R} \epsilon^{-2t/RC} \qquad (2\text{-}4\text{-}4)$$

The energy dissipated in the form of heat in the resistor is

$$W = \int_0^t P \, dt = \frac{[E + e(0)]^2C}{2} - \frac{[E + e(0)]^2C}{2} \epsilon^{-2t/RC} \qquad (2\text{-}4\text{-}5)$$

The total energy dissipated in the resistor while the circuit reaches the steady state is

$$W = \frac{[E + e(0)]^2C}{2} \qquad (2\text{-}4\text{-}6)$$

The amount of power delivered to C is

$$P = e_c i = \{E - [E + e(0)]\epsilon^{-t/RC}\} \left[\frac{E + e(0)}{R} \epsilon^{-t/RC} \right]$$
$$= \frac{E^2 + Ee(0)}{R} \epsilon^{-t/RC} - \frac{[E + e(0)]^2}{R} \epsilon^{-2t/RC} \qquad (2\text{-}4\text{-}7)$$

The energy stored in C is

$$W = \frac{Ce_c^2}{2} = \frac{C}{2} \{E - [E + e(0)]\epsilon^{-t/RC}\}^2$$
$$= \frac{CE^2}{2} - C[E^2 + Ee(0)]\epsilon^{-t/RC} + \frac{C}{2}[E + e(0)]^2\epsilon^{-2t/RC} \qquad (2\text{-}4\text{-}8)$$

The total energy stored in C when the circuit reaches the steady state is

$$W = \frac{CE^2}{2} \qquad (2\text{-}4\text{-}9)$$

It is interesting to notice that when $e(0) = 0$ the energy dissipated in the resistor while the circuit reaches steady state is the same as the energy stored in the capacitor. Hence in charging a capacitor the energy dissipated as heat in the resistor equals that stored in the capacitor. This fact is independent of the size of resistor used.

2-5. The E-R-L Circuit. Fig. 2–5-1 is an idealized version of a circuit containing battery, resistor, and inductor. The actual resistance of the

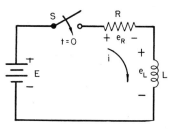

Fig. 2–5-1

battery and inductor is included in the resistance of the resistor R. At first it is assumed that no energy is stored in the inductor before $t = 0$; that is, the current is zero. When S is closed, the circuit is such that there is no impulse of voltage across the inductor; therefore the current cannot jump and at $t = 0+$ the current $i(0)$ is zero. Because $i(0) = 0$, $e_R(0) = i(0)R = 0$ and all the voltage E will appear across the inductor L, making

$$E = L \frac{di}{dt}(0)$$

where $(di/dt)(0)$ represents the derivative of the current with respect to time at the time $t = 0$. Therefore the initial rate of increase of the current is

$$\frac{di}{dt}(0) = \frac{E}{L}$$

After some time has elapsed, a current i exists and the resistor voltage e_R has a value. Thus the voltage across L will be less than E and di/dt will have a smaller value than E/L. The term di/dt continues to decrease and approaches the steady-state value of zero. With $di/dt = 0$ all the voltage E is across the resistance R and $E = i_{ss}R$; thus the steady-state current is $i_{ss} = E/R$.

After a direction for the current i is assumed as shown in Fig. 2–5-1, Kirchhoff's voltage equation is

$$E = e_R + e_L \quad \text{or} \quad E = Ri + L \frac{di}{dt} \tag{2-5-1}$$

Comparison of Eqs. 2–5-1 and 2–2-2 shows that the method of solution used for Eq. 2–2-2 must be modified in order to solve Eq. 2–5-1. This is true because in Eq. 2–2-2 the left side is zero, whereas in Eq. 2–5-1 it is equal to E. When the left side of an equation is equal to something other than zero, the current i has a steady-state value other than zero. The steady-state value of the current is found from Eq. 2–5–1 by noting that, as i_{ss} is a constant, $di_{ss}/dt = 0$; thus Eq. 2–5–1 becomes $Ri_{ss} = E$, from which i_{ss} is found as $i_{ss} = E/R$. The steady-state component of current can also be solved for by d-c circuit methods to give $i_{ss} = E/R$. If the current is considered as comprised of two components, one a steady-state component and the other a transient component,

$$i = i_{ss} + i_{tr} \qquad (2\text{–}5\text{–}2)$$

and methods similar to those used for the E-R-C circuit are possible. That this is so is demonstrated by substituting the two components for i in Eq. 2–5–1:

$$E = L \frac{di}{dt} + iR = L \left(\frac{d}{dt} i_{ss} + \frac{d}{dt} i_{tr} \right) + R(i_{ss} + i_{tr})$$

This yields

$$E = L \frac{di_{tr}}{dt} + R \left(\frac{E}{R} \right) + Ri_{tr}$$

giving finally

$$0 = L \frac{di_{tr}}{dt} + Ri_{tr} \qquad (2\text{–}5\text{–}3)$$

Eq. 2–5–3 can be solved in exactly the same manner as Eq. 2–2–2.

No matter how complicated an equation is, when $i_{ss} + i_{tr}$ is substituted for i, the i_{ss} term leaves an E on the right side of the equation which cancels the E on the left side. The result is an equation involving i_{tr} alone with a left-hand side of zero.

Since a current of the form $i = A\epsilon^{st}$ leads to a solution in the preceding example, it seems reasonable to try the same form again, remembering additionally that here this is used for i_{tr}, which is only one component of the total current. Therefore the form of $i_{tr} = A\epsilon^{st}$ is used, giving

$$0 = A\epsilon^{st}[Ls + R]$$

which leads to the value of s:

$$Ls + R = 0 \qquad s = -\frac{R}{L} \qquad (2\text{–}5\text{–}4)$$

The total current can be written

$$i = i_{ss} + i_{tr} = \frac{E}{R} + A\epsilon^{-Rt/L} \qquad (2\text{–}5\text{–}5)$$

Before the constant A is evaluated, an interesting point to notice is that Eqs. 2–2–2 and 2–5–3 are identical in form except that R is replaced by L and $1/C$ by R. The solution of Eq. 2–5–3 could have been obtained from the solution already obtained for Eq. 2–2–2 by making the appropriate substitution:

$$i_{tr} = A \exp \left(-\frac{t}{L(1/R)} \right) = A\epsilon^{-Rt/L}$$

which checks the i_{tr} just found.

To evaluate A, the known initial condition that $i(0)$ is zero at $t = 0$ is utilized in Eq. 2–5-5; thus

$$0 = \frac{E}{R} + A\epsilon^{-0}$$

yielding for A

$$A = -\frac{E}{R}$$

Upon substitution, Eq. 2–5-5 becomes

$$i = \frac{E}{R} - \frac{E}{R}\epsilon^{-Rt/L} = \frac{E}{R}\left(1 - \epsilon^{-Rt/L}\right) \tag{2–5-6}$$

The voltage across the inductor is

$$e_L = L\frac{di}{dt} = L\left(-\frac{E}{R}\right)\left(-\frac{R}{L}\right)\epsilon^{-(R/L)t} = E\epsilon^{-Rt/L} \tag{2–5-7}$$

and the voltage across the resistor is

$$e_R = iR = E(1 - \epsilon^{-Rt/L}) \tag{2–5-8}$$

Fig. 2–5-2 shows a plot of i, e_L, and e_R.

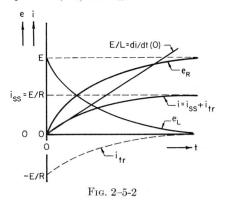

Fig. 2–5-2

2–6. Time Constant. The time constant is, again, defined as the value of time for which the exponent is equal to unity; in this case it is $t_c = L/R$. Fig. 2–6-1a shows the variation of current in the E-R-L circuit with E and R held constant and L increased, thus increasing $t_c = L/R$. It is apparent that, the larger the value of L, the longer time the current takes to reach a given value. Fig. 2–6-1b shows the current of the E-R-L circuit with E and L held constant and R increased, thus decreasing the $t_c = L/R$. The initial slope is the same for each value of R, and for a small value of resistance, such as R_1, the current reaches a given value in less time than it does for a large value, such as R_4. The R_1 curve, however, takes a longer time to reach a given percentage of its final value than does the R_4 curve.

The various methods described previously for the E-R-C circuit may be used to determine the time constant of the E-R-L circuit. The 63.2

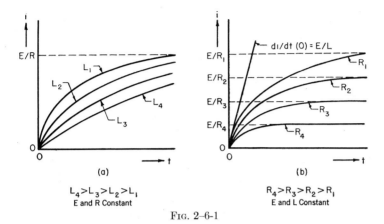

FIG. 2-6-1

percent method could be used to determine the time it takes the current to reach 63.2 percent of its final E/R value. The log-plot method may be modified as follows:

$$i = \frac{E}{R} - \frac{E}{R}\,\epsilon^{-t/t_c} = i_{ss} - i_{ss}\epsilon^{-t/t_c}$$

$$i_{ss} - i = i_{ss}\epsilon^{-t/t_c}, \qquad \frac{i_{ss} - i}{i_{ss}} = \epsilon^{-t/t_c} \tag{2-6-1}$$

$$\log_{10}\left(\frac{i_{ss} - i}{i_{ss}}\right) = t\left(\frac{-\log_{10}\epsilon}{t_c}\right) \tag{2-6-2}$$

The log-plot is made as before and the time constant t_c is determined from the slope.

2-7. Power and Energy in the E-R-L Circuit. The power delivered by the battery is

$$P = Ei = \frac{E^2}{R}[1 - \epsilon^{-Rt/L}] \tag{2-7-1}$$

and the energy delivered by the battery is

$$W = \int_0^t P\,dt = \frac{E^2}{R}\,t - \frac{E^2}{R^2}\,L + \frac{E^2 L}{R^2}\,\epsilon^{-Rt/L} \tag{2-7-2}$$

The power dissipated in the resistor is

$$P = i^2 R = \frac{E^2}{R}[1 - 2\,\epsilon^{-Rt/L} + \epsilon^{-2Rt/L}] \tag{2-7-3}$$

and the energy dissipated in the resistor is

$$W = \int_0^t P\,dt = \frac{E^2}{R}\left[t + \frac{2L}{R}\,\epsilon^{-Rt/L} - \frac{L}{2R}\,\epsilon^{-2Rt/L} - \frac{3}{2}\frac{L}{R}\right] \tag{2-7-4}$$

The power delivered to the inductor is

$$P = e_L i = \frac{E^2}{R}[\epsilon^{-Rt/L} - \epsilon^{-2Rt/L}] \tag{2-7-5}$$

and the energy stored in the inductor is

$$W = \frac{Li^2}{2} = \frac{L}{2}\frac{E^2}{R^2}[1 - 2\,\epsilon^{-Rt/L} + \epsilon^{-2Rt/L}] \tag{2-7-6}$$

In the steady state the total energy stored in the inductor is

$$W_t = \frac{L}{2}\frac{E^2}{R^2} \tag{2-7-7}$$

2–8. Compound Transients. Before leaving the study of transients with circuits of one storage element, it is worth while to study the solutions in more general cases. As a start, the circuit shown in Fig. 2–8-1 is con-

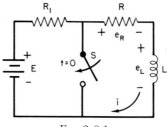

Fig. 2–8-1

sidered; the switch S has been open long enough for the circuit to reach the steady state. Before the switch is closed the current i has the value $i = E/(R + R_1)$. When switch S is closed at time $t = 0$, the inductor maintains the value of current at $t = 0+$ so that $i(0) = E/(R + R_1)$. For the direction of the assumed current, Kirchhoff's voltage equation around the loop containing the inductor is

$$0 = Ri + L\frac{di}{dt} \tag{2-8-1}$$

A current of the form $i = A\epsilon^{st}$ is assumed. This leads to

$$0 = A\epsilon^{st}[Ls + R]$$

giving for s

$$s = -\frac{R}{L}$$

and for the current

$$i = A\epsilon^{-Rt/L} \tag{2-8-2}$$

The constant A is found by imposing conditions at time $t = 0$ as $i(0) = A\epsilon^{-0}$ or $A = i(0)$, which yield for the current and voltages

$$i = i(0)\epsilon^{-Rt/L} \tag{2-8-3}$$

$$e_R = i(0)R\epsilon^{-Rt/L} \tag{2-8-4}$$

$$e_L = L\frac{di}{dt} = -i(0)R\epsilon^{-Rt/L} \tag{2-8-5}$$

These quantities are sketched in Fig. 2–8-2.

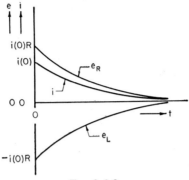

Fig. 2–8-2

An example of the application for the case of the discharge of current in a series R-L circuit is the discharge-resistor type of switch used to open a highly inductive circuit, such as the field of a large generator or motor. If a switch were opened on such a circuit without taking precautions, very large voltages would appear across the switch, and arcs would form at the contactors of the switch which could cause serious damage not only to the switch but also to the insulation of the windings. Fig. 2–8-3 is a schematic

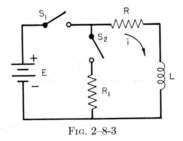

Fig. 2–8-3

way of showing how a discharge switch operates. Just before S_1 opens, S_2 is closed; thus, when S_1 does open, R_1 is in the discharge circuit. After the switching operation, the circuit is a discharge circuit with an $i(0) = E/R$ and a total resistance equal to $(R_1 + R)$. The equation for i then becomes

$$i = i(0) \, \exp\left[\frac{-(R_1 + R)}{L} t\right] \tag{2–8-6}$$

The voltage across the R_1 resistor is

$$iR_1 = i(0)R_1 \exp\left[-\frac{(R_1 + R)}{L} t\right] = \frac{E}{R} R_1 \exp\left[-\frac{(R_1 + R)}{L} t\right] \tag{2–8-7}$$

It should be noticed that the current i exists in R_1 from the bottom to the top, so that the polarity reference for Eq. 2–8-7 is plus on the bottom and minus on the top.

This voltage is maximum at $t = 0$ and has the value

$$e_M = \frac{ER_1}{R} \qquad (2\text{-}8\text{-}8)$$

It should also be noticed that the maximum voltage across the opened switch S is $E(1 + R_1/R)$. For the transient to pass quickly the time constant of the circuit should be small; therefore R_1 should be large. However, a large R_1 means that e_M will be large. A choice of R_1 in any specific design will have to balance these two factors against each other.

As a continuation of the study of circuits with one storage element, the circuit of Fig. 2–8–4a is analyzed. It is assumed that S has been open long enough for the current to reach its steady-state value, $i = 50/18 = 2.78$ amp. Then, at $t = 0$, S is closed. The equation for the current i through the inductor is desired. At $t = 0$ the inductor L maintains the current at 2.78 amp. After S is closed, Thevenin's theorem can be used to simplify the circuit to the left of A–B.

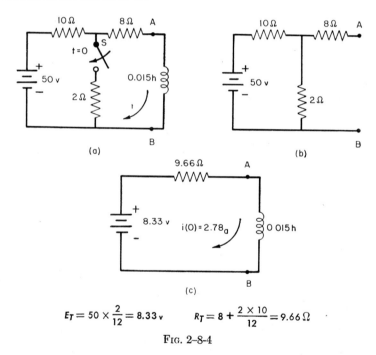

$$E_T = 50 \times \frac{2}{12} = 8.33 \text{ v} \qquad R_T = 8 + \frac{2 \times 10}{12} = 9.66\,\Omega$$

Fig. 2–8–4

The equivalent circuit for Fig. 2–8–4a with S closed becomes that of Fig. 2–8–4c, which is an E-R-L circuit. The only difference between this case and previous work stems from the initial current $i(0)$. Kirchhoff's voltage equation is

$$0.015 \frac{di}{dt} + 9.66\, i = 8.33 \text{ volts} \qquad (2\text{-}8\text{-}9)$$

whence

$$i_{ss} = \frac{8.33}{9.66} = 0.862 \text{ amp} \qquad (2\text{-}8\text{-}10)$$

Eq. 2-8-9 can be solved as before by letting $i = i_{ss} + i_{tr}$ and assuming $i_{tr} = A\epsilon^{st}$. Upon evaluation, s becomes

$$s = -\frac{R}{L} = -\frac{9.66}{0.015} = -644 \qquad (2\text{-}8\text{-}11)$$

and the total current is

$$i = 0.862 + A\epsilon^{-644t} \qquad (2\text{-}8\text{-}12)$$

When known conditions at time $t = 0$ are imposed, the value of A is found to be

$$2.78 = 0.862 + A\epsilon^0 \qquad A = 1.918 \qquad (2\text{-}8\text{-}13)$$

leading to the solution for i:

$$i = 0.862 + 1.918 \, \epsilon^{-644t} \qquad (2\text{-}8\text{-}14)$$

The general form for the circuit of Fig. 2-8-4c, with $i(0)$ in the same direction as i, is

$$i = i_{ss} + [i(0) - i_{ss}]\epsilon^{-Rt/L} \qquad (2\text{-}8\text{-}15)$$

The circuit of Fig. 2-8-4a can be used as a relay oscillator to produce a tone with a fundamental frequency of any desired value within reason. Let it be supposed that the 8-ohm resistor and the 0.015-henry inductor are the resistance and inductance, respectively, of a relay. Also let it be assumed that when the current in the relay reaches a value of 2.5 amp the relay operates, closing the switch S; and when the current reaches a value of 0.9 amp the relay again operates and opens S. The problem can best be solved by considering the solution in two intervals of time. The first interval of time used is that when S is closed, and the second interval is that when S is open.

For the first interval of time, $t = 0$ is taken at the time S closes; therefore $i(0)$ is equal to 2.5 amp and i_{ss} is equal to 0.862 amp. The equivalent circuit of Fig. 2-8-4c applies to this situation and the form of the current

$$i = i_{ss} + [i(0) - i_{ss}]\epsilon^{-Rt/L}$$

upon substitution becomes

$$i = 0.862 + (2.5 - 0.862)\epsilon^{-644t}$$

or

$$i = 0.862 + 1.638 \, \epsilon^{-644t} \qquad (2\text{-}8\text{-}16)$$

When the current drops to a value of 0.9 amp in t_1 seconds, the switch opens. The time t_1 can be found through

$$0.9 = 0.862 + 1.638 \, \epsilon^{-644t_1}$$

Thus

$$\epsilon^{-644t_1} = 0.0232; \quad \text{whence} \quad t_1 = 0.00585 \text{ sec} \qquad (2\text{-}8\text{-}17)$$

For the second interval of time a new $t=0$ is chosen when S opens. In this interval $i(0)$ is equal to 0.9 amp and i_{ss} is equal to 2.78 amp. The current of the form

$$i = i_{ss} + [i(0) - i_{ss}]\epsilon^{-Rt/L}$$

upon substitution becomes

$$i = 2.78 + (0.9 - 2.78)\epsilon^{-18t/0.015}$$

whence

$$i = 2.78 - 1.88\ \epsilon^{-1200t} \qquad (2\text{–}8\text{–}18)$$

When the current rises to a value of 2.5 amp in t_2 seconds, the switch S closes, completing one cycle of operation. The time t_2 can be found through

$$2.5 = 2.78 - 1.88\ \epsilon^{-1200t_2} \qquad \epsilon^{-1200t_2} = 0.145$$

whence

$$t_2 = 0.00158\ \text{sec} \qquad (2\text{–}8\text{–}19)$$

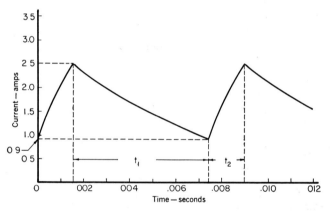

Fig. 2–8-5

The current has the wave shape over one cycle shown in Fig. 2–8-5 with $t = 0$ arbitrarily chosen. This is repeated continually.

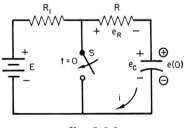

Fig. 2–8-6

In continuing the subject of compound transients, the capacitor-discharge circuit of Fig. 2–8–6 is analyzed. It is assumed that the switch S is open long enough for the circuit to reach the steady state; and, at time $t = 0$, S is closed. The original voltage $e(0)$ on the capacitor is therefore equal to the battery voltage E. Kirchhoff's voltage law is

$$0 = e_R + e_c = iR + \frac{1}{C}\int_0^t i\,dt + E \qquad (2\text{-}8\text{-}20)$$

The initial current $i(0)$ can be found by substituting the known initial conditions into Eq. 2–8–20; this gives

$$i(0)R + 0 + E = 0 \qquad i(0) = -\frac{E}{R} \qquad (2\text{-}8\text{-}21)$$

When Eq. 2–8–20 is differentiated, the result is

$$R\frac{di}{dt} + \frac{i}{C} = 0 \qquad (2\text{-}8\text{-}22)$$

This is exactly the same as Eq. 2–2–2; therefore the solution is the same, $i = A\epsilon^{-t/RC}$. The constant A can be found by imposing the conditions $i(0) = -E/R$; thus

$$i(0) = -\frac{E}{R} = A\epsilon^0; \text{ hence } A = -\frac{E}{R}$$

and upon substitution the final solution is

$$i = -\frac{E}{R}\epsilon^{-t/RC} \qquad (2\text{-}8\text{-}23)$$

The voltage on the capacitor is

$$e_c = \frac{1}{C}\int_0^t i\,dt + E$$
$$e_c = \frac{1}{C}\int_0^t \left(-\frac{E}{R}\epsilon^{-t/RC}\right)dt + E$$
$$e_c = E\epsilon^{-t/RC} - E + E = E\epsilon^{-t/RC} \qquad (2\text{-}8\text{-}24)$$

Fig. 2–8–7 contains plots of e_c and i for this circuit.

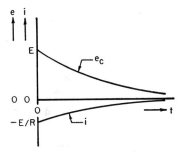

FIG. 2–8–7

As a continuation of the study of circuits with one storage element, the circuit of Fig. 2–8–8a is analyzed. It is assumed that the switch S has been open long enough for the circuit to reach the steady state. Therefore, before $t = 0$, the voltage e_c is equal to 50 volts and the current i is zero.

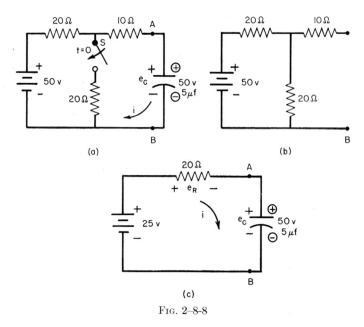

Fig. 2–8–8

After $t = 0$ the equation for the current i through the capacitor C is desired. After S is closed, Thevenin's theorem can be used for the circuit to the left of A–B. The resulting circuit is shown in Fig. 2–8–8c: this is an equivalent circuit for Fig. 2–8–8a as far as the capacitor is concerned.

The solution for the current i of the equivalent circuit has already been found (Eq. 2–2–13); it is

$$i = \frac{E - e(0)}{R} \epsilon^{-t/RC}$$

which for this problem becomes

$$i = \frac{25 - 50}{20} \epsilon^{-t/20 \times 5 \times 10^{-6}} = -1.25 \, \epsilon^{-10^4 t} \qquad (2\text{–}8\text{–}25)$$

An application illustrating the charging and discharging of a capacitor is the relaxation oscillator, used as a time base generator in cathode-ray oscilloscopes. The circuit is shown in Fig. 2–8–9a; the wave shape of the capacitor voltage e_c is shown in Fig. 2–8–9b. If the switch S is closed at $t = 0$ and the capacitor C is initially uncharged, the capacitor voltage starts at zero and increases until it reaches the breakdown voltage E_1 of the gas diode. The capacitor is discharged almost instantly to the extinction voltage E_2 of the gas diode. Then C is again charged to the voltage E_1

and the cycle repeats. As far as the study of the relaxation oscillator is concerned, the portion of the cycle that repeats is the one of interest.

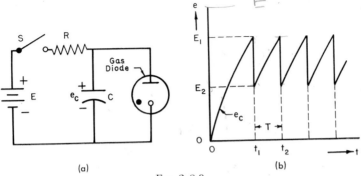

(a)   (b)

Fig. 2–8–9

Therefore the $t = 0$ axis can be shifted to the original $t = t_1$ and the equation, which is similar to Eq. 2–2–19, can be written

$$e_c = E - (E - E_2)\epsilon^{-t/RC} \qquad (2\text{–}8\text{–}26)$$

The period of oscillation T can be expressed as $T = t_2 - t_1$; and, when t in Eq. 2–8–26 reaches the time T, the capacitor voltage e_c has reached E_1:

$$E_1 = E - (E - E_2)\epsilon^{-T/RC} \qquad (2\text{–}8\text{–}27)$$

from which T can be obtained:

$$T = RC \ln \frac{E - E_2}{E - E_1} \qquad (2\text{–}8\text{–}28)$$

2–9. Parallel _R-C_ and _R-L_ Circuits with a Constant-Current Source. Many sources of power have such high internal resistance that they tend to act as a constant-current source. An example of this is a vacuum-tube circuit involving a tetrode or pentode tube. The source can be idealized by assuming it to be a source of a constant-current I, just as the battery

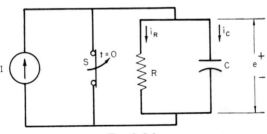

Fig. 2–9–1

source is idealized by assuming it to be a constant-voltage E. For the circuit shown in Fig. 2–9–1 Kirchhoff's current law can be written

$$I = i_R + i_C \qquad (2\text{–}9\text{–}1)$$

or

$$I = \frac{e}{R} + C\frac{de}{dt} \tag{2-9-2}$$

and with the substitution

$$G = \frac{1}{R}$$

finally as

$$I = Ge + C\frac{de}{dt} \tag{2-9-3}$$

An inspection of Eq. 2–9-3 shows that the voltage e can be divided into two terms, a steady-state voltage term, $e_{ss} = I/G = IR$, and a transient term, e_{tr}. If $e = e_{ss} + e_{tr}$ is substituted in Eq. 2–9-3, the result is

$$0 = Ge_{tr} + C\frac{de_{tr}}{dt} \tag{2-9-4}$$

where the form for e_{tr} can be found:

$$e_{tr} = A\epsilon^{-Gt/C} \tag{2-9-5}$$

The constant A can be evaluated by applying $t = 0$ conditions to the equation

$$e = \frac{I}{G} + A\epsilon^{-Gt/C} \tag{2-9-6}$$

The $t = 0$ conditions can be found by the following reasoning. Before $t = 0$ there is a direct short across the R and C; therefore e is equal to zero. At $t = 0$ the voltage on the C cannot jump unless an impulse of current occurs; this is impossible in this circuit. Therefore $e(0)$ is equal to zero, and with these conditions Eq. 2–9-6 becomes

$$0 = \frac{I}{G} + A \qquad A = -\frac{I}{G} \tag{2-9-7}$$

Upon substitution the final solution is

$$e = \frac{I}{G}[1 - \epsilon^{-Gt/C}] \tag{2-9-8}$$

When the equation for the I-G-C parallel circuit,

$$I = Ge + C\frac{de}{dt} \tag{2-9-9}$$

is compared with Eq. 2–5-1 for the E-R-L series circuit,

$$E = Ri + L\frac{di}{dt} \tag{2-9-10}$$

it can be seen that these equations have exactly the same form and the analogous quantities are

E is analogous to I
i is analogous to e
R is analogous to G
L is analogous to C

$$\tag{2-9-11}$$

This analogy again evidences duality, and it can be seen that the E-R-L series circuit is the dual of the I-G-C parallel circuit. It should be noted that a parallel connection is the dual of a series connection.

The solution for the I-G-C parallel circuit can be obtained from the solution to the E-R-L series circuit from the concept of duality. That is, the solution to Eq. 2–9-10 is

$$i = \frac{E}{R} \left(1 - \epsilon^{-Rt/L}\right) \qquad (2\text{–}9\text{–}12)$$

and, by replacing i, E, R, L with their dual counterparts from 2–9-11, the solution to Eq. 2–9-9 can be written

$$e = \frac{I}{G} \left(1 - \epsilon^{-Gt/C}\right) \qquad (2\text{–}9\text{–}13)$$

which checks the previous solution.

As a second example of a circuit that is driven by a current source, the circuit of Fig. 2–9-2 is analyzed. It is assumed that the current in the

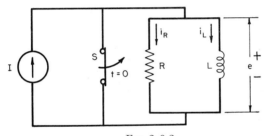

Fig. 2–9-2

inductor before $t = 0$ is zero; therefore $i(0)$ is also zero. Kirchhoff's current law for this circuit is

$$I = i_R + i_L \qquad (2\text{–}9\text{–}14)$$

or

$$I = \frac{e}{R} + \frac{1}{L} \int_0^t e\, dt = eG + \frac{1}{L} \int_0^t e\, dt \qquad (2\text{–}9\text{–}15)$$

The initial conditions can be found from Eq. 2–9-15:

$$I = e(0)G + 0 \qquad e(0) = \frac{I}{G}$$

The differential equation, as obtained by differentiating Eq. 2–9-15, is

$$0 = G \frac{de}{dt} + \frac{e}{L} \qquad (2\text{–}9\text{–}16)$$

where the form for e can be found:

$$e = A\epsilon^{-t/GL} \qquad (2\text{–}9\text{–}17)$$

The constant A is found by using the conditions at time $t = 0$:

$$A = \frac{I}{G}$$

and upon substitution the solution is

$$e = \frac{I}{G} \epsilon^{-t/GL} \qquad (2\text{-}9\text{-}18)$$

A comparison of Eqs. 2-2-2 and 2-9-16 shows that the E-R-C series circuit is the dual of the I-G-L parallel circuit.

2–10. General Case Using One Storage Element. If there is only one storage element in a complicated circuit, and if the equation for current or voltage associated with the storage element is the desired solution, the required current or voltage may be obtained with the aid of Thevenin's theorem or Norton's theorem and the equations already derived.

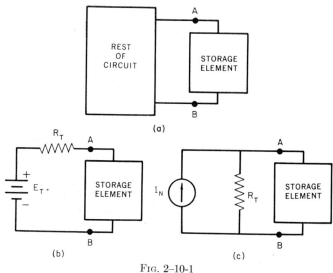

FIG. 2–10-1

The entire circuit can be divided into the storage element and the rest of the circuit as shown in Fig. 2–10-1a. No matter how complicated the rest of the circuit is, by use of Thevenin's theorem it can be replaced by the voltage E_T and the resistor R_T in series with storage element, resulting in the circuit of Fig. 2–10-1b; or by use of Norton's theorem the circuit may be replaced by the current I_N and the resistor R_T in parallel with the storage element, resulting in the circuit of Fig. 2–10-1c. Also, no matter what switching operations have gone on before time $t = 0$, these switching operations contribute only an initial current $i(0)$ in the case of an inductive storage element, or an initial voltage $e(0)$ in the case of a capacitive storage element.

Two examples of the use of Thevenin's theorem to simplify circuits have already been presented in the material associated with Figs. 2-8-4 and 2-8-8. A third example of the simplification of circuits is presented next by

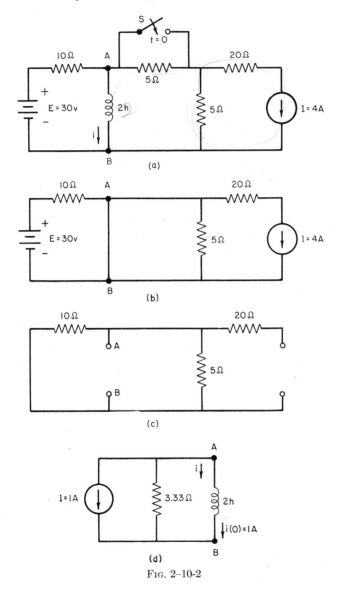

Fig. 2–10-2

using the circuit of Fig. 2–10-2a, except that this time Norton's theorem is used. In this circuit the switch S is open until steady-state conditions are reached, and S is closed at $t = 0$. The current i in the direction shown in the inductor is the desired solution. This example demonstrates a situation where Norton's theorem can be used to advantage: when the inductor is removed and a short is placed across the two terminals $A-B$ (as shown in Fig. 2–10-2b), the circuit is divided into two portions. After S is closed, the current in the inductor due to the 30-volt voltage source in the direction shown for i is 3 amp. The current in the inductor due to the 4-amp current source is -4 amp; therefore the total current in the direction shown for i is equal to -1 amp. The Norton's theorem resistance, which is the same as the Thevenin's theorem resistance, is obtained as the input resistance after removing the energy sources and replacing them with their internal resistance. The internal resistance of the voltage source is zero and that of the current source is infinity, as shown in Fig. 2–10-2c. The resistance looking into points $A-B$ is a 5- and a 10-ohm resistor in parallel; it is 3.33 ohms. The Norton theorem equivalent of this circuit is shown in Fig. 2–10-2d. The direction of the current source is chosen so that the current through a short across terminals $A-B$ is in the same direction as for the original circuit with $A-B$ shorted.

Before $t = 0$ in the steady state, the inductor is a short and by a reasoning process similar to the above $i(0)$ is found as $+1$ amp. Upon substituting in the form

$$i = i_{ss} + [i(0) - i_{ss}]\, \epsilon^{-Rt/L}$$

the solution is

$$i = -1 + [1 - (-1)]\, \epsilon^{(-3.33/2)t} = -1 + 2\, \epsilon^{-1.67t} \qquad (2\text{–}10\text{-}1)$$

If some voltage or current in the original circuit other than that associated with the storage element is desired, it can be found in a number of different ways. As an example, let it be supposed the current from left to right through the 10-ohm resistor is desired. One method of finding the current is to find the voltage across the resistor. As a start, the voltage across the 2-henry inductor is found. The voltage e_{AB} is

$$e_{AB} = L\frac{di}{dt} = -6.67\, \epsilon^{-1.67t} \qquad (2\text{–}10\text{-}2)$$

The voltage across the resistor is

$$e_R = E - e_{AB} = 30 + 6.67\, \epsilon^{-1.67t} \qquad (2\text{–}10\text{-}3)$$

Therefore the desired current is

$$i_R = \frac{e_R}{R} = 3 + 0.667\, \epsilon^{-1.67t} \qquad (2\text{–}10\text{-}4)$$

It should be noted that the time constants of i, e_{AB}, e_R, and i_R are all the same. This would be true for all other voltages and currents throughout the entire circuit, because all these currents and voltages are found by differentiation and addition (or subtraction) and none of these operations affects the exponent.

In still other circuits there is no obvious advantage in using either Thevenin's theorem or Norton's theorem, and either may be used with equal ease. The circuit of Fig. 2–10-3a is an example of this. The circuit of Fig. 2–10-3b is the Norton's theorem equivalent circuit and that of Fig. 2–10-3c the Thevenin's theorem equivalent circuit. The development of the two equivalent circuits is left as an exercise. A quick check

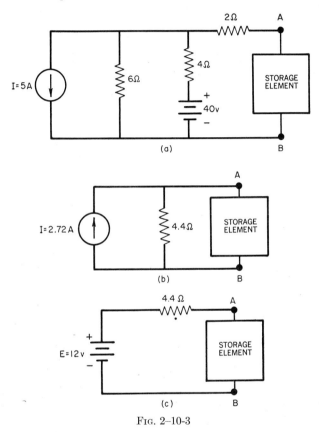

Fig. 2–10-3

on the circuit to the left of the A–B terminals shows that the open-circuit voltages of Figs. 2–10-3b and 2–10-3c are equal, and also that the short-circuit currents of these two circuits are equal. The two circuits are equivalent for any load across terminals A–B. Therefore any current generator with a finite internal resistance may be changed into a voltage generator, and vice versa. This fact is of importance in the equivalent circuits of electronic vacuum tubes and elsewhere.

2–11. The Impulse Function. The impulse function is introduced earlier in connection with a jump of voltage on a capacitor and with a jump of current in an inductor. It is worth while to consider further this concept which could have been introduced without regard to a circuit application. The configuration shown in Fig. 2–11-1a leads to the unit impulse. The area under this curve is unity, and as δ approaches zero the height $1/\delta$ increases without bound. The limiting case of this process yields that of the unit impulse. The configuration of Fig. 2–11-1b also has unit area, and as δ approaches zero the height $2/\delta$ increases without bound. The limiting case of this process also yields that of a unit impulse. The area

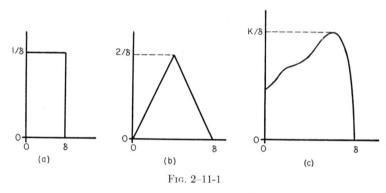

Fig. 2–11-1

under the curve of Fig. 2–11-1c is also assumed to be unity, and as δ approaches zero the height increases without bound and in the limit this wave shape also yields the unit impulse. The point being made is that a function with a plot of any configuration can be used if, as the width approaches zero, the height increases without bound and the area under the curve remains constant. In the limit all these functions lead to the same concept.

A unit impulse is shown in Fig. 2–11-2a, and the integral of the impulse is shown in Fig. 2–11-2b. That the second curve is the integral of the first

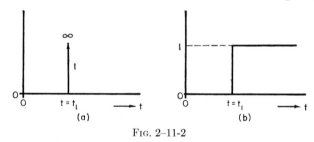

Fig. 2–11-2

can be seen by visualizing the integral as the area under the curve to the left of the time t as t moves from left to right across Fig. 2–11-2a. This integral is zero until time t_1, at which time the unit area under the unit impulse contributes 1 to the integral; and, since there is no other area under the plot of the function being integrated, the value of the integral remains as unity from t_1 onward.

Since integration and differentiation are in a certain sense inverse processes, the curve of Fig. 2–11-2a is the derivative of the curve of Fig. 2–11-2b. Therefore, when a function is being differentiated, an impulse is generated whenever there is a discontinuity in the function and the value of the impulse is equal to the magnitude of the discontinuity.

This point of view is utilized in the situation shown in Fig. 2–11-3. Before $t = 0$ the 2-henry inductor has a current $i_1 = 10$ amp and the 4-henry

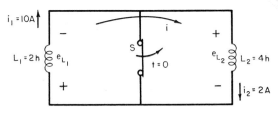

Fig. 2–11-3

inductor has a current $i_2 = 2$ amp, in the directions shown. Since the two inductors are divided by a switch, these two currents need not be the same. However, when the switch S is opened at $t = 0$, the two inductors are put in series and both must carry the same current (labeled i in the figure). It is to be reasoned that, if one current jumps, an impulse of voltage appears across that inductor; this must also appear across the other inductor, whence both currents must jump to some common value as indicated in Fig. 2–11-4. The current in the 4-henry inductor jumps from 2 amp to i

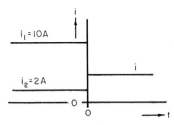

Fig. 2–11-4

amperes, or the magnitude of the discontinuity is $i - 2$ and this is equal to the value of the impulse created by di_2/dt at $t = 0$. Multiplication of this value by $L_2 = 4$ henrys gives the value of the voltage impulse appearing across L_2 at $t = 0$ as $4(i - 2)$. The current in the 2-henry inductor jumps from 10 amp to i amperes, the magnitude of the discontinuity is $i - 10$, and this is equal to the value of the impulse created by di_1/dt at $t = 0$. Multiplication of this value by $L_1 = 2$ henrys gives the value of the voltage impulse appearing across L_1 at $t = 0$ as $2(i - 10)$. Since the two inductors are in parallel, these two voltage impulses are the same; and with proper care with respect to signs the following equation can be written:

$$4(i-2) = -2(i-10) \qquad (2\text{-}11\text{-}1)$$

which gives for i a value

$$i = \frac{20+8}{6} = 4.66 \text{ amp} \qquad (2\text{-}11\text{-}2)$$

This equation can be written in more general form:

$$(L_1 + L_2)i = L_1 i_1 + L_2 i_2 \qquad (2\text{-}11\text{-}3)$$

The significance of Eq. 2–11-3 can be stated in words as: When some switching such as that shown in Fig. 2–11-3 occurs, the current jumps to a new value such that the product of inductance and current remains constant. The product of inductance and current can be interpreted by using the definition of inductance:

$$LI = \left(\frac{N\phi}{I}\right)I = N\phi \qquad (2\text{-}11\text{-}4)$$

Therefore the fact that the product LI remains constant evidences the concept of the conservation of flux linkages.

The dual of the situation just discussed is shown in Fig. 2–11-5. In this circuit, before $t = 0$ the 5-μf capacitor has an initial charge with $e_1 = 100$

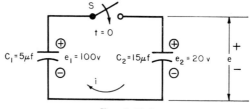

Fig. 2–11-5

volts and the 15-μf capacitor has an initial charge with $e_2 = 20$ volts. After S is closed, the two capacitors are in parallel and both voltages jump to a common value termed e volts. Since this situation is the dual of the one just presented, the results should also be duals. The equation just obtained,

$$(L_1 + L_2)i = L_1 i_1 + L_2 i_2 \qquad (2\text{-}11\text{-}5)$$

has a dual with L_1 replaced by C_1, L_2 by C_2, and the currents by the corresponding voltages. Therefore, for the circuit containing capacitors, the corresponding equation is

$$(C_1 + C_2)e = C_1 e_1 + C_2 e_2 \qquad (2\text{-}11\text{-}6)$$

Since the product of Ce is charge, Eq. 2–11-6 is a statement of the conservation-of-charge concept. This concept can be applied to the problem at hand as follows. Before $t = 0$ the charge on C_1 is

$$q_1 = e_1 C_1 = 100 \times 5 \times 10^{-6} = 500 \times 10^{-6} \qquad (2\text{-}11\text{-}7)$$

and the charge on C_2 is

$$q_2 = e_2C_2 = 20 \times 15 \times 10^{-6} = 300 \times 10^{-6} \qquad (2\text{-}11\text{-}8)$$

and the total charge is

$$q = q_1 + q_2 = 800 \times 10^{-6} \qquad (2\text{-}11\text{-}9)$$

After $t = 0$ the total charge remains the same and the total C is 20 μf; therefore the voltage can be found:

$$e = \frac{q}{C} = \frac{800 \times 10^{-6}}{20 \times 10^{-6}} = 40 \text{ volts} \qquad (2\text{-}11\text{-}10)$$

The value of the impulse of current that causes the voltage on the capacitors to jump can be found from

$$i = C \frac{de}{dt} \qquad (2\text{-}11\text{-}11)$$

The value of the impulse at $t = 0$ contained in de_2/dt is equal to the magnitude of the discontinuity in e_2, which is $(40 - 20)$ volts, and therefore the value of the impulse is 20. When this is multiplied by C_2, the value of the current impulse is

$$15 \times 10^{-6} \times 20 = 300 \times 10^{-6} \qquad (2\text{-}11\text{-}12)$$

The correctness of the work can be checked by also determining the value of the current impulse from C_1 and de_1/dt.

2-12. Certain Circuits Containing More Than One Storage Element of the Same Kind. If a circuit has two or more inductors in series, as in Fig. 2-12-1a where R_1 is the resistance of the L_1 inductor, etc., the fact

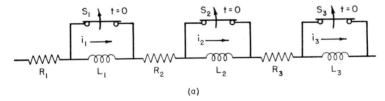

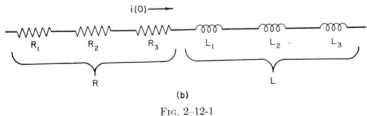

Fɪɢ. 2-12-1

that each inductor may have a different current before $t = 0$ is indicated by i_1 existing through S_1, etc. At $t = 0$ all the switches S are open and $i(0)$ can be found by the concept of conservation of flux linkages. The total R is equal to $R_1 + R_2 + R_3$, the total L is equal to $L_1 + L_2 + L_3$, and the rest of the problem involves an R-L circuit with an initial current $i(0)$ (shown in Fig. 2-12-1b) and can be solved by methods already presented.

The dual of this situation is shown in Fig. 2–12-2a, where C_1 has an initial voltage e_1, etc., and S_1 and S_2 are closed at $t = 0$. At $t = 0$ the com-

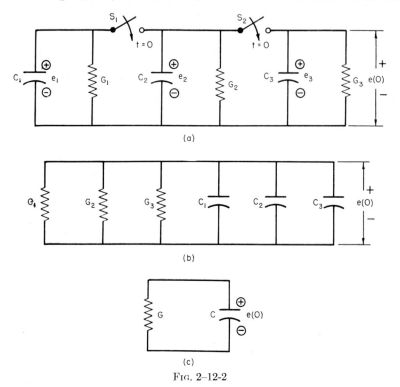

(a)

(b)

(c)

FIG. 2–12-2

mon voltage $e(0)$ can be found by the concept of conservation of charge, and the three G's and C's are in parallel, giving

$$G = G_1 + G_2 + G_3$$
$$C = C_1 + C_2 + C_3$$

(2–12-1)

The equivalent circuit is shown in Fig. 2–12-2c.

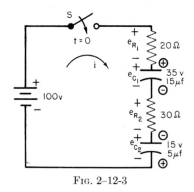

FIG. 2–12-3

If a circuit has two or more capacitors in series, the solution may be considered in a manner illustrated in the following example for the circuit of Fig. 2–12-3. Kirchhoff's voltage equation can be written

$$100 = e_{R_1} + e_{c_1} + e_{R_2} + e_{c_2} \tag{2-12-2}$$

whence

$$100 = 20\,i + \frac{\displaystyle\int_0^t i\,dt}{15 \times 10^{-6}} + 35 + 30\,i + \frac{\displaystyle\int_0^t i\,dt}{5 \times 10^{-6}} - 15 \tag{2-12-3}$$

or

$$80 = 50\,i + \frac{1}{3.75 \times 10^{-6}} \int_0^t i\,dt \tag{2-12-4}$$

The solution for the current i is

$$80 = 50\,i(0) + 0; \quad \text{whence } i(0) = \frac{80}{50} = 1.6$$

Then

$$i = A \exp\left(-\frac{t}{50 \times 3.75 \times 10^{-6}}\right) = 1.6\,\epsilon^{-5333\,t} \tag{2-12-5}$$

The voltage e_{c_1} is

$$e_{c_1} = \frac{\displaystyle\int_0^t i\,dt}{15 \times 10^{-6}} + 35 = \frac{\displaystyle\int_0^t 1.6\,\epsilon^{-5333\,t}\,dt}{15 \times 10^{-6}} + 35 \tag{2-12-6}$$

whence

$$e_{c_1} = 55 - 20\,\epsilon^{-5333\,t}$$

The voltage e_{c_2} is

$$e_{c_2} = \frac{1}{5 \times 10^{-6}} \int_0^t 1.6\,\epsilon^{-5333t}\,dt - 15 \tag{2-12-7}$$

whence

$$e_{c_2} = 45 - 60\,\epsilon^{-5333t}$$

The following technique may prove helpful in some situations. A capacitor C with an initial voltage of $e(0)$ with the polarity as shown in Fig. 2–12-4a can be replaced by a capacitor C with no initial charge in series with a constant-voltage source of $e(0)$ volts as shown in Fig. 2–12-4b.

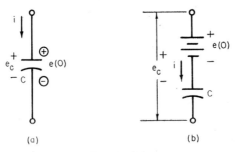

(a)   (b)

FIG. 2–12-4

The equation for voltage across the terminals of these two circuits shows that they are equivalent. The equation referred to is

$$e_c = \frac{1}{C} \int_0^t i \, dt + e(0) \qquad (2\text{-}12\text{-}8)$$

With this technique the circuit of Fig. 2–12-3 can be redrawn as shown in Fig. 2–12-5a. With respect to the current i, the circuit of Fig. 2–12-5b is

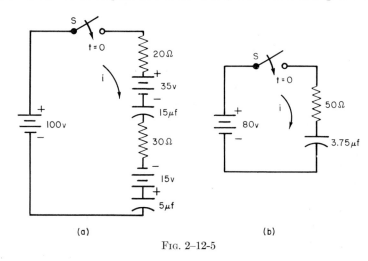

(a)   (b)

Fig. 2–12-5

an equivalent circuit. The voltage sources are combined to give 80 volts, the resistors are combined to give 50 ohms, and the capacitors are combined to give 3.75 μf. The switch S is closed at $t = 0$ on this circuit and the current i is

$$i = \frac{E}{R} \epsilon^{-t/RC} = \frac{80}{50} \exp\left(-\frac{t}{50 \times 3.75 \times 10^{-6}}\right) = 1.6 \, \epsilon^{-5333\,t} \qquad (2\text{-}12\text{-}9)$$

The voltages e_{c_1} and e_{c_2} can then be found in exactly the same manner as in Eqs. 2–12-6 and 2–12-7.

A dual situation to that shown in Fig. 2–12-3 is depicted in Fig. 2–12-6. The problem is to find the voltage e across the circuit after S is opened. The problem is worked by using the dual concept to the equivalent-circuit approach, as just done for the E-R-C series circuit. As an introduction to

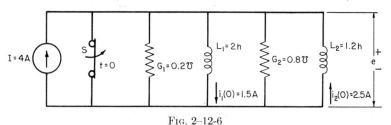

Fig. 2–12-6

this, it can be shown that an inductor L with an initial current $i(0)$ as shown in Fig. 2–12-7a can be replaced by an inductor L with no initial

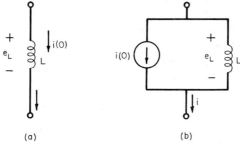

(a)   (b)

FIG. 2–12-7

current in parallel with a constant-current source, as shown in Fig. 2–12-7b. When the equations for currents are written in these two cases as

$$i = \frac{1}{L} \int_0^t e \, dt + i(0) \tag{2–12-10}$$

the equivalents of the two circuits can be seen.

With this technique the circuit of Fig. 2–12-6 can be redrawn as shown

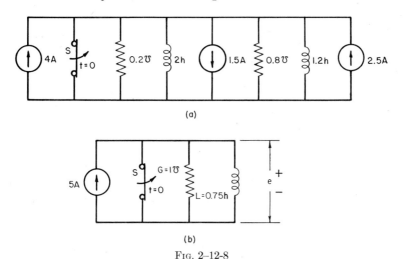

(a)

(b)

FIG. 2–12-8

in Fig. 2–12-8a. The equation for voltage across this circuit is

$$e = \frac{I}{G} \epsilon^{-t/GL} = \frac{5}{1} \epsilon^{-t/(1 \times 0.75)} = 5 \, \epsilon^{-1.33t} \tag{2–12-11}$$

The current in the L_1 inductor in the downward direction is

$$i_{L_1} = \frac{1}{L_1} \int_0^t e \, dt + i_1(0) = 3.38 - 1.88 \, \epsilon^{-1.33t} \tag{2–12-12}$$

and the current in the L_2 inductor in the downward direction is

$$i_{L_2} = \frac{1}{L_2} \int_0^t e \, dt - i_2(0) = 0.62 - 3.12 \, \epsilon^{-1.33t} \qquad (2\text{-}12\text{-}13)$$

A capacitor with an initial charge can be analyzed as a capacitor with no initial charge in series with a constant-voltage source. An inductor with an initial current can be analyzed as an inductor with no initial current in parallel with a constant-current source. Therefore, if one wished to pursue these techniques, all circuits involving R, L, and C elements could be solved by developing an equivalent circuit that contains no energy storage at $t = 0$.

2–13. Differentiating and Integrating Circuits. The series or parallel R-C and R-L circuits are often used as differentiating or integrating circuits. To show the meaning of these terms, consider a voltage e placed on a quiescent series R-C circuit.

$$e = iR + \frac{1}{C} \int_0^t i \, dt$$
$$\frac{e}{R} = i + \frac{1}{RC} \int_0^t i \, dt \qquad (2\text{-}13\text{-}1)$$

If the time constant RC is sufficiently large, the second term on the right side of Eq. 2–13-1 can be neglected by comparison with the first term. The equation then becomes

$$\frac{e}{R} \approx i \qquad (2\text{-}13\text{-}2)$$

and the current i is approximately proportional to the voltage e. The voltage e_c on the capacitor C is

$$e_c = \frac{1}{C} \int_0^t i \, dt \approx \frac{1}{RC} \int_0^t e \, dt \qquad (2\text{-}13\text{-}3)$$

Thus voltage e_c is approximately proportional to the integral of the applied voltage e. Hence this series R-C circuit with a "large" time constant is termed an integrating circuit.

Again from Eq. 2–13-1, if the time constant RC is sufficiently small, the equation can be approximated:

$$\frac{e}{R} \approx \frac{1}{RC} \int_0^t i \, dt \qquad (2\text{-}13\text{-}4)$$

or

$$i = C \frac{de}{dt} \qquad (2\text{-}13\text{-}5)$$

The voltage e_R across the resistor R is

$$e_R = iR \approx RC \frac{de}{dt} \qquad (2\text{-}13\text{-}6)$$

which indicates that e_R is approximately proportional to the derivative of the applied voltage e. Hence this series R-C circuit with a small time constant is termed a differentiating circuit.

In a similar manner, the series R-L circuit with an applied voltage e may be examined; thus

$$e = iR + L\frac{di}{dt}$$

or

$$\frac{e}{R} = i + \frac{L}{R}\frac{di}{dt} \tag{2-13-7}$$

If the time constant L/R is sufficiently large, the equation can be approximated:

$$\frac{e}{R} \approx \frac{L}{R}\frac{di}{dt} \tag{2-13-8}$$

or

$$i \approx \frac{1}{L}\int_0^t e\,dt \tag{2-13-9}$$

The voltage e_R becomes

$$e_R = iR \approx \frac{R}{L}\int_0^t e\,dt \tag{2-13-10}$$

This series R-L circuit with a large time constant is termed an integrating circuit.

If the time constant L/R is sufficiently small, Eq. 2—13-7 can be approximated:

$$i \approx \frac{e}{R} \tag{2-13-11}$$

and

$$e_L = L\frac{di}{dt} \approx \frac{L}{R}\frac{de}{dt} \tag{2-13-12}$$

which indicates that a series R-L circuit with a small time constant is a differentiating circuit.

A similar development can be made for the parallel R-C and R-L circuits, and the results will be the duals of those just presented. This dual development is left as an exercise.

The result of this work is tabulated in Table 2–13.

TABLE 2–13

Circuit	Derivative appears as (small t_c)	Integral appears as (large t_c)
Series R-L	e_L	e_R
Series R-C	e_R	e_C
Parallel R-L	i_R	i_L
Parallel R-C	i_C	i_R

PROBLEMS

2–1. Given the circuit shown in Fig. 2–2-1, find $(di/dt)(0)$, $(d^2i/dt^2)(0)$, $(de_c/dt)(0)$, and $(d^2e_c/dt^2)(0)$ from the differential equation. Do not use the solution obtained in the text.

2–2. The wave shape of current shown in Fig. 1–4-2a passes through an R-C circuit where $R = 1000$ ohms and $C = 40$ μf. Assume that $e(0) = 0$. Calculate and sketch the voltage across the R-C circuit. What is the peak value of this voltage?

2–3. Given an E-R-C circuit as shown in Fig. 2–2-1 where $E = 50$ volts, $R = 1000$ ohms, $C = 0.5$ μf, and $e(0) = 30$ volts with the polarity as shown. When the current reaches a value of 0.030 amp, how much power is being dissipated in R? how much power is going into the electric field? how much energy is stored in the electric field?

2–4. Given the data from an E-R-C circuit that has been plotted as shown in Fig. 2–P-1. From this plot, obtain t_c for the circuit.

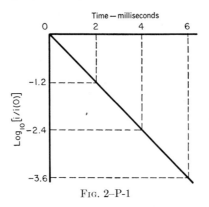

Fig. 2–P-1

2–5. Given the circuit shown in Fig. 2–5-1 with $i(0) = 0$, find $(d^2i/dt^2)(0)$, $(d^3i/dt^3)(0)$, $(de_L/dt)(0)$, and $(d^2e_L/dt^2)(0)$ from the differential equation. Do not use the solution in the text.

2–6. Starting from Eq. 2–2-1, written in terms of q such as $E = R(dq/dt) + q/C$, solve for Eq. 2–2-19 in terms of q without first getting the current equation and integrating.

2–7. The field coil of a relay has a resistance of 50 ohms and an inductance of 4 henrys. The contacts of the relay do not close until the current in the field of the relay has reached 0.14 amp.

(a) If the relay is to be used with a 10-volt battery, find the time required for the contacts to close after the voltage is applied to the field.

(b) To what value must the battery voltage be increased in order to cut the time of operation of the relay in half?

2–8. The wave shape of current shown in Fig. 1–5-2a passes through an R-L circuit, where $R = 1$ ohm and $L = 0.10$ henry. Calculate and sketch the voltage across the R-L circuit.

2–9. Given an E-R-L circuit as shown in Fig. 2–5-1, where $E = 50$ volts, $R = 15$ ohms, and $L = 0.3$ henry. When the current reaches a value of 2 amp, how much power is being dissipated in R? how much power is going into the magnetic field? how much energy is stored in the magnetic field?

2-10. Given data taken from an *E-R-L* circuit that has been plotted as shown in Fig. 2–P-2. From this plot obtain t_c for the circuit.

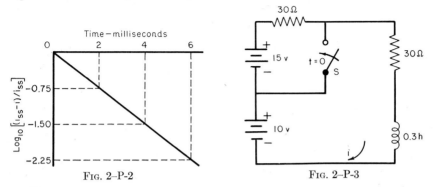

FIG. 2–P-2   FIG. 2–P-3

2-11. Given the circuit shown in Fig. 2–P-3. The switch *S* is open until steady-state conditions are reached, and then, at $t = 0$, *S* is closed. Find the equation for the current i after $t = 0$. Make a rough sketch of the current.

2-12. Given the circuit shown in Fig. 2–P-4. Switch S_1 is closed, and then 0.09 sec later switch S_2 is closed. Find the charge q on the capacitor 0.04 sec after S_2 is closed.

$$Q = 1.08 \times 10^{-3} \ cuuL$$

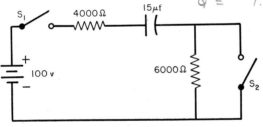

FIG. 2–P-4

2-13. Given the circuit shown in Fig. 2–P-5. The gas tube breaks down when $E_1 = 90$ volts. Assume that E_2, the voltage on the capacitor after the tube discharges, is 32 volts. Determine the value of *R* necessary for the circuit to repeat the entire cycle at a rate of 400 cps. Neglect the time involved to discharge the capacitor.

$$R = 374 \ \Omega$$

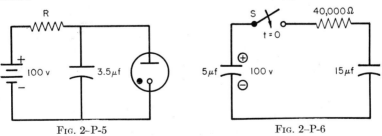

FIG. 2–P-5   FIG. 2–P-6

2-14. Find the equation for the voltage across the 5-μf capacitor in the circuit shown in Fig. 2–P-6. $e_{c5} = 25 + 75 e^{-6.66t}$

2-15. Given the circuit shown in Fig. 2–P-7. The switch S_1 is closed, and 0.005

$$e_{c15} = 25 - 25 e^{-6.66t}$$

sec later switch S_2 is closed at time $t = 0$. Find the equation for the voltage on the 5-μf capacitor after $t = 0$.

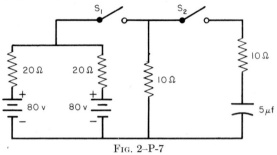

FIG. 2–P-7

2–16. In the circuit shown in Fig. 2–P-8 the switch S is open until steady-state conditions have been reached. At time $t = 0$, S is closed. Find the equation for the current i through the inductor as shown after $t = 0$.

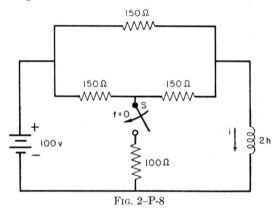

FIG. 2–P-8

2–17. Given the circuit shown in Fig. 2–P-9, find the equation for the voltage on the 25-μf capacitor written with a polarity reference (+) on top, (−) on bottom.

$e_{C_{25}} = 22.5 - 7.5e^{-8000t}$

$e_{C_{15}} = 22.5 + 12.5e^{-8000t}$

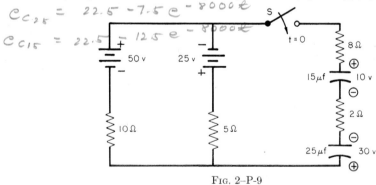

FIG. 2–P-9

2–18. The switch S is open until steady-state conditions have been reached in the circuit of Fig. 2–P-10. Then at $t = 0$ switch S is closed. Find the equation for the current i in the direction shown after $t = 0$.

2–19. Verify the bottom two entries in Table 2–13.

2–20. The current of Fig. 1–P–4 is passed through a series circuit consisting of

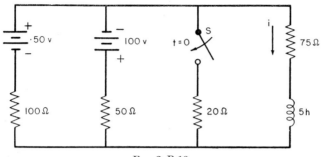

Fig. 2–P–10

2000-ohm resistor and 2.5-μf capacitor. Sketch the voltage across the circuit and the instantaneous power taken by the circuit.

2–21. The voltage of Fig. 1–P–5 is impressed across a parallel circuit of a 185-μh inductor and a 3-ohm resistor. Plot the total current, power, and energy taken by the circuit.

2–22. The relay of the relay oscillator circuit shown in Fig. 2–P–11 picks up (S is

$$t_1 + t_2 = 0.085 + 0.054$$
$$f = 7.17 \ cps$$

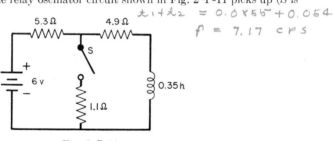

Fig. 2–P–11

closed) at a current of 0.52 amp and drops out (S is open) at 0.26 amp. What is the frequency of oscillation?

2–23. For Fig. 2–P–12 assume that before $t = 0$ the switch S (double-pole single-throw) is open and that the circuit is in steady-state condition. At $t = 0$, S is closed. Calculate and plot the current in the 0.3-henry inductance.

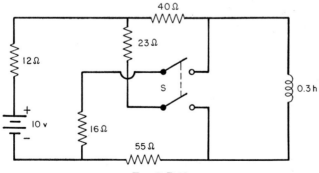

Fig. 2–P–12

2–24. In the circuit of Fig. 2–2–1 determine at what time the power received by the capacitor is a maximum. What is this maximum power?

2–25. In the circuit of Fig. 2–5–1 determine at what time the power received by the inductor is a maximum. What is this maximum power? $t_{max} = \frac{L}{R} Ln\,2$

2–26. The circuit of Fig. 2–P–13 is that of a capacitor relay oscillator. The 3000-ohm resistor is that of the relay coil whose inductance is assumed small enough to

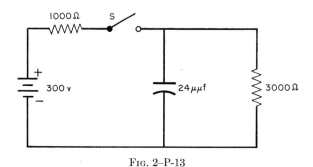

FIG. 2–P–13

be neglected. The relay contact S is closed initially and the current builds up in the relay coil until at 60 ma the contact S opens. The current in the relay coil decreases until at 15 ma the contact S again closes. Find the frequency of oscillation.

2–27. A 440-volt d-c source is suddenly applied to a series R-L circuit. The following current results: $R = 241\,\Omega$, $L = 0.86\,h$

t (milliseconds)	0	1	2	4	6	∞
i (amperes)	0	0.45	0.78	1.23	1.48	1.82

Calculate the values of the resistance and the inductance.

2–28. For the circuit of Fig. 2–P–14 and before $t = 0$, the switch S is on contact A and the steady state is attained. S makes contact with B, remains there for 0.5 sec,

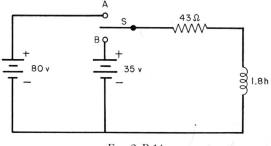

FIG. 2–P–14

and then switches back to A at $t = 0$. Obtain the equations for the current flowing in the inductor after S returns to A at $t = 0$.

2–29. If the switch S is opened at $t = 0$, find the equation for the voltage across the constant-current generator of Fig. 2–P-15.

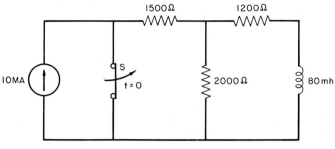

1500Ω   1200Ω

IOMA   S   t = 0   2000Ω   80 mh

FIG. 2–P-15

2–30. The circuit of Fig. 2–P-16 is in the steady state at $t = 0$, when switch S is closed. What is the expression for the voltage across the capacitor after $t = 0$?

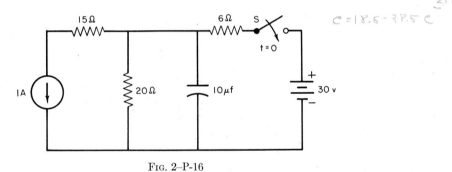

2170

$C = 18.5 - 37.5 C$

15Ω   6Ω   S   t = 0

1A   20Ω   10μf   30 v

FIG. 2–P-16

2–31. Assume that switches S_1 and S_2 are closed and that the circuit of Fig. 2–P-17 is in the steady state. At $t = 0$ both switches S_1 and S_2 are opened. Obtain the equations for the voltages across C_1 and C_2 after $t = 0$.

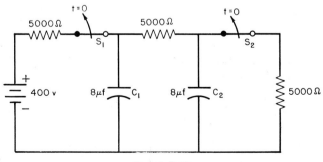

t = 0   5000Ω   5000Ω   t = 0

5000Ω   S₁   S₂

400 v   8μf   C₁   8μf   C₂   5000Ω

FIG. 2–P-17

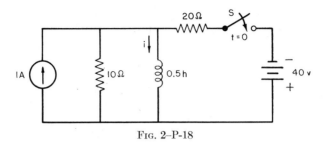

FIG. 2–P-18

2-32. In the circuit of Fig. 2–P-18, S is open until the steady state is reached and, at $t = 0$, S is closed. Find the equation for the current in the 0.5-henry inductor in the direction shown.

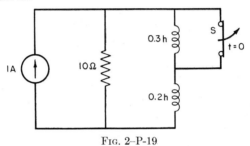

FIG. 2–P-19

2-33. In the circuit of Fig. 2–P-19, S is closed until steady state is reached (the current in the 0.3-henry inductor is zero) and, at $t = 0$, S is opened. Find the equa-

$$i_L = 1 - 0.6e^{-20t}$$

$$i_R = 0.6e^{-20t}$$

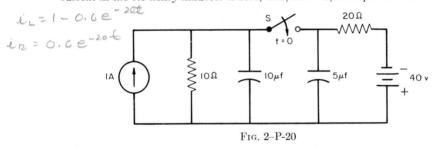

FIG. 2–P-20

tion for the current in the 0.2-henry inductor. Also find the current through the 10-ohm resistor.

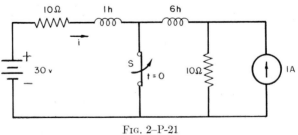

FIG. 2–P-21

$e c_6 = -6.66$

2-34. In the circuit of Fig. 2–P-20, S is opened until the steady state is reached and, at $t = 0$, S is closed. Find the equation for the voltage on the 5-μf capacitor.

2-35. In the circuit of Fig. 2–P-21, S is closed until the steady state is reached and, at $t = 0$, S is opened. Find the equation for the current in the 1-henry inductor in the direction shown.

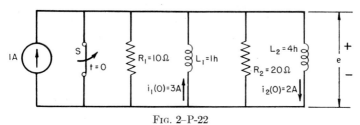

FIG. 2–P-22

2-36. In the circuit of Fig. 2–P-22 the switch S is opened at $t = 0$. Find the equation for the voltage e and the current in the 4-henry inductor in the down direction.

CHAPTER 3

CIRCUITS WITH TWO STORAGE ELEMENTS

The first part of this chapter is intended as a very brief introduction to or review of second-order differential equations and hyperbolic functions. The last part of the chapter is concerned with the application of these topics to the solution of problems arising from series and parallel circuits having two storage elements.

3–1. Second-Order Differential Equations. The example of the second-order differential equation to be considered is

$$\frac{d^2i}{dt^2} + 5\frac{di}{dt} + 6\,i = 0 \tag{3-1-1}$$

with the initial conditions

$$i(0) = 0 \qquad \frac{di}{dt}\,(0) = 4 \tag{3-1-2}$$

The desired solution must satisfy both the differential equation and the initial conditions. Since a current of the form $i = A\epsilon^{st}$ provided the solution for previous problems, it is reasonable to try the same form again. Thus

$$i = A\epsilon^{st} \qquad \frac{di}{dt} = sA\epsilon^{st} \qquad \frac{d^2i}{dt^2} = s^2A\epsilon^{st}$$

When these are substituted in Eq. 3–1-1, the result is

$$A\epsilon^{st}[s^2 + 5\,s + 6] = 0 \tag{3-1-3}$$

Since $A\epsilon^{st}$ is not zero, the term inside the brackets must be

$$s^2 + 5\,s + 6 = 0 \tag{3-1-4}$$

or, when factored,

$$(s+2)(s+3) = 0 \tag{3-1-5}$$

the characteristic roots are

$$s_1 = -2 \qquad s_2 = -3 \tag{3-1-6}$$

Eq. 3–1-4 is termed the characteristic equation of the differential Eq. 3–1-1, and s_1 and s_2 are the roots of the characteristic equation. At first glance the fact that there are two roots seems to indicate the possibility of two solutions. Both of the terms $i_1 = A_1\epsilon^{-2t}$ and $i_2 = A_2\epsilon^{-3t}$ satisfy the differential equation for any values of the A's. However, when either i_1 or i_2 is used in an attempt to satisfy both initial conditions of Eqs. 3–1-2, it is found that one of the conditions can be satisfied but the other cannot. For example, if i_1 is forced to satisfy the initial condition $i(0) = 0$, A_1 is found to be zero: $\quad i(0) = 0 = A_1\epsilon^0 = A_1 \quad$ or $\quad A_1 = 0$

62

If A_1 is zero, the solution i_1 is $i_1 = 0$ and the condition $(di/dt)(0) = 4$ cannot be satisfied. A linear combination of i_1 and i_2, however, can satisfy these conditions in the following manner. The terms i_1 and i_2 both satisfy the differential equation, 3–1-1, in that when they are substituted into the equation the equation equals zero. In a similar manner, if the sum $i_1 + i_2$ is substituted into the equation, the equation equals zero, and hence it is satisfied. The sum i_1 plus i_2 can be written

$$i = A_1 \epsilon^{-2t} + A_2 \epsilon^{-3t} \qquad (3\text{–}1\text{–}7)$$

and the two constants A_1 and A_2 make it possible to satisfy the two initial conditions. When the condition $i(0) = 0$ is imposed on Eq. 3–1-7, the sum of the two constants is

$$0 = A_1 + A_2 \quad \text{or} \quad A_2 = - A_1 \qquad (3\text{–}1\text{–}8)$$

and, upon substitution, Eq. 3–1-7 becomes

$$i = A_1[\epsilon^{-2t} - \epsilon^{-3t}] \qquad (3\text{–}1\text{–}9)$$

The derivative of the current is

$$\frac{di}{dt} = A_1[- 2\,\epsilon^{-2t} + 3\,\epsilon^{-3t}] \qquad (3\text{–}1\text{–}10)$$

and, when the condition $(di/dt)(0) = 4$ is imposed, A_1 is found to be

$$4 = A_1[- 2 + 3] \quad \text{or} \quad A_1 = 4 \qquad (3\text{–}1\text{–}11)$$

and, upon substitution, the solution is

$$i = 4[\epsilon^{-2t} - \epsilon^{-3t}] \qquad (3\text{–}1\text{–}12)$$

Therefore, as Eq. 3–1-12 satisfies both the differential equation and the initial conditions, it is the desired solution.

As a second example, consider the equation

$$4\frac{d^2e}{dt^2} + 5\frac{de}{dt} + e = 12 \qquad (3\text{–}1\text{–}13)$$

and associated initial conditions

$$e(0) = 0 \qquad \frac{de}{dt}(0) = 0 \qquad (3\text{–}1\text{–}14)$$

Since the right side of Eq. 3–1-13 is not zero, e has a steady-state term as well as a transient term; thus

$$e = e_{ss} + e_{tr} \qquad (3\text{–}1\text{–}15)$$

As time t becomes large, the transient term e_{tr} approaches zero, and only the steady-state term e_{ss} is left. Since e_{ss} is a constant,

$$\frac{de_{ss}}{dt} = 0 \quad \text{and} \quad \frac{d^2e_{ss}}{dt^2} = 0$$

and Eq. 3–1-13 reduces to

$$e_{ss} = 12 \qquad (3\text{–}1\text{–}16)$$

When Eq. 3-1-15 is substituted into Eq. 3-1-13:

$$4 \frac{d^2(e_{ss} + e_{tr})}{dt^2} + 5 \frac{d(e_{ss} + e_{tr})}{dt} + (e_{ss} + e_{tr}) = 12$$

the result is

$$4 \frac{d^2 e_{tr}}{dt^2} + 5 \frac{d e_{tr}}{dt} + e_{tr} = 0 \qquad (3\text{-}1\text{-}17)$$

As for the previous example, e_{tr} can be assumed to be of the form

$$e_{tr} = A \epsilon^{st}$$

resulting in

$$A \epsilon^{st} [4 \, s^2 + 5 \, s + 1] = 0 \qquad (3\text{-}1\text{-}18)$$

and the characteristic equation is

$$[4 \, s^2 + 5 \, s + 1] = (4 \, s + 1)(s + 1) = 0 \qquad (3\text{-}1\text{-}19)$$

which has the two roots

$$s_1 = -\tfrac{1}{4} \qquad s_2 = -1 \qquad (3\text{-}1\text{-}20)$$

The voltage equation is

$$e = e_{ss} + e_{tr} = 12 + A_1 \epsilon^{-t/4} + A_2 \epsilon^{-1t} \qquad (3\text{-}1\text{-}21)$$

When the initial condition $e(0) = 0$ is imposed on this equation, the result is

$$0 = 12 + A_1 + A_2 \quad \text{or} \quad A_1 + A_2 = -12 \qquad (3\text{-}1\text{-}22)$$

When Eq. 3-1-21 is differentiated,

$$\frac{de}{dt} = -\tfrac{1}{4} A_1 \epsilon^{-t/4} - A_2 \epsilon^{-1t} \qquad (3\text{-}1\text{-}23)$$

and the initial condition $(de/dt)(0) = 0$ is imposed, the result is

$$0 = -\tfrac{1}{4} A_1 - A_2 \quad \text{or} \quad A_1 = -4 A_2 \qquad (3\text{-}1\text{-}24)$$

Eqs. 3-1-22 and 3-1-24 can be solved simultaneously:

$$A_1 = -16 \qquad A_2 = 4 \qquad (3\text{-}1\text{-}25)$$

The desired solution is

$$e = 12 - 16 \, \epsilon^{-t/4} + 4 \, \epsilon^{-1t} \qquad (3\text{-}1\text{-}26)$$

3-2. Hyperbolic Functions. Hyperbolic functions are related to the hyperbola in a manner somewhat similar to the way trigonometric functions are related to the circle. The geometry of hyperbolic functions is not of interest here, but the analytic similarities and differences between the hyperbolic and the trigonometric functions are useful. Euler's relation states

$$\epsilon^{j\beta t} = \cos \beta t + j \sin \beta t$$

and

$$\epsilon^{-j\beta t} = \cos \beta t - j \sin \beta t$$

$$(3\text{-}2\text{-}1)$$

Eqs. 3–2–1 yield the relationships

$$\cos \beta t = \frac{\epsilon^{+j\beta t} + \epsilon^{-j\beta t}}{2} \qquad \sin \beta t = \frac{\epsilon^{+j\beta t} - \epsilon^{-j\beta t}}{2j} \qquad (3\text{-}2\text{-}2)$$

Hyperbolic functions can be defined in a manner quite similar to Eqs. 3–2–2:

$$\cosh bt = \frac{\epsilon^{bt} + \epsilon^{-bt}}{2} \qquad \sinh bt = \frac{\epsilon^{bt} - \epsilon^{-bt}}{2} \qquad (3\text{-}2\text{-}3)$$

Eqs. 3–2–3 yield the relationships

$$\begin{aligned}
\epsilon^{bt} &= \cosh bt + \sinh bt \\
\epsilon^{-bt} &= \cosh bt - \sinh bt
\end{aligned} \qquad (3\text{-}2\text{-}4)$$

Often in circuit work b may be imaginary; thus $b = j\beta$, where β is real. In such a situation the hyperbolic functions become

$$\cosh bt = \frac{\epsilon^{bt} + \epsilon^{-bt}}{2} = \cosh j\beta t = \frac{\epsilon^{j\beta t} + \epsilon^{-j\beta t}}{2} = \cos \beta t \qquad (3\text{-}2\text{-}5)$$

and

$$\sinh bt = \frac{\epsilon^{bt} - \epsilon^{-bt}}{2} =$$

$$\sinh j\beta t = \frac{\epsilon^{j\beta t} - \epsilon^{-j\beta t}}{2} = j\left[\frac{\epsilon^{j\beta t} - \epsilon^{-j\beta t}}{2j}\right] = j \sin \beta t \qquad (3\text{-}2\text{-}6)$$

Similarly β may be imaginary, or $\beta = jb$, where b is real and the trigonometric functions become

$$\cos \beta t = \frac{\epsilon^{j\beta t} + \epsilon^{-j\beta t}}{2} = \cos jbt = \frac{\epsilon^{j(jb)t} + \epsilon^{-j(jb)t}}{2} = \frac{\epsilon^{-bt} + \epsilon^{bt}}{2} = \cosh bt$$

$$(3\text{-}2\text{-}7)$$

and

$$\sin \beta t = \frac{\epsilon^{+j\beta t} - \epsilon^{-j\beta t}}{2j} =$$

$$\sin jbt = \frac{\epsilon^{j(jb)t} - \epsilon^{-j(jb)t}}{2j} = j\left[\frac{\epsilon^{bt} - \epsilon^{-bt}}{2}\right] = j \sinh bt \qquad (3\text{-}2\text{-}8)$$

By use of the preceding equations, a complete set of identities for hyperbolic functions may be derived from known trigonometric functions. In the following example the trigonometric identity for the sum of two angles is the starting point.

$$\sin (\beta_1 t + \beta_2 t) = \sin \beta_1 t \cos \beta_2 t + \sin \beta_2 t \cos \beta_1 t \qquad (3\text{-}2\text{-}9)$$

Let it be supposed that both β_1 and β_2 become imaginary:

$$\beta_1 = jb_1 \qquad \beta_2 = jb_2$$

The equation becomes

$$\sin j(b_1 t + b_2 t) = \sin jb_1 t \cos jb_2 t + \sin jb_2 t \cos jb_1 t$$

or

$$j \sinh (b_1 t + b_2 t) = j \sinh b_1 t \cosh b_2 t + j \sinh b_2 t \cosh b_1 t$$

and, finally, the corresponding hyperbolic identity is obtained:

$$\sinh (b_1 t + b_2 t) = \sinh b_1 t \cosh b_2 t + \sinh b_2 t \cosh b_1 t \qquad (3\text{-}2\text{-}10)$$

As a second example, the trigonometric identity is the starting point:

$$\cos (\beta_1 t + \beta_2 t) = \cos \beta_1 t \cos \beta_2 t - \sin \beta_1 t \sin \beta_2 t \qquad (3\text{-}2\text{-}11)$$

Again let it be assumed that β_1 and β_2 become imaginary:

$$\beta_1 = jb_1 \qquad \beta_2 = jb_2$$

The equation becomes

$$\cos j(b_1 t + b_2 t) = \cos jb_1 t \cos jb_2 t - \sin jb_2 t \sin jb_1 t$$

or

$$\cosh (b_1 t + b_2 t) = \cosh b_1 t \cosh b_2 t - j^2 \sinh b_1 t \sinh b_2 t$$

and finally the corresponding hyperbolic identity is obtained:

$$\cosh (b_1 t + b_2 t) = \cosh b_1 t \cosh b_2 t + \sinh b_1 t \sinh b_2 t \qquad (3\text{-}2\text{-}12)$$

The derivatives for $\sinh bt$ and $\cosh bt$ may be obtained from the exponential definitions:

$$\frac{d}{dt} \cosh bt = \frac{d}{dt} \left[\frac{\epsilon^{bt} + \epsilon^{-bt}}{2} \right] = b \frac{\epsilon^{bt} - \epsilon^{-bt}}{2} = b \sinh bt \qquad (3\text{-}2\text{-}13)$$

and

$$\frac{d}{dt} \sinh bt = \frac{d}{dt} \left[\frac{\epsilon^{bt} - \epsilon^{-bt}}{2} \right] = b \frac{\epsilon^{bt} + \epsilon^{-bt}}{2} = b \cosh bt \qquad (3\text{-}2\text{-}14)$$

When other identities are needed in the text, they are derived in a similar manner.

3–3. The *E-R-L-C* Series Circuit. The first circuit containing two storage elements to be considered is the series *E-R-L-C* circuit shown in Fig. 3–3-1. Let it be assumed for the first part of this discussion that the

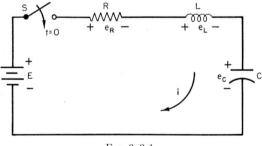

FIG. 3–3-1

initial current $i(0)$ and the initial capacitor voltage $e(0)$ are both zero. Before the mathematical solution is attempted, an analysis of the physical behavior of the circuit is presented. First let it be assumed that the resistor R is zero. When the switch S is closed, the inductor maintains the current initially at zero. Since the voltage on the capacitor C is initially zero, all E volts appear across the inductor L; thus

$$\frac{di}{dt}(0) = \frac{E}{L}$$

Shortly the voltage on C has increased so that less than E volts appear across L, and di/dt is less than the original value E/L. When the voltage on C increases to the point where it equals E, the voltage across L is then equal to zero, and di/dt is zero. This corresponds to the t_1 point in Fig. 3–3-2, at which time a current I_M exists in the inductor L. The current

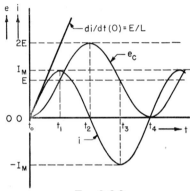

FIG. 3–3-2

cannot stop instantly, for if it did di/dt would be infinite. Thus the current continues to exist, causing the voltage on C to go above the voltage E. At the same time a negative voltage increases across L and causes di/dt to become negative. The current i decreases until it is zero at the t_2 point. As the i curve is symmetrical about t_1, there is as much area under the curve from t_1 to t_2 as there is from t_0 to t_1. Since the value of charge q is equal to the area under the i curve, the total q at t_2 is twice that at t_1. Hence the capacitor voltage e_c at t_2 is twice the voltage E. At point t_2 the voltage across C is $2E$ and the voltage across L is $-E$; therefore $di/dt = -E/L$. The current then goes through exactly the same set of values as for the first half-cycle, except that the sign of the current is negative. At t_4, i and e_c are again zero, and the circuit is again ready to repeat the cycle as if it were back at t_0.

Between t_0 and t_1 the battery E is supplying energy to both L and C. Between t_1 and t_2 the inductor L gives up energy and E is still supplying energy; all this energy appears on C at t_2. Between t_2 and t_3 the capacitor C is giving up energy, some of it going to L and the rest to E. Between t_3 and t_4 both L and C give up energy which is returned to E. At t_4 neither L nor C has any energy; all of it has gone back to E. Therefore some of the energy goes through the cycle from E to L, from L to C, from C to L, and from L to E.

Now let it be supposed that a resistor R of small value is added to the circuit. Some energy is dissipated as heat in the i^2R loss over each cycle so that the energy is transferred from one storage element to the other. Thus

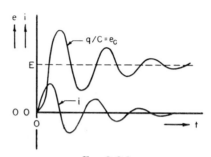

FIG. 3-3-3

not all the energy reaches the other storage element. Hence the capacitor voltage e_c never reaches $2E$, and the second loop of current is smaller than the first. The current i still oscillates, but the oscillations decrease in magnitude and gradually approach zero. In a similar manner, the capacitor voltage e_c oscillates and the voltage gradually approaches E. This situation is shown in Fig. 3-3-3. If R is increased, the i^2R loss increases and i and e_c approach their steady-state values more quickly. If R is further increased, R finally reaches a value such that the oscillations disappear and the plots of e_c and i follow curves similar to those in Fig. 3-3-4.

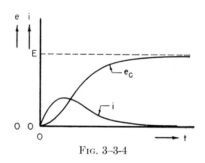

FIG. 3-3-4

3-4. Mathematical Analysis. After the current direction shown in Fig. 3-3-1 is assumed, the equation becomes

$$E = e_R + e_L + e_c = Ri + L\frac{di}{dt} + \frac{\int^t i\,dt}{C} \qquad (3\text{-}4\text{-}1)$$

This equation is differentiated in order to obtain the differential equation

$$0 = L\frac{d^2i}{dt^2} + R\frac{di}{dt} + \frac{i}{C} \qquad (3\text{-}4\text{-}2)$$

Again a solution of the form

$$i = A\epsilon^{st}$$

is assumed, and upon substitution Eq. 3–4-2 becomes

$$A\epsilon^{st}\left[s^2L + Rs + \frac{1}{C}\right] = 0 \tag{3-4-3}$$

The characteristic equation is

$$s^2L + Rs + \frac{1}{C} = 0 \tag{3-4-4}$$

and the roots obtained are

$$s_1 \text{ and } s_2 = -\frac{R}{2L} \pm \sqrt{\frac{R^2}{4L^2} - \frac{1}{LC}} \tag{3-4-5}$$

For the moment let it be assumed that $R^2/4L^2 > 1/LC$, and for convenience in writing let $a = R/2L$ and $b = \sqrt{R^2/4L^2 - 1/LC}$. Therefore the two roots become $s_1 = -a + b$ and $s_2 = -a - b$, and the solution for the current has the form

$$i = A_1\epsilon^{(-a+b)t} + A_2\epsilon^{(-a-b)t} \tag{3-4-6}$$

One equation involving A_1 and A_2, found by using the initial condition $i(0) = 0$, is

$$0 = A_1 + A_2$$

Substitution of $A_2 = -A_1$ in Eq. 3–4-6 gives

$$i = A_1[\epsilon^{(-a+b)t} - \epsilon^{(-a-b)t}] \tag{3-4-7}$$

The derivative of the current is

$$\frac{di}{dt} = A_1[(-a + b)\epsilon^{(-a+b)t} + (a + b)\epsilon^{(-a-b)t}] \tag{3-4-8}$$

Before this equation can be used, $(di/dt)(0)$ has to be found. This is done by putting in the original Eq. 3–4-1 the known value of the quantities at $t = 0$. When $i(0) = 0$ is substituted in this equation, $(di/dt)(0)$ is found to be

$$E = R(0) + L\frac{di}{dt}(0) + 0 \qquad \frac{di}{dt}(0) = \frac{E}{L}$$

Eq. 3–4-8 can now be used at $t = 0$ to evaluate A_1:

$$\frac{E}{L} = A_1[-a + b + a + b] \quad \text{or} \quad A_1 = \frac{E}{2bL} \tag{3-4-9}$$

Upon substitution, the final solution is

$$i = \frac{E}{2bL}[\epsilon^{(-a+b)t} - \epsilon^{(-a-b)t}] = \frac{E}{bL}\epsilon^{-at}\left[\frac{\epsilon^{bt} - \epsilon^{-bt}}{2}\right]$$

which may be written

$$i = \frac{E}{bL}\epsilon^{-at}\sinh bt \tag{3-4-10}$$

In the work leading up to Eq. 3–4-10 it is assumed that $R^2/4\,L^2 > 1/LC$, which can also be written $R > 2\sqrt{L/C}$ or $b^2 > 0$. In the physical reasoning above, this corresponds to the case where R was sufficiently large that oscillations did not occur. This case, shown in Fig. 3–3-4, is known as the overdamped or nonoscillatory case.

If now the circuit is considered as having fixed E, L, and C, but an R that starts in the region $R > 2\sqrt{L/C}$ and is gradually decreased, eventually a value of R is reached such that $R_c = 2\sqrt{L/C}$. This, of course, implies that $b = 0$. If zero is substituted for b in Eq. 3–4-10, the indeterminate form results:

$$i = \frac{E}{L}\,\epsilon^{-at}\left[\frac{0}{0}\right] \tag{3–4-11}$$

This indeterminate form can be evaluated by using l'Hospital's rule:

$$i = \frac{E}{L}\,\epsilon^{-at}\left.\frac{\dfrac{d\,\sinh bt}{db}}{\dfrac{d}{db}\,(b)}\right|_{b=0} = \frac{E}{L}\,\epsilon^{-at}t\,\cosh bt\,\bigg|_{b=0} = \frac{E}{L}\,t\epsilon^{-at} \tag{3–4-12}$$

The value $R_c = 2\sqrt{L/C}$ is termed the critical resistance, and Eq. 3–4-12 is the current for the critically damped case.

As R is decreased below the value $R_c = 2\sqrt{L/C}$, the $R^2/4\,L^2$ term becomes less than the $1/LC$ term and b becomes imaginary. A new coefficient β is defined: $\beta = \sqrt{1/LC - R^2/4\,L^2}$; and, for these lower values of R, $b = j\beta$, where β is real. Eq. 3–4-10 can be written

$$i = \frac{E}{bL}\,\epsilon^{-at}\sinh bt = \frac{E}{j\beta L}\,\epsilon^{-at}\sinh j\beta t = \frac{E}{\beta L}\,\epsilon^{-at}\sin \beta t \tag{3–4-13}$$

This is the expression for the current of the underdamped or oscillatory case. Eqs. 3–4-10, 3–4-12, and 3–4-13 are different forms of the same general solution in that hyperbolic functions and trigonometric functions are continuations of each other.

If R is decreased to the limiting value of zero, $a = 0$, $\beta = 1/\sqrt{LC}$, and Eq. 3–4-13 becomes

$$i = \frac{E}{(1/\sqrt{LC})L}\,\epsilon^{0}\sin\frac{1}{\sqrt{LC}}t = \frac{E}{\sqrt{L/C}}\sin\frac{1}{\sqrt{LC}}t \tag{3–4-14}$$

This can be written

$$i = I_M\sin\frac{1}{\sqrt{LC}}t \quad \text{where} \quad I_M = \frac{E}{\sqrt{L/C}} \tag{3–4-15}$$

The $\sqrt{L/C}$ term appears in a position in Eq. 3–4-15 analogous to impedance in a-c circuits; hence the name surge impedance for this term. A sketch of the function of Eq. 3–4-13 is shown in Fig. 3–3-3 and of Eq. 3–4-14 in Fig. 3–3-2.

In the preceding analysis the equation for current was derived for $R > 2\sqrt{L/C}$, $R_c = 2\sqrt{L/C}$, and $R < 2\sqrt{L/C}$. Each of these cases is now examined in more detail.

3–5. The Underdamped Case. When the resistance is zero, the equation for current is

$$i = \frac{E}{\sqrt{L/C}} \sin \frac{1}{\sqrt{LC}} t \qquad (3\text{–}5\text{-}1)$$

The equation for the charge q may be found by integrating Eq. 3–5-1:

$$q = \int_0^t i \, dt = \int_0^t \frac{E}{\sqrt{L/C}} \sin \frac{1}{\sqrt{LC}} t \, dt$$

$$= \frac{E}{\sqrt{LC}} \sqrt{LC} \left[- \cos \frac{1}{\sqrt{LC}} t \, \Big|_0^t \right] = EC \left[1 - \cos \frac{1}{\sqrt{LC}} t \right] \quad (3\text{–}5\text{-}2)$$

The equation for the voltage on the capacitor C is

$$e_c = \frac{q}{C} = E \left[1 - \cos \frac{1}{\sqrt{LC}} t \right] \qquad (3\text{–}5\text{-}3)$$

and the equation for the voltage e_L is

$$e_L = E - e_c = E \cos \frac{1}{\sqrt{LC}} t \qquad (3\text{–}5\text{-}4)$$

The current is an undamped sine function where

$$\beta = \frac{1}{\sqrt{LC}} = 2\pi f$$

giving for f

$$f = \frac{1}{2\pi\sqrt{LC}} \qquad (3\text{–}5\text{-}5)$$

The frequency of oscillation of i and q is the same as the series resonance frequency in a-c analysis. As R is increased, i and q become

$$i = \frac{E}{\beta L} \epsilon^{-at} \sin \beta t \qquad (3\text{–}5\text{-}6)$$

$$q = \int_0^t i \, dt = EC \left[1 - \epsilon^{-at} \left(\frac{a}{\beta} \sin \beta t + \cos \beta t \right) \right] \qquad (3\text{–}5\text{-}7)$$

The voltages across the circuit elements are

$$e_c = \frac{q}{C} = E \left[1 - \epsilon^{-at} \left(\frac{a}{\beta} \sin \beta t + \cos \beta t \right) \right] \qquad (3\text{–}5\text{-}8)$$

$$e_R = iR = \frac{ER}{\beta L} \epsilon^{-at} \sin \beta t \qquad (3\text{–}5\text{-}9)$$

$$e_L = L \frac{di}{dt} = E\epsilon^{-at} \left[\cos \beta t - \frac{a}{\beta} \sin \beta t \right] \qquad (3\text{–}5\text{-}10)$$

Another way of obtaining e_c which does not involve an integration is to use the equation

$$e_c = E - Ri - L\frac{di}{dt} \qquad (3\text{-}5\text{-}11)$$

The power for each element may be found by using the appropriate e in

$$P = ei$$

The energy stored in C and L may be found from

$$P_L = \frac{Li^2}{2} \quad \text{or} \quad P_c = \frac{Ce_c^2}{2}$$

The sketch for i and q is shown in Fig. 3–3–3; the current i is shown in Fig. 3–5–1 in greater detail. The envelopes for the current equation, curves

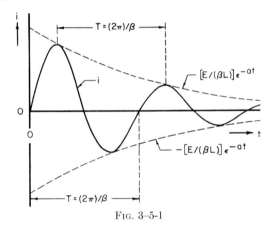

Fig. 3–5–1

of $\pm (E/\beta L)\,\epsilon^{-at}$, are sketched with the i curve. The current is a damped sine function where

$$\beta = 2\,\pi f = \sqrt{\frac{1}{LC} - \frac{R^2}{4\,L^2}}$$

giving the damped natural frequency of oscillation

$$f = \frac{1}{2\,\pi}\sqrt{\frac{1}{LC} - \frac{R^2}{4\,L^2}} \qquad (3\text{-}5\text{-}12)$$

This natural frequency of oscillation starts at the value $f = 1/(2\,\pi\sqrt{LC})$ with R zero, and decreases as R increases. As the frequency decreases, the period $T = 1/f = 2\,\pi/\beta$ increases. The time constant for this case is the time required to make the exponent of the envelope equal to one, or $\epsilon \exp[(-R/2\,L)t_c] = \epsilon^{-1}$, from which it can be seen that $t_c = 2\,L/R$.

The first point where the i curve touches the envelope is where $\beta t = \pi/2$ or $t = T/4$. This can be seen by substituting $t = T/4$ in Eq. 3–5–6:

$$i = \frac{E}{\beta L}\,\epsilon^{-aT/4}\sin\frac{\pi}{2} = \frac{E}{\beta L}\,\epsilon^{-aT/4} \qquad (3\text{-}5\text{-}13)$$

which is the equation for the envelope at this point. Similarly it can be shown that successive points where i touches the upper part of the envelope are $\beta t = 2\,\pi$ radians apart. Also i touches the lower part of the envelope at $\beta t = 3\,\pi/2$ the first time, and successive points of contact are $2\,\pi$ radians apart.

The current reaches its first maximum at a point before $\beta t = \pi/2$. The i curve touches and is tangent to the positive envelope at the $\pi/2$ point and hence has a negative slope there. The point of zero slope for i is therefore to the left of $\pi/2$. To solve for the time for maximum i, Eq. 3–5-6 is differentiated and the result set equal to zero:

$$\frac{di}{dt} = \frac{E}{\beta L}\,\epsilon^{-at}\,[\beta\cos\beta t - a\sin\beta t] = 0$$

and solved for the time t:

$$t = \frac{1}{\beta}\tan^{-1}\frac{\beta}{a} \qquad\qquad (3\text{–}5\text{-}14)$$

This is a multivalued function and gives the various times corresponding to both the maximum and minimum points. It can be observed from this equation that the maximum points for current occur $\beta t = 2\,\pi$ radians apart. In a similar fashion the first minimum is $\beta t = \pi$ radians after the maximum, and the minimum points occur $2\,\pi$ radians apart. To find the values for a maximum i or minimum i, these values of time from Eq. 3–5-14 can be substituted in Eq. 3–5-6. The ratio of one maximum to the next maximum may be shown to be $\epsilon^{2\pi a/\beta}$; and this is sometimes called the decrement of the wave. The larger the decrement, the quicker the oscillatory wave dies away with time.

The points where the current goes through zero can be determined by observing that $\sin\beta t$ must equal zero; this gives $\beta t = \pi$ and all integral multiples of π.

EXAMPLE 3–5-1. One application of the underdamped or oscillatory case is the charging-choke circuit shown schematically in Fig. 3–5-2. In the

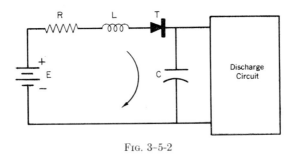

FIG. 3–5-2

actual circuit the battery E would be a d-c power supply. When the capacitor C is discharged, the rectifier T conducts current in the reference direction but does not let the current reverse. The current flowing through the rectifier then charges C. At some time after C is charged, the discharge circuit removes the energy from C in a short length of time. This results in deliverance of a large amount of power in the form of a pulse to some other part of the circuit. This charging-choke circuit is used in radar and similar applications. The current i which charges C exists for a much longer period of time than does the discharge current, so the power required from the battery E is not very great. Since C is charged to almost twice the voltage E, the voltage required from the battery is about half what it otherwise would have to be.

To analyze this circuit the following values are assumed: $E = 60$ volts, $R = 175$ ohms, $L = 2.5$ henrys, and $C = 5$ μf. It is also assumed that the initial charge $q(0) = 0$. For these values a and β become $a = R/2L = 175/5 = 35$; $\beta = \sqrt{1/LC - R^2/4L^2} = 281$. The capacitor voltage e_c, from $t = 0$ up to a value of time when the current i tries to reverse, has the form

$$e_c = E\left[1 - \epsilon^{-at}\left(\frac{a}{\beta}\sin \beta t + \cos \beta t\right)\right] \qquad (3\text{-}5\text{-}15)$$

which, for this example, becomes

$$e_c = 60[1 - \epsilon^{-35t}(0.124 \sin 281t + \cos 281t)] \qquad (3\text{-}5\text{-}16)$$

The voltage e_c follows this equation until the current becomes zero. After this value of time, e_c remains constant until the discharge circuit operates at t_1 and removes the charge. The circuit then repeats this cycle, as shown in Fig. 3–5–3. The voltage e_c is a maximum when q is a maximum, and

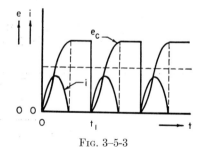

FIG. 3–5–3

q is a maximum when $dq/dt = i = 0$. The current i is zero when $\beta t = \pi$ or $t = \pi/\beta = 0.0112$. The maximum voltage is

$$e_{c(max)} = 60[1 - \epsilon^{-35(0.0112)}(0.124 \sin \pi + \cos \pi)]$$
$$= 60(1.675) = 100.5 \qquad (3\text{-}5\text{-}17)$$

If R were zero, $e_{(max)}$ would equal 120 volts.

3–6. The Critically Damped Case. As R is increased, the frequency f of oscillation in the underdamped case becomes less and the period T becomes greater. When $R_c = 2\sqrt{L/C}$ the circuit no longer oscillates,

f is zero, and T is infinitely large. This critical value of R is the least value of resistance for which no oscillation takes place. The equation for current for this case was found to be

$$i = \frac{E}{L} t\epsilon^{-at} \qquad (3\text{-}6\text{-}1)$$

The equation for q can be found by integrating the current i:

$$q = \int_0^t i\, dt = \int_0^t \frac{E}{L} t\epsilon^{-at}\, dt = EC[1 - \epsilon^{-at}(at + 1)] \qquad (3\text{-}6\text{-}2)$$

The current is maximum when

$$\frac{di}{dt} = \frac{E}{L} \epsilon^{-at}[1 - at] = 0$$

or when the time t equals

$$t = \frac{1}{a} = \frac{2L}{R} \qquad (3\text{-}6\text{-}3)$$

The equations for voltage, power, and energy of the various circuit elements may be found in a manner similar to that shown in Art. 3–5.

3–7. The Overdamped Case. When the resistance R is increased so that $R > 2\sqrt{L/C}$ the current becomes

$$i = \frac{E}{bL} \epsilon^{-at} \sinh bt \qquad (3\text{-}7\text{-}1)$$

The equation for the charge q can be found by integrating the current i:

$$q = \int_0^t i\, dt = \int_0^t \frac{E}{bL} \epsilon^{-at} \sinh bt\, dt$$

$$= EC\left[1 - \epsilon^{-at}\left(\frac{a}{\beta} \sinh bt + \cosh bt\right)\right] \qquad (3\text{-}7\text{-}2)$$

The current is a maximum when

$$\frac{di}{dt} = \frac{E}{L} \epsilon^{-at}\left[\cosh bt - \frac{a}{b} \sinh bt\right] = 0 \qquad\qquad D\,i_o = \frac{R}{2L}$$

from which the time t can be found:

$$t = \frac{1}{b} \tanh^{-1}\left(\frac{b}{a}\right) \qquad (3\text{-}7\text{-}3)$$

When t of Eq. 3–7-3 is expanded in a series, the result is

$$t = \frac{1}{a} + \frac{b^2}{3\, a^3} + \cdots \qquad (3\text{-}7\text{-}4)$$

Comparison of Eq. 3–7-4 with Eq. 3–6-3 evidences that the maximum current for the critically damped case occurs in time before that of the overdamped case. Hence the current in the critically damped case rises faster; also, it is possible to show that it decays faster than in the overdamped case.

3–8. General Solutions in Another Form. In the preceding work on the
E-R-L-C circuit, it is assumed that the initial conditions $e(0)$ and $i(0)$ are
zero. Before circuits where the initial conditions are not zero are taken up,
Eq. 3–4-6 is put in another form. This equation is repeated:

$$i = A_1\epsilon^{(-a+b)t} + A_2\epsilon^{(-a-b)t} \tag{3–8-1}$$

and is a general solution to the second-order differential equation which
has no steady-state component. This equation can be written

$$i = \epsilon^{-at}[A_1\epsilon^{bt} + A_2\epsilon^{-bt}] \tag{3–8-2}$$

The ϵ^{bt} and ϵ^{-bt} terms may be expanded as in Eq. 3–2-4 to give

$$i = \epsilon^{-at}[A_1(\cosh bt + \sinh bt) + A_2(\cosh bt - \sinh bt)]$$

which can be written

$$i = \epsilon^{-at}[(A_1 + A_2)\cosh bt + (A_1 - A_2)\sinh bt] \tag{3–8-3}$$

Since A_1 and A_2 are constants, their sum and difference are also constants
and with the substitutions

$$A_1 + A_2 = B_1 \qquad A_1 - A_2 = B_2$$

Eq. 3–8-3 can be written

$$i = \epsilon^{-at}(B_1 \cosh bt + B_2 \sinh bt) \tag{3–8-4}$$

In a similar manner the general form for the oscillatory case can be
written

$$i = \epsilon^{-at}(B_3 \cos \beta t + B_4 \sin \beta t) \tag{3–8-5}$$

Often the B_1 and B_2 (or B_3 and B_4) constants can be evaluated more easily
than can A_1 and A_2. This is particularly true in the oscillatory case.
Another very common form for the current of the oscillatory case is

$$i = D\epsilon^{-at} \sin (\beta t + \alpha) \tag{3–8-6}$$

which is sometimes more useful for computation than is Eq. 3–8-5. If
B_3 and B_4 are known, D and α can be found:

$$D = \sqrt{B_3{}^2 + B_4{}^2}$$

$$\alpha = \sin^{-1}\frac{B_3}{\sqrt{B_3{}^2 + B_4{}^2}} = \cos^{-1}\frac{B_4}{\sqrt{B_3{}^2 + B_4{}^2}} \tag{3–8-7}$$

It is to be noticed that one and only one angle α between zero and 360
degrees satisfies Eq. 3–8-7.

The preceding discussion assumes that the solution is either the overdamped case or the underdamped case. Obviously there is the third
possibility, that of the critically damped case. The general form for this
case can be obtained from the overdamped case by letting b go to zero,
or from the underdamped case by letting β go to zero. Either way, the
same form results. The following explanation is based on the overdamped
case. When the B_2 term of Eq. 3–8-4 is evaluated, it contains a b in the

denominator. In the limit, as b goes to zero, the second term of Eq. 3–8–4 yields $0/0$, which can be evaluated as before. Hereby, the general form for the critically damped case becomes

$$i = B_5 \epsilon^{-at} + B_6 t \epsilon^{-at} \qquad (3\text{–}8\text{–}8)$$

If the voltage across the capacitor is desired the following forms hold for the three cases.

Overdamped case:

$$e_c = e_{ss} + \epsilon^{-at}[B_1 \cosh bt + B_2 \sinh bt] \qquad (3\text{–}8\text{–}9)$$

Underdamped case:

$$e_c = e_{ss} + \epsilon^{-at}[B_3 \cos \beta t + B_4 \sin \beta t] \qquad (3\text{–}8\text{–}10)$$

Critically damped case:

$$e_c = e_{ss} + B_5 \epsilon^{-at} + B_6 t \epsilon^{-at} \qquad (3\text{–}8\text{–}11)$$

3–9. E-R-L-C Series Circuit with Initial Conditions. Three circuits that have different initial conditions are analyzed as a drill in the material already presented and to show how problems with different initial conditions can be solved.

EXAMPLE 3–9–1. The first circuit to be studied is that shown in Fig. 3–9-1. The switch S is thrown to position 1 until steady-state conditions

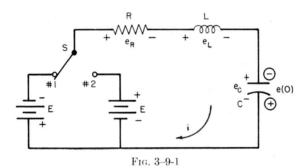

FIG. 3–9-1

exist; then, at time $t = 0$, S is thrown to position 2. This means that before $t = 0$ the capacitor C is charged to $e(0) = E$ volts in the polarity shown and the current $i = 0$. At $t = 0$ the problem then is concerned with a series E-R-L-C circuit with $i(0) = 0$ and $e(0) = E$ with the polarity shown. The following equations can be written:

$$E = e_R + e_L + e_c$$

whence

$$E = Ri + L\frac{di}{dt} + \frac{1}{C}\int_0^t i\,dt - E$$

Thus

$$2\,E = L\frac{di}{dt} + Ri + \frac{1}{C}\int_0^t i\,dt \qquad (3\text{–}9\text{–}1)$$

When Eq. 3-9-1 is differentiated, the result is

$$0 = L\frac{d^2i}{dt^2} + R\frac{di}{dt} + \frac{i}{C} \tag{3-9-2}$$

The current $i(0)$ is known, but to solve the problem $(di/dt)(0)$ must be found. Since Eq. 3-9-1 is true for all values of time t greater than or equal to zero, $(di/dt)(0)$ can be found from this equation by substituting the known conditions at $t = 0$:

$$2E = L\frac{di}{dt}(0) + R(0) + 0 \quad \text{or} \quad \frac{di}{dt}(0) = \frac{2E}{L}$$

The differential equation 3-9-2 is of exactly the same form as Eq. 3-4-2. If numerical values are used for R, L, and C and if the roots of the characteristic equation are real, that is,

$$s_1 = -a + b \qquad s_2 = -a - b$$

the solution has the form

$$i = \epsilon^{-at}[B_1 \cosh bt + B_2 \sinh bt] \tag{3-9-3}$$

If the roots of the characteristic equation are imaginary, that is,

$$s_1 = -a + j\beta \qquad s_2 = -a - j\beta$$

the solution has the form

$$i = \epsilon^{-at}[B_1 \cos \beta t + B_2 \sin \beta t] \tag{3-9-4}$$

If the roots of the characteristic equation correspond to the critically damped case, that is,

$$s_1 = -a \qquad s_2 = -a$$

the solution has the form

$$i = B_1\epsilon^{-at} + B_2 t\epsilon^{-at} \tag{3-9-5}$$

Before the constants B_1 and B_2 are evaluated, the other two circuits to be considered are analyzed in a similar manner.

EXAMPLE 3-9-2. The second circuit to be studied is that shown in Fig. 3-9-2. The switch S is closed long enough for the circuit to reach

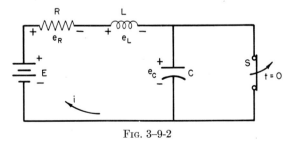

FIG. 3-9-2

steady-state conditions, for which $i(0) = E/R$ and $e(0) = 0$. The circuit equation

$$E = e_R + e_L + e_c$$

gives

$$E = Ri + L\frac{di}{dt} + \frac{1}{C}\int_0^t i\,dt \qquad (3\text{–}9\text{–}6)$$

When this is differentiated, the result is

$$0 = L\frac{d^2i}{dt^2} + R\frac{di}{dt} + \frac{i}{C} \qquad (3\text{–}9\text{–}7)$$

To find $(di/dt)(0)$ the known initial conditions are put into Eq. 3–9–6:

$$E = R\frac{E}{R} + L\frac{di}{dt}(0) + 0 \quad \text{or} \quad \frac{di}{dt}(0) = 0 \qquad (3\text{–}9\text{–}8)$$

Again it is to be noticed that Eq. 3–9–7 is of exactly the same form as Eqs. 3–9–2 and 3–4–2 and hence has the solution of the forms shown in Eq. 3–9–3, 3–9–4, or 3–9–5.

EXAMPLE 3–9–3. The third circuit to be studied is that shown in Fig. 3–9–3. The switch S is closed long enough for steady-state conditions to be

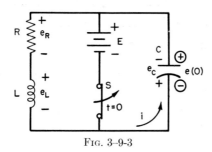

FIG. 3–9–3

reached, for which $i(0) = E/R$ and $e(0) = E$ with the polarity shown. Then the switch S is opened at time $t = 0$. When the reference direction for the current is used, the circuit equation

$$0 = e_R + e_L + e_c$$

gives

$$0 = Ri + L\frac{di}{dt} + \frac{1}{C}\int_0^t i\,dt - E$$

or

$$E = Ri + L\frac{di}{dt} + \frac{1}{C}\int_0^t i\,dt \qquad (3\text{–}9\text{–}9)$$

When the last equation is differentiated, the result is

$$0 = L\frac{d^2i}{dt^2} + R\frac{di}{dt} + \frac{i}{C} \qquad (3\text{–}9\text{–}10)$$

To find $(di/dt)(0)$, the known initial conditions are put into Eq. 3–9–9:

$$E = R\frac{E}{R} + L\frac{di}{dt}(0) + 0 \quad \text{or} \quad \frac{di}{dt}(0) = 0 \qquad (3\text{–}9\text{–}11)$$

Again it is to be noted that Eq. 3-9-10 is of the same form as Eqs. 3-9-7, 3-9-2, and 3-4-2; thus the solution has the forms shown in Eq. 3-9-3, 3-9-4, or 3-9-5.

All series R-L-C circuits, no matter what the initial conditions, have exactly the same differential equation, the same characteristic equation, and the same characteristic roots. These equations and roots are determined by the values of R, L, and C and are not affected by initial conditions. The solution to such problems then has the same form, but the values of B_1 and B_2 differ depending on the initial conditions.

To complete the solutions to the three examples, 3-9-1, 3-9-2, and 3-9-3, actual values for R, L, and C are considered.

Example 3-9-1. The following values are assumed: $E = 10$ volts, $R = 100$ ohms, $L = 0.1$ henry, and $C = 150$ μf. The constants a and b are

$$a = \frac{R}{2L} = 500 \qquad b = \sqrt{\frac{R^2}{4L^2} - \frac{1}{LC}} = 427 \qquad (3\text{-}9\text{-}12)$$

Since the characteristic roots are real, the solution has the form

$$i = \epsilon^{-500t}[B_1 \cosh 427\ t + B_2 \sinh 427\ t] \qquad (3\text{-}9\text{-}13)$$

When the known condition $i(0) = 0$ is imposed, the result is

$$0 = \epsilon^0[B_1 \cosh 0 + B_2 \sinh 0] \qquad (3\text{-}9\text{-}14)$$

An inspection of the definition of hyperbolic functions shows that

$$\cosh 0 = 1 \qquad \sinh 0 = 0$$

Therefore $B_1 = 0$ and the solution has the form

$$i = \epsilon^{-500t}[B_2 \sinh 427\ t] \qquad (3\text{-}9\text{-}15)$$

B_2 can be found by differentiating this equation:

$$\frac{di}{dt} = \epsilon^{-500t}[B_2\ 427 \cosh 427t - B_2\ 500 \sinh 427t] \qquad (3\text{-}9\text{-}16)$$

and by imposing the other condition known at $t = 0$:

$$\frac{di}{dt}(0) = \frac{2E}{L} = 200$$

whence

$$200 = \epsilon^0[B_2\ 427 \cosh 0 - B_2\ 500 \sinh 0]$$

and thus

$$B_2 = \tfrac{200}{427} = 0.468 \qquad (3\text{-}9\text{-}17)$$

Therefore the desired solution is

$$i = 0.468\ \epsilon^{-500t} \sinh 427\ t \qquad (3\text{-}9\text{-}18)$$

Example 3-9-2. The following values are assumed: $E = 25$ volts, $R = 175$ ohms, $L = 2.5$ henrys, and $C = 5$ μf. The constants a and b are

$$a = \frac{R}{2L} = 35 \qquad b = \sqrt{\frac{R^2}{4L^2} - \frac{1}{LC}} = j\ 281 \qquad (3\text{-}9\text{-}19)$$

Since $b = j\,281$, the oscillatory case occurs. The current has the form

$$i = \epsilon^{-35t}[B_1 \cos 281\,t + B_2 \sin 281\,t] \tag{3-9-20}$$

When the known initial condition $i(0) = E/R = 25/175 = 0.143$ is imposed, the result is

$$0.143 = \epsilon^0[B_1 \cos 0 + B_2 \sin 0]$$
$$B_1 = 0.143 \tag{3-9-21}$$

Upon substitution, Eq. 3-9-20 becomes

$$i = \epsilon^{-35t}[0.143 \cos 281\,t + B_2 \sin 281\,t]$$

B_2 can be found by differentiating this equation:

$$\frac{di}{dt} = \epsilon^{-35t}[-0.143(281) \sin 281\,t + B_2\,(281) \cos 281\,t]$$
$$-35\,\epsilon^{-35t}[0.143 \cos 281\,t + B_2 \sin 281\,t] \tag{3-9-22}$$

and by using the other initial condition $(di/dt)(0) = 0$:

$$0 = B_2\,(281) - 35(0.143) \qquad B_2 = \frac{35(0.143)}{281} = 0.0178 \tag{3-9-23}$$

Therefore the desired solution is

$$i = \epsilon^{-35t}[0.143 \cos 281\,t + 0.0178 \sin 281\,t] \tag{3-9-24}$$

Example 3-9-3. The following values are assumed: $E = 15$ volts, $R = 12$ ohms, $L = 0.05$ henry, and $C = 400\ \mu\text{f}$. The roots are $-a \pm b = -120 \pm j\,189$. Thus the solution has the form

$$i = \epsilon^{-120t}[B_1 \cos 189\,t + B_2 \sin 189\,t] \tag{3-9-25}$$

B_1 and B_2 are evaluated as

$$i(0) = \frac{E}{R} = \frac{15}{12} = 1.25 \quad \text{and} \quad B_1 = 1.25$$
$$i = \epsilon^{-120t}[1.25 \cos 189\,t + B_2 \sin 189\,t] \tag{3-9-26}$$
$$\frac{di}{dt} = \epsilon^{-120t}[-1.25(189) \sin 189\,t + B_2\,189 \cos 189\,t$$
$$-120(1.25 \cos 189\,t + B_2 \sin 189\,t)] \tag{3-9-27}$$
$$\frac{di}{dt}(0) = 0$$
$$0 = B_2\,189 - 120(1.25) \qquad B_2 = \frac{120(1.25)}{189} = 0.793$$

The desired solution is

$$i = \epsilon^{-120t}[1.25 \cos 189\,t + 0.793 \sin 189\,t] \tag{3-9-28}$$

3-10. Parallel R-L-C Circuits. The dual of the series R-L-C circuit excited by a voltage source is the parallel G-L-C circuit excited by a current source. This circuit is shown in Fig. 3–10-1, where it is assumed that no initial energy is stored in either the inductor or the capacitor and that the

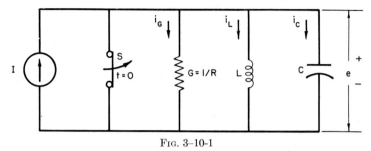

FIG. 3–10-1

switch S is opened at $t = 0$. Kirchhoff's current law can be written

$$I = i_G + i_L + i_c \tag{3–10-1}$$

or

$$I = Ge + \frac{1}{L} \int_0^t e\, dt + C \frac{de}{dt} \tag{3–10-2}$$

When the derivative is taken, this equation yields

$$0 = C \frac{d^2e}{dt^2} + G \frac{de}{dt} + \frac{e}{L} \tag{3–10-3}$$

This equation indicates that the steady-state component of e is zero; the transient component is

$$e = e_{tr} = A\epsilon^{st} \tag{3–10-4}$$

After the usual steps the characteristic equation is found to be

$$Cs^2 + Gs + \frac{1}{L} = 0 \tag{3–10-5}$$

and the roots can be written

$$s_1 \text{ and } s_2 = -a \pm b \quad \text{or} \quad -a \pm j\beta$$

where a, b, and β are defined as

$$a = \frac{G}{2C} \qquad b = \sqrt{a^2 - \frac{1}{LC}} \qquad \beta = \sqrt{\frac{1}{LC} - a^2} \tag{3–10-6}$$

If the roots are assumed real, the solution is

$$e = \epsilon^{-at} [B_1 \cosh bt + B_2 \sinh bt] \tag{3–10-7}$$

When the known initial condition $e(0) = 0$ is used, B_1 is

$$B_1 = 0 \tag{3–10-8}$$

and the equation becomes

$$e = \epsilon^{-at}[B_2 \sinh bt] \tag{3–10-9}$$

Before B_2 can be evaluated, $(de/dt)(0)$ must be found. At $t = 0$ all the current exists in the capacitor and

$$i_c(0) = I = C \frac{de}{dt}(0) \quad \text{or} \quad \frac{de}{dt}(0) = \frac{I}{C} \tag{3–10-10}$$

B_2 can now be found by differentiating Eq. 3-10-9:

$$\frac{de}{dt} = \epsilon^{-at}[B_2 b \cosh bt - B_2 a \sinh bt] \tag{3-10-11}$$

and using the condition just found:

$$\frac{I}{C} = B_2 b \quad \text{or} \quad B_2 = \frac{I}{bC} \tag{3-10-12}$$

The final solution is

$$e = \frac{I}{bC} \epsilon^{-at} \sinh bt \tag{3-10-13}$$

Since the roots were assumed real, this equation is the solution for the overdamped case. Herefrom the solution for the oscillatory case can be found by letting $b = j\beta$:

$$e = \frac{I}{\beta C} \epsilon^{-at} \sin \beta t \tag{3-10-14}$$

Likewise the critically damped case is

$$e = \frac{I}{C} t\epsilon^{-at} \tag{3-10-15}$$

The solution for each of these cases can be found from the solutions for the E-R-L-C series circuit and by use of the concept of duality, as a comparison of the corresponding solutions shows.

The parallel I-G-C-L circuit has the following relationship among the various constants for the various cases.

Overdamped case:

$$G > 2\sqrt{\frac{C}{L}} \tag{3-10-16}$$

Critically damped case:

$$G_c = 2\sqrt{\frac{C}{L}} \tag{3-10-17}$$

Oscillatory case:

$$G < 2\sqrt{\frac{C}{L}} \tag{3-10-18}$$

A comparison of the parallel and series connections is made in Table 3-10. In this table G is replaced by $1/R$ and the relationships are shown in terms of R for comparison.

TABLE 3-10

Case	E-R-L-C Series Circuit	I-G-L-C Parallel Circuit
Overdamped	$R > 2\sqrt{\frac{L}{C}}$	$R < \frac{1}{2}\sqrt{\frac{L}{C}}$
Critically damped	$R_c = 2\sqrt{\frac{L}{C}}$	$R_c = \frac{1}{2}\sqrt{\frac{L}{C}}$
Oscillatory	$R < 2\sqrt{\frac{L}{C}}$	$R > \frac{1}{2}\sqrt{\frac{L}{C}}$

An observant reader will have noted that the E-R-L series circuit and the I-G-L parallel circuit have the same characteristic equation. For the series circuit the root of the characteristic equation is $s_1 = -R/L$, and for the parallel circuit it is $s_1 = -1/GL = -R/L$. (The same is also true for R-C circuits.) This same reader in studying Table 3–10 will wonder why there is similarity in one case and difference in the other. This point is clarified if it is realized that the characteristic equation is determined by the parameters of the circuit alone. The same circuit can be excited in any number of ways, yet the characteristic equation remains the same. That is, if the voltage source in the series E-R-L circuit shown in Fig. 3–10-2a is replaced by its internal resistance, which is zero, the circuit is

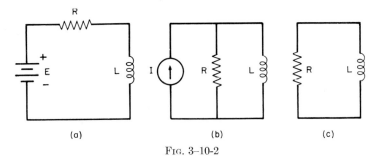

(a) (b) (c)

Fig. 3–10-2

that of Fig. 3–10-2c. Also, if the current source in the parallel I-R-L circuit of Fig. 3–10-2b is replaced by its internal resistance, which is infinite, the circuit is again that of Fig. 3–10-2c. Therefore, circuitwise, these two circuits are the same.

If this same line of reasoning is followed for the E-R-L-C series circuit and the I-R-L-C parallel circuit, it is seen that the circuits are not the same. This is shown in Fig. 3–10-3. Since the circuits are different, their

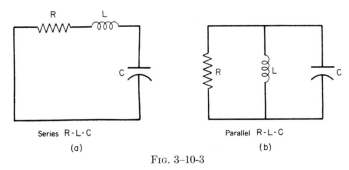

Series R-L-C Parallel R-L-C

(a) (b)

Fig. 3–10-3

responses in terms of variation of R will be different. If R in the series R-L-C circuit is made zero and R in the parallel R-L-C circuit is made infinite, both reduce to the same circuit, and this oscillates indefinitely, no matter how excited. This should help to explain the entry in Table 3–10 for the oscillatory case. In the series circuit, R has to be less than a certain value. In the parallel circuit, R has to be greater than a certain value.

EXAMPLE 3–10-1. The following example illustrates the analysis of the parallel R-L-C circuit with initial conditions. For this example both the

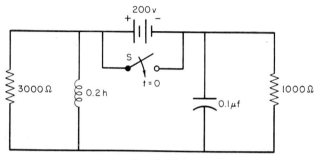

FIG. 3–10-4

inductor and the capacitor have some initial energy storage because the circuit is assumed to be in steady state before the switch is closed. The object is to determine the voltage across the capacitor after S is closed.

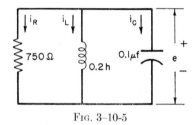

FIG. 3–10-5

Once S is closed, the two resistors may be replaced by one resistor, as shown in Fig. 3–10-5. The initial conditions are:

$$e(0) = -\, 200 \text{ volts}$$
$$i_L(0) = 0.2 \text{ amp}$$
$$i_R(0) = -\, 0.2667 \text{ amp}$$
$$i_c(0) = 0.0667 \text{ amp}$$

In this circuit the steady-state voltage is zero and the roots of the characteristic equation are

$$a = \frac{1}{2\,RC} = \frac{1}{2(750)(10^{-7})} = 6667$$

$$b = \sqrt{a^2 - \frac{1}{LC}} = \sqrt{(6667)^2 - \frac{1}{(0.2)(10^{-7})}} = j\,2357$$

Since b is imaginary, the solution can be put in the form

$$e = \epsilon^{-6667\,t}[B_1 \cos 2357\,t + B_2 \sin 2357\,t] \qquad (3\text{–}10\text{-}19)$$

The initial condition $e(0) = -200$ volts gives for B_1

$$B_1 = -200 \qquad (3\text{-}10\text{-}20)$$

Also, at $t = 0$, $i_c(0) = 10^{-7}(de/dt)(0) = 0.0667$ amp or

$$\frac{de}{dt}(0) = 6.67 \times 10^5 \text{ volts/sec}$$

B_2 is

$$6.67 \times 10^5 = (-6667)(-200) + 2357\, B_2$$

or

$$B_2 = -282.8 \qquad (3\text{-}10\text{-}21)$$

The final solution is

$$e = \epsilon^{-6667\,t}[-282.8 \sin 2357\, t - 200 \cos 2357\, t] \qquad (3\text{-}10\text{-}22)$$

3–11. The Calculation of Certain Roots. The quadratic equation

$$as^2 + bs + c = 0 \qquad (3\text{-}11\text{-}1)$$

has as roots

$$s_1 \text{ and } s_2 = -\frac{b}{2\,a} \pm \sqrt{\left(\frac{b}{2\,a}\right)^2 - \frac{c}{a}} \qquad (3\text{-}11\text{-}2)$$

When $c/a \ll (b/2\,a)^2$, the roots are approximately $-b/a$ and zero. More exact determinations can be obtained by using the binomial expansion:

$$(x + y)^n = x^n + nx^{n-1}y + \frac{n(n-1)}{2!}\, x^{n-2}y^2 + \cdots \qquad (3\text{-}11\text{-}3)$$

which is valid for $|\,y\,| < |\,x\,|$. Thus, from Eq. 3–11-2,

$$\sqrt{\left(\frac{b}{2\,a}\right)^2 - \frac{c}{a}} = \frac{b}{2\,a}\sqrt{1 - \frac{c}{a}\left(\frac{2\,a}{b}\right)^2} \qquad (3\text{-}11\text{-}4)$$

Since $(c/a)(2\,a/b)^2 \ll 1$, the quantity in the left side of the equation may be expanded by using the binomial expansion. Only the first two terms of the expansion need be kept, as the others are small by comparison. Thus

$$\sqrt{\left(\frac{b}{2\,a}\right)^2 - \frac{c}{a}} \approx \left(\frac{b}{2\,a}\right)\left[1 - \frac{c}{2\,a}\left(\frac{2\,a}{b}\right)^2 + \cdots\right] \qquad (3\text{-}11\text{-}5)$$

When Eq. 3–11-5 is substituted in Eq. 3–11-2, the result is

$$s_1 \text{ and } s_2 \approx -\frac{b}{2\,a} \pm \left(\frac{b}{2\,a}\right)\left[1 - \frac{c}{2\,a}\left(\frac{2\,a}{b}\right)^2\right]$$

or

$$s_1 \approx \left(-\frac{b}{a} + \frac{c}{b}\right) \quad \text{and} \quad s_2 \approx -\frac{c}{b} \qquad (3\text{-}11\text{-}6)$$

which are more exact values for the roots. As an example, the quadratic equation $s^2 + 600\,s + 1 = 0$ has as its roots

$$s_1 \approx \left(-\frac{b}{a} + \frac{c}{b}\right) = -\frac{600}{1} + \frac{1}{600} = -600 \qquad (3\text{-}11\text{-}7)$$

and

$$s_2 \approx -\frac{c}{b} = -\frac{1}{600} = -0.001667 \qquad (3\text{-}11\text{-}8)$$

The roots of a quadratic equation such as $s^2 + 600\,s + 1 = 0$ can be approximated by another technique. For the moment it is supposed that the two roots are

$$s_1 = -\sigma_1 \quad \text{and} \quad s_2 = -\sigma_2 \qquad (3\text{--}11\text{--}9)$$

and the quadratic as constructed from the roots is

$$(s + \sigma_1)(s + \sigma_2) = s^2 + (\sigma_1 + \sigma_2)s + \sigma_1\sigma_2 = 0 \qquad (3\text{--}11\text{--}10)$$

When the coefficients are compared, it can be seen that the following relationships exist:

$$\sigma_1 + \sigma_2 = 600 \qquad \sigma_1\sigma_2 = 1 \qquad (3\text{--}11\text{--}11)$$

If it is assumed that σ_1 is the larger root, then, since the sum of the two roots is equal to 600 and the product is equal to 1, $\sigma_1 \gg \sigma_2$; therefore

$$\sigma_1 \approx 600 \qquad \sigma_2 \approx \frac{1}{\sigma_1} = \frac{1}{600} = 0.001667 \qquad (3\text{--}11\text{--}12)$$

which check the previous solutions.

3–12. Geometric Interpretation of Root Location. The R-L-C series circuit has the characteristic equation

$$s^2 + \frac{R}{L}s + \frac{1}{LC} = 0 \qquad (3\text{--}12\text{-}1)$$

which has the roots

$$s_1 = -\frac{R}{2\,L} + \sqrt{\frac{R^2}{4\,L^2} - \frac{1}{LC}}$$

and $\qquad (3\text{--}12\text{-}2)$

$$s_2 = -\frac{R}{2\,L} - \sqrt{\frac{R^2}{4\,L^2} - \frac{1}{LC}}$$

These roots can both be real or they can be a complex conjugate pair. In either case the roots can be located as points in a complex s-plane. In

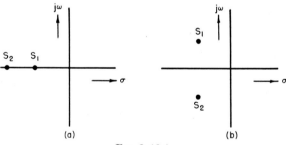

$$(a) \qquad\qquad\qquad\qquad (b)$$

FIG. 3–12-1

general, s has a real part denoted by σ and an imaginary part denoted by ω. In other words, s is given by

$$s = \sigma + j\omega \qquad (3\text{--}12\text{-}3)$$

The complex s-plane is shown in Fig. 3–12-1. In (a) the location of two real roots is shown; in (b) the location of two imaginary roots is shown.

It is of interest to observe the movement of the roots of Eq. 3–12-2 as the circuit parameters are varied. In the following discussion it is assumed that L and C are held constant and R is varied, starting with $R = 0$. When $R = 0$, the roots are

$$s_1 = +j\sqrt{\frac{1}{LC}} \qquad s_2 = -j\sqrt{\frac{1}{LC}} \qquad (3\text{–}12\text{-}4)$$

and appear on the $j\omega$ axis as shown in Fig. 3–12-2. Since the coefficient of the s^0 term of Eq. 3–12-1 is $1/LC$ and does not contain R, the product of the two roots must be independent of R, as R is varied. When the roots are complex, one root can be written $A\epsilon^{j\alpha}$ and the other root as the complex conjugate $A\epsilon^{-j\alpha}$. The product of these two roots is A^2 and is a constant. Therefore as R is increased the roots move along a semicircular path that has a radius $\sqrt{1/LC}$. When R is increased to the value of critical resistance $R_c = 2\sqrt{L/C}$, the two roots meet on the negative real axis. As R is increased above the value of critical resistance, the product of the two roots still remains constant and they are both real; so, as one root moves along the negative real axis toward the origin, the other root moves along the negative real axis to the left toward minus infinity.

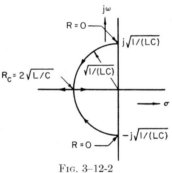

FIG. 3–12-2

PROBLEMS

3–1. Find the solution that satisfies the differential equation and the given initial conditions.

(a)

$$20\frac{d^2i}{dt^2} + 9\frac{di}{dt} + i = 0$$

$$i(0) = 0 \qquad \frac{di}{dt}(0) = 0.5$$

(b)

$$\frac{d^2i}{dt^2} + 4\frac{di}{dt} + 3\,i = 0$$

$$i(0) = 0 \qquad \frac{di}{dt}(0) = 6$$

(c)

$$5\frac{d^2e}{dt^2} + 6\frac{de}{dt} + e = 15$$

$$e(0) = 0 \qquad \frac{de}{dt}(0) = 0$$

3–2. Show that

(a) $\tanh j\beta t = j \tan \beta t$

(b) $\sinh(-bt) = -\sinh(bt)$

(c) $\cosh(-bt) = +\cosh(bt)$

(d) $\sinh(b_1 t - b_2 t) = \sinh b_1 t \cosh b_2 t - \sinh b_2 t \cosh b_1 t$

(e) $\cosh(b_1 t - b_2 t) = \cosh b_1 t \cosh b_2 t - \sinh b_1 t \sinh b_2 t$

(f) $\cosh^2 bt - \sinh^2 bt = 1$

3–3. For an E-L-C circuit, assuming $R = 0$ and given $E = 10$ volts, $L = 2.5$ henrys, and $C = 5$ μf, find:

(a) The maximum current I_{max}. *14.14 ma*

(b) The natural frequency f and the natural period T. *45.1   0.02215*

(c) The energy stored in L at times $t = t_1$, t_2, t_3, and t_4. These times correspond to the points shown in Fig. 3–3-2. *$w_1 = 0.25 \times 10^{-3}$ $w_2 = 0$ $w_3 = 0.25 \times 10^{-3}$ joules*

(d) The energy stored on C at $t = t_1$, t_2, t_3, and t_4. *$w_4 = 0$ $w_1 = 0.25 \times 10^{-7}$ $w_2 = 1 \times 10^{-3}$*

(e) The maximum capacitor voltage $e_{c(max)}$. *20 V $w_3 = 0.25 \times 10^{-3}$ $w_4 = 0$*

3–4. For an E-R-L-C circuit, assuming that $E = 10$ volts, $R = 500$ ohms, $L = 2.5$ henrys, and $C = 5$ μf, find: *0.005 54*

(a) The time t at which the first maximum of current occurs. *0.00457 sec*

(b) The value of the first maximum of current. *0.00890a*

(c) The natural frequency f and the natural period T. *42.2)   0.0237 sec*

(d) The time t at which the first maximum of capacitor voltage occurs. *0.0137 sec*

(e) The value of the first maximum of capacitor voltage. *13.06*

(f) The time constant for the circuit. *0.01 sec*

3–5. For an E-R-L-C circuit, assuming that $E = 10$ volts, $R = 1414$ ohms $L = 2.5$ henrys, and $C = 5$ μf, find:

(a) The time t at which maximum current occurs.

(b) The value of the maximum current.

(c) The value of the maximum capacitor voltage.

3–6. For an E-R-L-C circuit, assuming that $E = 10$ volts, $R = 5000$ ohms, $L = 2.5$ henrys, and $C = 5$ μf, find:

(a) The time t at which maximum current occurs. *0.002 sec*

(b) The value of the maximum current. *0.0019 amh*

(c) The value of the maximum capacitor voltage. *10 V*

3–7. Derive Eq. 3–5-7 directly by starting from Eq. 3–4-1 written in terms of the charge q, instead of first solving for the current i and integrating. Then differentiate the solution for q to check Eq. 3–4-13 for i.

3–8. Given the circuit shown in Fig. 3–P-1. The switch S is thrown to position 1 until steady-state conditions have been reached. At time $t = 0$, S is thrown to

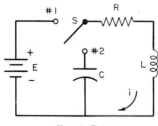

FIG. 3–P-1

position 2. For $E = 10$ volts, $R = 100$ ohms, $L = 0.1$ henry, and $C = 150$ μf, find the equation for the current i in the direction shown.

3-9. Given the circuit shown in Fig. 3–P-2. The switch S is closed until steady-

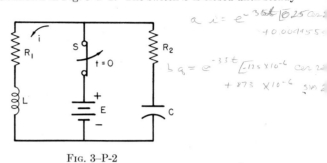

$$a \quad i = e^{-35t} [0.25 \cos 2 + 0.00195 ...$$

$$b \quad q = e^{-35t} [-12.5 \times 10^{-6} \cos 2 + 873 \times 10^{-6} \sin 2 ...$$

Fig. 3–P-2

state conditions are reached. Then S is opened at $t = 0$. For $E = 25$ volts, $R_1 = 100$ ohms, $R_2 = 75$ ohms, $L = 2.5$ henrys, and $C = 5$ μf, find:

   (a) The equation for the current i in the direction shown.

   (b) The equation for the charge q on C written with the polarity reference (+) on the bottom plate, (−) on the top.

3-10. In the circuit shown in Fig. 3–P-3, the switch S is closed until steady-state

$$i = e^{-42.9t} [0.15 \cos 376t + 0.00945 \sin 376t]$$

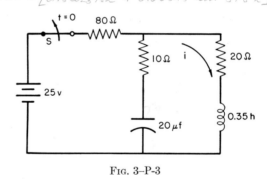

Fig. 3–P-3

conditions are reached, and then is opened at $t = 0$. Find i in the direction shown after $t = 0$.

3-11. (a) For

$$0.1 \frac{d^2 i}{dt^2} + 6 \frac{di}{dt} + 17\, i = 50$$

$$i(0) = 2 \qquad \frac{di}{dt}(0) = 40$$

What is i?

(b) For

$$3.5 \frac{d^2 e}{dt^2} + 15 \frac{de}{dt} + 85\, e = 300$$

$$e(0) = -100 \qquad \frac{de}{dt}(0) = 1000$$

What is e?

3-12. The circuit of Fig. 3-P-4 is in the steady state when the switch S is opened at time $t = 0$. Determine the voltage across the resistor after $t = 0$.

$$e = 38.8 \; e^{-2.5 \times 10^5 t} \; \sin \; 2.58 \times 10^7 t$$

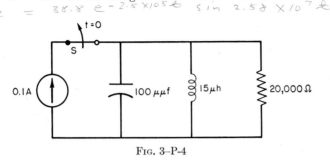

FIG. 3-P-4

3-13. In Fig. 3-P-5 switch S is open and steady-state conditions apply; at $t = 0$, S is closed. Obtain the expression for the voltage across the capacitor after $t = 0$.

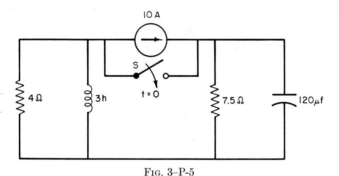

FIG. 3-P-5

3-14. Obtain the series for t of Eq. 3-7-4 from Eq. 3-7-3.

3-15. A certain oscillatory series R-L-C circuit similar to that of Fig. 3-3-1 has $E = 150$ volts. The first current maximum is 0.8 ma, the decrement is 1.8, and the frequency is 100 cps. Determine the R, L, and C of the circuit.

3-16. In the circuit of Fig. 3-P-6 the capacitor C is charged to 500 volts and then is discharged by closing the switch S. The discharge current is overdamped and

$$R = 1000 \; \Omega$$
$$L = 2.08 \; h$$
$$C = 8.6 \; \mu f$$

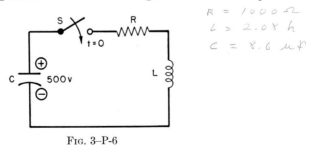

FIG. 3-P-6

has a maximum of 0.37 amp at a time of 4.2 msec. If the initial slope of the current is 240 amp/sec, calculate the R, L, and C of the circuit.

3–17. Art. 3–3 discusses the behavior of a series E-R-L-C circuit through use of physical reasoning. Develop the same type of reasoning, using the parallel I-G-L-C circuit of Fig. 3–10-1.

3–18. The circuit of Fig. 3–P-7 is in the steady state when the switch S is closed

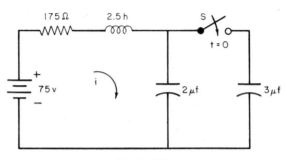

Fig. 3–P-7

at $t = 0$. Before $t = 0$ no energy is stored on the 3-μf capacitor. Find the equation for i after $t = 0$.

3–19. The circuit of Fig. 3–P-8 is in steady state when the switch S is opened at

$$e = 35.7 \left[e^{-1.43\,t} - e^{-50,000\,t} \right]$$

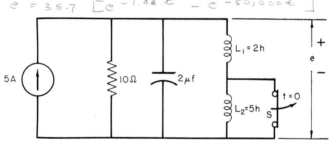

Fig. 3–P-8

$t = 0$. Before $t = 0$ no energy is stored in the 5-henry inductor. Find the equation for e.

$$i = 0.1425\ e^{-35\,t}\ \sin 281\,t$$

3–20. The circuit of Fig. 3–P-9 has two capacitors in series, both containing ini-

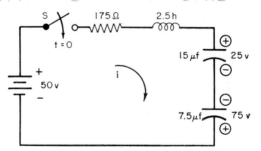

Fig. 3–P-9

$$e_c = -832 + e^{-35\,t} \left[-66.68 \cos 281\,t - 8.3 \sin 281\,t \right]$$

tial charges. S is closed at $t = 0$. Find the equation for current i and the equation for the voltage on the 7.5-μf capacitor.

3–21. The circuit of Fig. 3–P-10 has two inductors in parallel, both containing

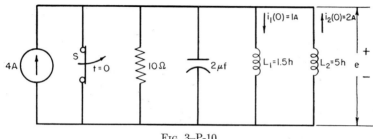

Fɪɢ. 3–P-10

initial currents. The switch S is opened at $t = 0$. Find the equation for e and the equation for the current in the 5-henry inductor in the downward direction.

CHAPTER 4

SERIES–PARALLEL CIRCUITS WITH TWO STORAGE ELEMENTS

4–1. Introduction. Certain series-parallel circuits can be solved by methods developed in the preceding chapters. An example of a circuit of

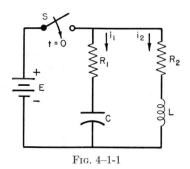

FIG. 4–1-1

this type is shown in Fig. 4–1-1. In this circuit E volts are placed across both the R_1-C branch and the R_2-L branch; i_1 and i_2 are given by

$$i_1 = \frac{E}{R_1}\, \epsilon^{-t/R_1 C} \qquad i_2 = \frac{E}{R_2}\, [1 - \epsilon^{-R_2 t/L}] \tag{4-1-1}$$

The i_1 current does not affect the R_2-L branch, and the i_2 current does not affect the R_1-C branch. If a resistor is placed in series with the switch S, then i_1 will affect i_2 and i_2 will affect i_1. Circuits of this type are analyzed in subsequent articles.

Another example of circuits that can be solved by methods already developed is shown in Fig. 4–1-2. An examination of this circuit shows that

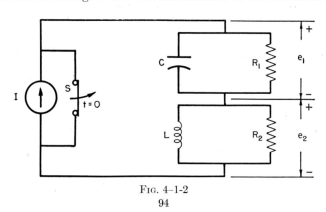

FIG. 4–1-2

it is the dual of the circuit of Fig. 4–1-1 just discussed. In this circuit, the
current I flows into the R_1-C parallel combination and into the R_2-L
parallel combination. Therefore e_1 and e_2 are given by

$$e_1 = IR_1[1 - \epsilon^{-t/R_1 C}] \qquad e_2 = IR_2\epsilon^{-R_2 t/L} \qquad (4\text{–}1\text{-}2)$$

If a resistor is placed in parallel with the current source, e_1 and e_2 will
interact. The remainder of this chapter is concerned with series-parallel
circuits in which the presence of one portion of the circuit affects the current
(or voltage) in the other portion of the circuit.

The method of solution for the series-parallel circuits consists of the
following major steps:

  (a) Set up the integro-differential equations for the circuit, and differentiate, to
remove the integral sign.
  (b) Solve the equations for the one current (or voltage) that is desired.
  (c) Obtain and factor the characteristic equation.
  (d) Put the solution in the desired form with the number of arbitrary constants
corresponding to the order of the differential equation.
  (e) By use of the equations of step (a) obtain the number of initial conditions
necessary to determine the arbitrary constants in step (d).
  (f) Determine the arbitrary constants of step (d) by use of the results of step (e)
and thus determine the solution.

An additional step that could be listed is that of checking the solution.
Two simple items to check are the initial value and the final (or steady-
state) value of the current (or voltage). The initial value of the solution
can be checked by putting $t = 0$ in the solution of step (f) and checking
the value obtained against the initial current (or voltage) obtained in
step (e). The final value can be checked in a similar manner except that
$t = \infty$ is put into the solution.

4–2. Series-Parallel Circuits with a Voltage Source. It is possible to
solve the series-parallel circuit of Fig. 4–2-1 in general terms, as was done

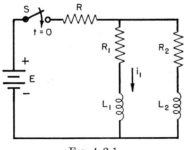

FIG. 4–2-1

in the E-R-L-C series circuit and for the I-G-C-L parallel circuit. However,
the results of such a procedure are so unwieldy that it is almost impossible

to study the variation of one parameter on the over-all solution. As an example to illustrate this, the characteristic equation for this circuit is

$$L_1L_2s^2 + (RL_1 + RL_2 + R_1L_2 + R_2L_1)s + R_1R + R_2R + R_1R_2 = 0 \quad (4\text{-}2\text{-}1)$$

and the two roots are

$$s_1 = -a + b \qquad s_2 = -a - b \qquad (4\text{-}2\text{-}2)$$

where

$$a = \frac{R}{2\,L_2} + \frac{R}{2\,L_1} + \frac{R_1}{2\,L_1} + \frac{R_2}{2\,L_2}$$

$$b = \sqrt{a^2 - \frac{R_1R + R_2R + R_1R_2}{L_1L_2}} \qquad (4\text{-}2\text{-}3)$$

The solution of i_1 is of the form

$$i = \epsilon^{-at}[B_1 \cosh bt + B_2 \sinh bt] \qquad (4\text{-}2\text{-}4)$$

If in these equations R_1 is a variable, the effect of the variation of R_1 on the solution can be determined with considerable labor, and the amount of work involved hardly seems appropriate for a book of this nature.

For these reasons numerical coefficients are used in the examples which follow. It is believed that the method of solution, which is the important thing, can be followed with less difficulty if the work is not cluttered with equations such as 4-2-1 and 4-2-3.

4–3. Examples of Series-Parallel Circuits with a Voltage Source. EXAMPLE 4–3-1. The circuit shown in Fig. 4–3-1 is studied first. It is

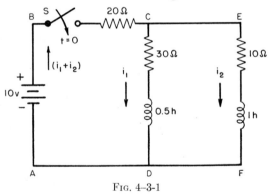

FIG. 4–3-1

assumed that the circuit is at rest before S is closed; that is, no energy is stored in either inductor before $t = 0$. The necessary Kirchhoff's law equations can be set up in many ways. The currents shown in the figure are the currents arbitrarily chosen at this time. The first equation is written by traversing the loop A-B-C-D and the second by traversing A-B-E-F:

$$10 = 20(i_1 + i_2) + 30\,i_1 + 0.5\frac{di_1}{dt}$$

$$10 = 20(i_1 + i_2) + 10\,i_2 + 1\frac{di_2}{dt} \qquad (4\text{-}3\text{-}1)$$

The terms of Eqs. 4–3–1 are combined.

$$10 = 50\, i_1 + 0.5 \frac{di_1}{dt} + 20\, i_2$$

$$10 = 20\, i_1 + 30\, i_2 + 1 \frac{di_2}{dt} \tag{4-3-2}$$

To find $(di_1/dt)(0)$ and $(di_2/dt)(0)$ the known values of currents at $t = 0$ are put into Eqs. 4–3–2. As no energy is stored in the inductors before $t = 0$, $i_1(0) = i_2(0) = 0$ and, on substitution, $(di_1/dt)(0)$ and $(di_2/dt)(0)$ are found to be

$$10 = 50(0) + 0.5 \frac{di_1}{dt}(0) + 20(0) \quad \text{or} \quad \frac{di_1}{dt}(0) = \frac{10}{0.5} = 20$$

$$10 = 20(0) + 30(0) + 1 \frac{di_2}{dt}(0) \quad \text{or} \quad \frac{di_2}{dt}(0) = 10 \tag{4-3-3}$$

It is assumed that i_1 is desired. One procedure for eliminating i_2 from Eqs. 4–3–2 is to solve the first of these equations for i_2:

$$i_2 = \frac{10}{20} - \frac{50}{20}\, i_1 - \frac{0.5}{20} \frac{di_1}{dt} = 0.5 - 2.5\, i_1 - 0.025 \frac{di_1}{dt} \tag{4-3-4}$$

Then i_2 can be differentiated with respect to time:

$$\frac{di_2}{dt} = -\, 2.5 \frac{di_1}{dt} - 0.025 \frac{d^2 i_1}{dt^2} \tag{4-3-5}$$

When i_2 of Eq. 4–3–4 and di_2/dt of Eq. 4–3–5 are substituted into the second of Eqs. 4–3–2, the result is an equation containing only i_1:

$$10 = 20\, i_1 + 30 \left(0.5 - 2.5\, i_1 - 0.025 \frac{di_1}{dt} \right) + 1 \left(-2.5 \frac{di_1}{dt} - 0.025 \frac{d^2 i_1}{dt^2} \right) \tag{4-3-6}$$

Combining terms and making the coefficient of $d^2 i_1/dt^2$ equal to unity in Eq. 4–3–6 gives

$$\frac{d^2 i_1}{dt^2} + 130 \frac{di_1}{dt} + 2200\, i_1 = 200 \tag{4-3-7}$$

Since the right side of Eq. 4–3–7 is not zero, the solution for i_1 is comprised of $i_1 = i_{1ss} + i_{1tr}$, where $i_{1ss} = 200/2200 = 0.091$, and the characteristic equation is

$$s^2 + 130\, s + 2200 = 0 \tag{4-3-8}$$

which, when factored, is

$$(s + 65 - 45)(s + 65 + 45) = 0 \tag{4-3-9}$$

The solution for i_1 can be written in the form

$$i_1 = 0.091 + A_1 \epsilon^{-20t} + A_2 \epsilon^{-110t} \tag{4-3-10}$$

or in the form

$$i_1 = 0.091 + \epsilon^{-65t}[B_1 \cosh 45\,t + B_2 \sinh 45\,t] \qquad (4\text{-}3\text{-}11)$$

When the initial conditions are forced on Eq. 4-3-10, the result is

$$i_1 = 0 = 0.091 + A_1 + A_2 \qquad (4\text{-}3\text{-}12)$$

When Eq. 4-3-10 is differentiated, the result is

$$\frac{di_1}{dt} = -20\,A_1\epsilon^{-20t} - 110\,A_2\epsilon^{-110t}$$

which at $t = 0$ yields

$$\frac{di_1}{dt}(0) = 20 = -20\,A_1 - 110\,A_2 \qquad (4\text{-}3\text{-}13)$$

When Eqs. 4-3-12 and 4-3-13 are solved simultaneously, A_1 and A_2 are found to be $A_1 = 0.111$ and $A_2 = -0.202$. When A_1 and A_2 are substituted in Eq. 4-3-10, the solution for i_1 is given by

$$i_1 = 0.091 + 0.111\,\epsilon^{-20t} - 0.202\,\epsilon^{-110t} \qquad (4\text{-}3\text{-}14)$$

If the solution for i_2 is also desired, it may be obtained in exactly the same manner or by substituting i_1 and di_1/dt into Eq. 4-3-4:

$$i_2 = 0.5 - 2.5\,i_1 - 0.025\frac{di_1}{dt} = 0.5 - 2.5[0.091 + 0.111\,\epsilon^{-20t} - 0.202\,\epsilon^{-110t}]$$
$$- 0.025[0.111(20)\,\epsilon^{-20t} + 0.202(110)\,\epsilon^{-110t}]$$

This, upon simplification, gives

$$i_2 = 0.273 - 0.222\,\epsilon^{-20t} - 0.051\,\epsilon^{-110t} \qquad (4\text{-}3\text{-}15)$$

It is to be noted that i_1 of Eq. 4-3-14 and i_2 of Eq. 4-3-15 check their respective initial and final values.

With circuits involving two storage elements of the same kind, the solutions will never be those of the oscillatory case. For a circuit to oscillate, an exchange of energy from inductor to capacitor and from capacitor to inductor must occur. In circuits with two inductors, such as Fig. 4-3-1, or with two capacitors, the solutions will always be of the nonoscillatory form.

Examination of Eqs. 4-3-14 and 4-3-15 shows that both i_1 and i_2 are of the same form and have the same exponents (or roots to the characteristic equation). This form is

$$i = i_{ss} + A_1\epsilon^{-20t} + A_2\epsilon^{-100t} \qquad (4\text{-}3\text{-}16)$$

No matter how complicated a circuit may be, the currents and voltages in various parts of the circuit usually have the same form, but of course the various A's and the steady-state terms will differ. There is always the possibility that i_{ss} (or e_{ss}) may be zero.

EXAMPLE 4–3-2. As a second example, the circuit shown in Fig. 4–3-2 is considered. It is assumed that the circuit is at rest before S is closed,

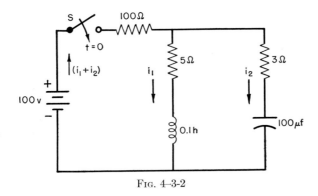

FIG. 4–3-2

whence $i_1(0)$ and $e_2(0)$ are both zero. When the arbitrary current directions are chosen, the voltage equations are

$$100 = 100(i_1 + i_2) + 5\,i_1 + 0.1\,\frac{di_1}{dt}$$

$$100 = 100(i_1 + i_2) + 3\,i_2 + \frac{\displaystyle\int_0^t i_2\,dt}{100 \times 10^{-6}} \qquad (4\text{–}3\text{-}17)$$

Combining terms yields

$$100 = 105\,i_1 + 0.1\,\frac{di_1}{dt} + 100\,i_2$$

$$100 = 100\,i_1 + 103\,i_2 + 10^4 \int_0^t i_2\,dt \qquad (4\text{–}3\text{-}18)$$

As stated, the circuit is at rest before $t = 0$; therefore $i_1(0) = 0$, since the inductor keeps i_1 from jumping to a new value at $t = 0$. However, this does not mean that $i_2(0)$ is equal to zero since there is an R-C path around the outside loop and the current through R can jump to a new value. One method of finding $i_2(0)$ is to take the second of Eqs. 4–3-18 and put in the known quantities at $t = 0$.

$$100 = 100(0) + 103\,i_2(0) + 10^4(0) \quad \text{or} \quad i_2(0) = \tfrac{100}{103} = 0.97 \quad (4\text{–}3\text{-}19)$$

To find $(di/dt)(0)$, $i_2(0)$ along with other known quantities at $t = 0$ can be substituted into the first of Eqs. 4–3-18:

$$100 = 105(0) + 0.1\,\frac{di_1}{dt}\,(0) + 100(0.97) \quad \text{or} \quad \frac{di_1}{dt}\,(0) = \frac{3}{0.1} = 30 \quad (4\text{–}3\text{-}20)$$

If i_1 is desired, the following steps yield the differential equation for i_1. First, i_2 is obtained from the first of Eqs. 4–3-18:

$$i_2 = 1 - 1.05\,i_1 - 1 \times 10^{-3}\,\frac{di_1}{dt} \qquad (4\text{–}3\text{-}21)$$

Then the differentiation of the second of Eqs. 4–3-18 and Eq. 4–3-21 gives

$$0 = 100 \frac{di_1}{dt} + 103 \frac{di_2}{dt} + 10^4 i_2$$

and   (4–3-22)

$$\frac{di_2}{dt} = -1.05 \frac{di_1}{dt} - 1 \times 10^{-3} \frac{d^2 i_1}{dt^2}$$

Eliminating i_2 between the equations of 4–3-21 and 4–3-22 gives

$$0 = 100 \frac{di_1}{dt} + 103 \left[-1.05 \frac{di_1}{dt} - 1 \times 10^{-3} \frac{d^2 i_1}{dt^2} \right]$$

$$+ 10^4 \left[1 - 1.05\, i_1 - 1 \times 10^3 \frac{di_1}{dt} \right] \qquad (4\text{–}3\text{-}23)$$

Collecting terms and making the coefficient of the $d^2 i_1/dt^2$ term equal to unity, and simplifying Eq. 4–3-23 give

$$9.7 \times 10^4 = \frac{d^2 i_1}{dt^2} + 176 \frac{di}{dt} + 1.02 \times 10^5\, i_1 \qquad (4\text{–}3\text{-}24)$$

from which i_{1ss} and the characteristic equation follow:

$$i_{1ss} = \frac{9.7 \times 10^4}{1.02 \times 10^5} = 0.952 \qquad (4\text{–}3\text{-}25)$$

and

$$s^2 + 176\, s + 1.02 \times 10^5 = 0 \qquad (4\text{–}3\text{-}26)$$

The characteristic equation can be factored:

$$(s + 88 + j\,307)(s + 88 - j\,307) = 0 \qquad (4\text{–}3\text{-}27)$$

and i_1 put in the form

$$i_1 = 0.952 + \epsilon^{-88t}[B_1 \cos 307\, t + B_2 \sin 307\, t] \qquad (4\text{–}3\text{-}28)$$

The arbitrary constants of Eq. 4–3-28 are determined by imposing the necessary initial conditions on Eq. 4–3-28 and its derivative.

$$0 = 0.952 + B_1 \quad \text{or} \quad B_1 = -0.952$$

$$i_1 = 0.952 + \epsilon^{-88t}[-0.952 \cos 307\, t + B_2 \sin 307\, t] \qquad (4\text{–}3\text{-}29)$$

$$\frac{di_1}{dt} = \epsilon^{-88t}[(-0.952)(-307) \sin 307\, t + B_2\, 307 \cos 307\, t]$$

$$+ [-0.952 \cos 307\, t + B_2 \sin 307\, t](-88)\, \epsilon^{-88t} \qquad (4\text{–}3\text{-}30)$$

From Eq. 4–3-20 di_1/dt is found to be 30, and from this B_2 is determined:

$$30 = B_2\, 307 + 88 \times 0.952 \quad \text{or} \quad B_2 = \frac{30 - 83.8}{307} = -0.175 \qquad (4\text{–}3\text{-}31)$$

Finally, i_1 can be written

$$i_1 = 0.952 - \epsilon^{-88t}[0.952 \cos 307\, t + 0.175 \sin 307\, t] \qquad (4\text{–}3\text{-}32)$$

Inspection of the circuit will show that $i_{2ss} = 0$, so i_2 has the form

$$i_2 = \epsilon^{-88t}[B_1 \cos 307\, t + B_2 \sin 307\, t] \qquad (4\text{–}3\text{-}33)$$

The determination of B_1 and B_2 is left as a problem at the end of the chapter.

In electric circuits the number of roots of the characteristic equation is often (but not always) equal to the number of storage elements. For example, the circuit of Fig. 4–3-1 has two storage elements, and the corresponding characteristic equation is that of Eq. 4–3-9 and has two roots. These roots can be plotted on the complex s-plane. For example, the roots corresponding to Eq. 4–3-9 are

$$s_1 = -20 \quad \text{and} \quad s_2 = -110 \tag{4-3-34}$$

These roots are plotted on the complex s-plane in Fig. 4–3-3.

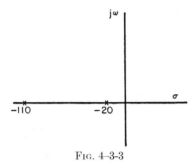

FIG. 4–3-3

As a second example, the circuit of Fig. 4–3-2 has two storage elements and the characteristic equation 4–3-26 has two roots:

$$s_1 = -88 - j\,307 \quad \text{and} \quad s_2 = -88 + j\,307 \tag{4-3-35}$$

These roots are plotted in Fig. 4–3-4.

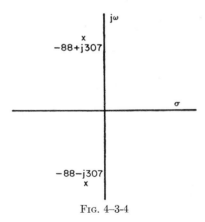

FIG. 4–3-4

For passive electric circuits the roots always lie on or to the left of the imaginary axis. If the roots are on the negative real axis (as in Fig. 4–3-3), the transient terms will be of an exponentially decaying type as in Eq. 4–3-14. If the roots are complex (as in Fig. 4–3-4), the transient terms will be of an exponentially decaying sinusoid type as in Eq. 4–3-32.

102   TRANSIENTS IN ELECTRICAL CIRCUITS

EXAMPLE 4–3-3. The two preceding examples are for circuits which were initially at rest. The method of solution for circuits of this type, but which have energy stored in either one or both storage elements, is quite similar and is demonstrated by this and the following example. The circuit shown in Fig. 4–3-5 is to be analyzed; it is given that S_1 is closed first and S_2 is

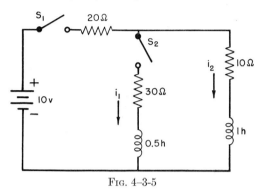

FIG. 4–3-5

closed 0.02 sec later. The current i_2 is desired after S_2 has been closed. After S_1 is closed but before S_2 is closed, the circuit is that of an E-R-L with $R = 20 + 10 = 30$ ohms and the solution written with $t = 0$ at the time when S_1 is closed becomes

$$i_2 = \frac{E}{R}[1 - \epsilon^{-Rt/L}] = \frac{10}{30}[1 - \epsilon^{-30t/1}] = 0.333(1 - \epsilon^{-30t}) \quad (4\text{–}3\text{-}36)$$

When $t = 0.02$ sec is substituted in this equation, the value for $i_2(0)$ at the start of the next transient is

$$i_2(0) = 0.333[1 - \epsilon^{-(30)(0.02)}] = 0.15$$

After S_2 is closed, the circuit is that of Ex. 4–3-1 with different initial conditions. Therefore the characteristic equation is exactly the same as before and, of course, this equation has exactly the same roots:

$$s_1 = -65 + 45 \quad \text{and} \quad s_2 = -65 - 45$$

The current i_2 can be put in exponential form as is done in Eq. 4–3-15 or in the hyperbolic form. For the sake of variety, this time i_2 is put in the hyperbolic form:

$$i_2 = 0.273 + \epsilon^{-65t}[B_1 \cosh 45\,t + B_2 \sinh 45\,t] \quad (4\text{–}3\text{-}37)$$

B_1 and B_2 can be determined from the initial conditions which, in turn, can be determined from Eqs. 4–3-2, which are repeated here for convenience:

$$10 = 50\,i_1 + 0.5\frac{di_1}{dt} + 20\,i_2$$
$$10 = 20\,i_1 + 30\,i_2 + 1\frac{di_2}{dt} \quad (4\text{–}3\text{-}38)$$

The term $(di_2/dt)(0)$ can be found by putting in the second of these equations the known conditions at $t = 0$, which are

$$i_1(0) = 0 \qquad i_2(0) = 0.15$$

$$10 = 20(0) + 30(0.15) + 1\frac{di_2}{dt}(0) \quad \text{or} \quad \frac{di_2}{dt}(0) = 5.5$$

B_1 can be found by imposing the conditions at $t = 0$ on Eq. 4–3-37:

$$0.15 = 0.273 + B_1 \quad \text{or} \quad B_1 = -0.123$$

Eq. 4–3-37 now becomes

$$i_2 = 0.273 + \epsilon^{-65t}[-0.123 \cosh 45\,t + B_2 \sinh 45\,t] \qquad (4\text{–}3\text{–}39)$$

B_2 can be determined in the following steps:

$$\frac{di_2}{dt} = \epsilon^{-65t}[-0.123 \cosh 45\,t + B_2 \sinh 45\,t](-65)$$
$$+ \epsilon^{-65t}[-0.123(45) \sinh 45\,t + B_2(45) \cosh 45\,t] \qquad (4\text{–}3\text{–}40)$$

which at $t = 0$ becomes

$$5.5 = 45\,B_2 + (65)(0.123) \quad \text{or} \quad B_2 = \frac{5.5 - 8.0}{45} = -0.0555$$

The solution for i_2 is

$$i_2 = 0.273 - \epsilon^{-65t}[0.123 \cosh 45\,t + 0.0555 \sinh 45\,t] \qquad (4\text{–}3\text{–}41)$$

EXAMPLE 4–3-4. As another example, the circuit shown in Fig. 4–3-6 is analyzed. Here S_1 is closed first and S_2 is closed 0.0012 sec later. The

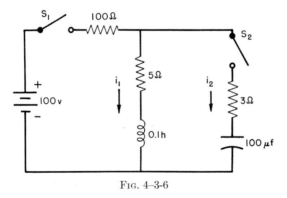

FIG. 4–3-6

current i_2 is desired, with $t = 0$ as the time when S_2 is closed. After S_1 is closed but before S_2 is closed, the equation for i_1 is

$$i_1 = \frac{E}{R}[1 - \epsilon^{-Rt/L}] = \frac{100}{105}[1 - \epsilon^{-105t/0.1}] = 0.952[1 - \epsilon^{-1050t}] \qquad (4\text{–}3\text{–}42)$$

When $t = 0.0012$ sec is put in this equation, the value for $i_1(0)$ at the start of the next transient is

$$i_1(0) = 0.952[1 - \epsilon^{-1050(0.0012)}] = 0.681 \qquad (4\text{–}3\text{–}43)$$

After S_2 is closed, the circuit is that of Ex. 4–3-2 with different initial conditions. Therefore the roots of the characteristic equation are $s_1 = -88 + j\,307$ and $s_2 = -88 - j\,307$ and i_2 has the form

$$i_2 = \epsilon^{-88t}[B_1 \cos 307\,t + B_2 \sin 307\,t] \qquad (4\text{–}3\text{–}44)$$

B_1 and B_2 can be found from the initial conditions; in turn, these can be found from the equations

$$100 = 105\,i_1 + 0.1\frac{di_1}{dt} + 100\,i_2$$

$$\qquad (4\text{–}3\text{–}45)$$

$$100 = 100\,i_1 + 103\,i_2 + 10^4\int_0^t i_2\,dt$$

The quantity $i_2(0)$ can be found by substituting in the second of these the known condition that $i_1 = 0.681$ at $t = 0$:

$$100 = 100(0.681) + 103\,i_2(0) + 0 \quad \text{or} \quad i_2(0) = \frac{31.9}{103} = 0.309 \qquad (4\text{–}3\text{–}46)$$

When this value of $i_2(0)$ is placed in the first of Eqs. 4–3-45, the quantity $(di_1/dt)(0)$ is

$$100 = 105(0.681) + 0.1\frac{di_1}{dt}(0) + 100(0.309) \quad \text{or} \quad \frac{di_1}{dt}(0) = -24 \qquad (4\text{–}3\text{–}47)$$

To find $(di_2/dt)(0)$ the second of equations 4–3-45 is differentiated, yielding

$$0 = 100\frac{di_1}{dt} + 103\frac{di_2}{dt} + 10^4\,i_2 \qquad (4\text{–}3\text{–}48)$$

and the known $(di_1/dt)(0)$ and $i_2(0)$ can be substituted in this equation:

$$0 = 100(-24) + 103\frac{di_2}{dt}(0) + 10^4(0.309) \quad \text{or} \quad \frac{di_2}{dt}(0) = -6.7 \qquad (4\text{–}3\text{–}49)$$

This process of working known initial conditions into these equations can be continued indefinitely, thereby yielding

$$\frac{d^2i_1}{dt^2}(0), \quad \frac{d^2i_2}{dt^2}(0), \quad \frac{d^3i_1}{dt^3}(0), \quad \text{etc.}$$

However, only two initial conditions are necessary in this particular problem. B_1 and B_2 can now be found from $i_2(0)$ and $(di_2/dt)(0)$ in the following steps. First impose $i_2(0)$ on Eq. 4–3-44 to find B_1:

$$0.309 = B_1 \qquad (4\text{–}3\text{–}50)$$

and, when the derivative of Eq. 4–3-44 is evaluated at $t = 0$, B_2 is

$$-6.7 = B_2\,307 - (88)(0.309) \quad \text{or} \quad B_2 = \frac{20.5}{307} = 0.0668 \qquad (4\text{–}3\text{–}51)$$

Upon substitution, the equation for i_2 is

$$i_2 = \epsilon^{-88t}[0.309 \cos 307\,t + 0.0668 \sin 307\,t] \qquad (4\text{–}3\text{–}52)$$

4–4. Examples of Series-Parallel Circuits with a Current Source.
EXAMPLE 4–4-1. The four preceding examples contain a voltage source

and the circuit equations are written with currents as the unknown quantities. This and the next example contain a current source and the circuit equations are written with voltages as the unknown quantities. The circuit configurations to be analyzed are the duals of the preceding examples. The circuit in this example is that shown in Fig. 4–4-1. The

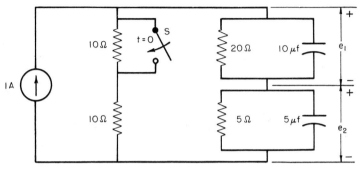

Fig. 4–4-1

switch S is open until the circuit reaches the steady state and is closed at $t = 0$.

Before $t = 0$ the two capacitors act as if they were open circuits and a current of 1 amp exists in an equivalent circuit consisting of a 20-ohm resistor in parallel with a 25-ohm resistor. The voltage across this combination is $e_1 + e_2$ and it is equal to 11.1 volts. The voltage e_1 is $4/5$ of this, and e_2 is $1/5$ of it. At $t = 0$ the voltages on the capacitors do not jump; therefore

$$e_1(0) = 8.88 \quad \text{and} \quad e_2(0) = 2.22 \qquad (4\text{–}4\text{-}1)$$

After $t = 0$ the circuit equations are

$$1 = \frac{e_1 + e_2}{10} + \frac{e_1}{20} + 10 \times 10^{-6} \frac{de_1}{dt}$$
$$1 = \frac{e_1 + e_2}{10} + \frac{e_2}{5} + 5 \times 10^{-6} \frac{de_2}{dt} \qquad (4\text{–}4\text{-}2)$$

When e_2 is eliminated between these equations, the differential equation for e_1 is

$$\frac{d^2e_1}{dt^2} + 7.5 \times 10^4 \frac{de_1}{dt} + 7 \times 10^8 \, e_1 = 40 \times 10^8 \qquad (4\text{–}4\text{-}3)$$

The characteristic equation for this circuit is

$$s^2 + 7.5 \times 10^4 \, s + 7 \times 10^8 = 0 \qquad (4\text{–}4\text{-}4)$$

which can be factored:

$$(s + 3.75 \times 10^4 + 2.66 \times 10^4)(s + 3.75 \times 10^4 - 2.66 \times 10^4) = 0 \quad (4\text{–}4\text{-}5)$$

The steady-state voltage e_{1ss} is found from Eq. 4–4-3 or from circuit:

$$e_{1ss} = \frac{40 \times 10^8}{7 \times 10^8} = 5.72 \qquad (4\text{--}4\text{--}6)$$

The voltage e_1 can now be written in the form

$$e_1 = 5.72 + \epsilon^{-3.75 \times 10^4 t}[B_1 \cosh 2.66 \times 10^4\, t + B_2 \sinh 2.66 \times 10^4\, t] \quad (4\text{--}4\text{--}7)$$

To find B_1 and B_2 a second initial condition is needed. To find $(de_1/dt)(0)$, the first of Eqs. 4–4-2 can be written, at $t = 0$,

$$1 = \frac{11.1}{10} + \frac{8.88}{20} + 10 \times 10^{-6}\frac{de_1}{dt}(0) \quad \text{or} \quad \frac{de_1}{dt}(0) = -5.54 \times 10^4 \qquad (4\text{--}4\text{--}8)$$

When the initial conditions are imposed on Eq. 4–4-7 in the usual manner, the resulting equation for e_1 is

$$e_1 = 5.72 + \epsilon^{-3.75 \times 10^4 t}[3.16 \cosh 2.66 \times 10^4\, t + 2.37 \sinh 2.66 \times 10^4\, t] \qquad (4\text{--}4\text{--}9)$$

EXAMPLE 4–4-2. The circuit of Fig. 4–4-2 is analyzed in this example. The switch S is closed until steady state is reached; at $t = 0$, S is opened.

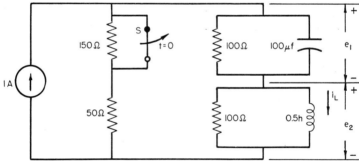

FIG. 4–4-2

Before $t = 0$ the capacitor acts as if it were an open circuit and the inductor as a short circuit, and a current of 1 amp exists in the equivalent circuit consisting of a 50-ohm resistor in parallel with a 100-ohm resistor. The voltage across this combination is 33.3 volts; therefore, before $t = 0$, $e_1 = 33.3$, $e_2 = 0$, and i_L can be found: $i_L = 0.333$.

At $t = 0$ the voltage on the capacitor does not jump, so that

$$e_1(0) = 33.3 \qquad (4\text{--}4\text{--}10)$$

but the voltage $e_2(0)$ can jump to a new value because the quantity that the inductor holds constant at $t = 0$ is the current, not the voltage. The voltage $e_2(0)$ can be found by first writing the circuit equations

$$1 = \frac{e_1 + e_2}{200} + \frac{e_1}{100} + 100 \times 10^{-6}\frac{de_1}{dt}$$

$$1 = \frac{e_1 + e_2}{200} + \frac{e_2}{100} + \frac{1}{0.5}\int_0^t e_2\, dt + 0.333 \qquad (4\text{--}4\text{--}11)$$

If $t = 0$ conditions are put into the second of these equations, $e_2(0)$ can be found:

$$1 = \frac{33.3 + e_2(0)}{200} + \frac{e_2(0)}{100} + 0.333 \quad \text{or} \quad e_2(0) = 33.3 \qquad (4\text{-}4\text{-}12)$$

In this example e_2 is desired; therefore the second initial condition $(de_2/dt)(0)$ is also required. This can be found in a two-step procedure by substituting known initial conditions into the first of Eqs. 4–4–11; $(de_1/dt)(0)$ is thus found:

$$1 = \frac{33.3 + 33.3}{200} + \frac{33.3}{100} + 100 \times 10^{-6} \frac{de_1}{dt}(0) \quad \text{or} \quad \frac{de_1}{dt}(0) = 3.33 \times 10^3$$

$$(4\text{-}4\text{-}13)$$

and, putting this into the second of Eqs. 4–4–11 after it is differentiated:

$$0 = \frac{\dfrac{de_1}{dt}(0) + \dfrac{de_2}{dt}(0)}{200} + \frac{\dfrac{de_2(0)}{dt}}{100} + \frac{1}{0.5} e_2(0)$$

or

$$0 = \frac{3.33 \times 10^3 + \dfrac{de_2}{dt}(0)}{200} + \frac{\dfrac{de_2}{dt}(0)}{100} + \frac{1}{0.5}(33.3)$$

giving

$$\frac{de_2}{dt}(0) = -5.55 \times 10^3 \qquad (4\text{-}4\text{-}14)$$

When e_1 is eliminated between the equations 4–4–11, the differential equation for e_2 is

$$\frac{d^2 e_2}{dt^2} + 266 \frac{de_2}{dt} + 20{,}000\, e_2 = 0 \qquad (4\text{-}4\text{-}15)$$

The characteristic equation for this circuit is

$$s^2 + 266\, s + 20{,}000 = 0 \qquad (4\text{-}4\text{-}16)$$

which can be factored as

$$(s + 133 + j\, 47.4)(s + 133 - j\, 47.4) \qquad (4\text{-}4\text{-}17)$$

The steady-state voltage e_{2ss} deduced from Eq. 4–4–15, or from inspection of the circuit, is zero.

The voltage e_2 can now be written in the form

$$e_2 = \epsilon^{-133t}[B_1 \cos 47.4\, t + B_2 \sin 47.4\, t] \qquad (4\text{-}4\text{-}18)$$

When the initial conditions are imposed on Eq. 4–4–18, the resulting equation for e_2 is

$$e_2 = \epsilon^{-133t}[33.3 \cos 47.4\, t - 23.7 \sin 47.4\, t] \qquad (4\text{-}4\text{-}19)$$

4–5. Various Methods of Writing Circuit Equations. It is not to be inferred from the examples presented thus far that when voltage sources are present the circuit equations should always be written with currents as the unknown, or that when current sources are present the circuit equations should always be written with voltages as the unknowns. Obviously, one circuit could have both current and voltage sources present, so that neither of the outlined procedures can be applied unless transformations are made on one type of source.

The circuit equations for any circuit can be written essentially in two different ways. The first of these can be called the loop method and the second the node method.

The loop method of writing the necessary equations is demonstrated on the circuit shown in Fig. 4–5-1. In this circuit, the 2-μf capacitor initially

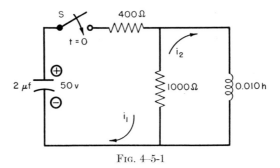

FIG. 4–5-1

has a voltage of 50 volts when the switch S is closed at $t = 0$. Mesh currents are set up as shown, and the circuit equations can be written

$$\frac{1}{2 \times 10^{-6}} \int_0^t i_1 \, dt - 50 + 400 \, i_1 + 1000[i_1 - i_2] = 0$$

$$0.01 \frac{di_2}{dt} + 1000(i_2 - i_1) = 0 \tag{4-5-1}$$

These equations are voltage equations with currents as the unknowns.

The node method of setting up the circuit equations is to write the necessary number of current equations with voltages as the unknowns. The circuit of Fig. 4–5-1 is redrawn in Fig. 4–5-2 to demonstrate the

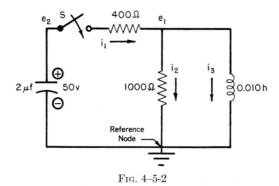

FIG. 4–5-2

method. One node is arbitrarily chosen as the reference node, and enough other nodes must be chosen so that the voltages of all other points in the circuit can be determined. An examination of Fig. 4–5-2 shows that the nodes labeled e_1 and e_2 are sufficient to determine all voltages. At both of these nodes, current equations are written. For example, at node e_1, the equation

$$i_1 = i_2 + i_3 \tag{4-5-2}$$

can be written. Each of these currents can be identified in terms of voltages:

$$\frac{e_2 - e_1}{400} = \frac{e_1}{1000} + \frac{1}{0.01} \int_0^t e_1 \, dt \tag{4-5-3}$$

At node e_2 the equation

$$i_1 = i_1 \tag{4-5-4}$$

can be written, where i_1 can be identified in two ways:

$$-2 \times 10^{-6} \frac{de_2}{dt} = \frac{e_2 - e_1}{400} \tag{4-5-5}$$

Eqs. 4–5-3 and 4–5-5 can be solved for e_1 and e_2, from which any of the currents can be determined if desired.

The circuit shown in Figs. 4–5-1 and 4–5-2 does not exhibit any particular advantages as to solution by the loop method or the node method, for in both cases there are two unknowns and the work in obtaining a solution is about the same in either. However, in many circuits one method may be more convenient to use than the other, because the circuit equations will contain fewer unknowns than they would if the equations were written by the other method. Therefore the student should become equally familiar with both methods so that he can use whichever is more convenient.

Other possible methods of writing circuit equations are mixtures of the loop method and the node method. This is demonstrated in the following example.

The circuit of Figs. 4–5-1 and 4–5-2 is redrawn in Fig. 4–5-3 for this

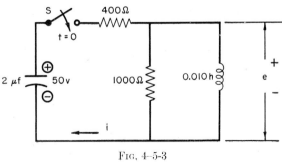

Fig. 4–5-3

example. Suppose that the voltage e is desired. The circuit equations can be written

$$e + \frac{1}{2 \times 10^{-6}} \int_0^t i \, dt - 50 + 400 \, i = 0$$

$$i = \frac{e}{1000} + \frac{1}{0.01} \int_0^t e \, dt \tag{4-5-6}$$

These equations are a mixture of an unknown voltage and an unknown current. The voltage e could be eliminated between the equations of 4-5-6, leaving an equation in current i, or the current i can be eliminated, leaving an equation in e. When the latter is done, the equation is

$$\frac{d^2 e}{dt^2} + 2.89 \times 10^4 \frac{de}{dt} + 3.57 \times 10^7 \, e = 0 \tag{4-5-7}$$

The steady-state voltage is zero, and the characteristic equation corresponding to Eq. 4-5-7 can be factored:

$$(s + 1286)(s + 27650) = 0 \tag{4-5-8}$$

The voltage e can be put in the form

$$e = A_1 \epsilon^{-1286t} + A_2 \epsilon^{-27650t} \tag{4-5-9}$$

Initially the current in the inductor is zero, so the 400-ohm and the 1000-ohm resistors act as a voltage divider, producing

$$e(0) = 50 \times \frac{1000}{1400} = 35.7 \text{ volts} \tag{4-5-10}$$

and

$$i(0) = \frac{e(0)}{1000} = \frac{35.7}{1000} = 0.0357 \text{ amp} \tag{4-5-11}$$

If Eqs. 4-5-6 are differentiated with conditions at $t = 0$ substituted, they become

$$\frac{de}{dt}(0) + 5 \times 10^5 (0.0357) + 400 \frac{di}{dt}(0) = 0$$

$$\frac{di}{dt}(0) + 10^{-3} \frac{de}{dt}(0) + 10^2 (35.7) = 0 \tag{4-5-12}$$

From Eqs. 4-5-12, the following can be obtained:

$$\frac{de}{dt}(0) = -1.033 \times 10^6 \tag{4-5-13}$$

When the initial conditions are imposed on Eq. 4-5-9, the resulting equation for e is

$$e = -1.73 \, \epsilon^{-1286t} + 37.45 \, \epsilon^{-27650t} \tag{4-5-14}$$

Many other examples could be supplied at this point, but those given are sufficient to demonstrate the method. In the next chapter the Laplace transform method of solution is taken up. After the fundamentals of this method are explained, other examples similar to the preceding ones are studied.

PROBLEMS

4–1. In the circuit of Fig. 4–P-1 the switch S is open until steady-state conditions are reached and is closed at $t = 0$. Find i_2 in the direction shown after $t = 0$.

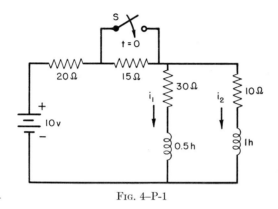

Fig. 4–P-1

4–2. Complete the solution of i_2 (Eq. 4–3-33) for Ex. 4–3-2.

4–3. Find i_1 in Ex. 4–3-3.

4–4. Find i_1 in Ex. 4–3-4.

4–5. Find e_2 in Ex. 4–4-1.

4–6. Find e_1 in Ex. 4–4-2.

4–7. Using Eq. 4–5-1, find i_2, then the voltage across the inductor.

4–8. Using Eqs. 4–5-3 and 4–5-5, solve for the voltage e_1.

4–9. In the circuit of Fig. 4–P-2 the switch S is closed until steady-state con-

$$i_1 = 0.953 + e^{-88t}(3.047 \cos 307t + 0.68 \sin 307t)$$

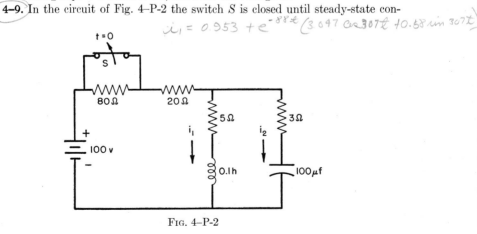

Fig. 4–P-2

ditions are reached and is opened at $t = 0$. Find the equation for i_1 in direction shown.

4–10. In the circuit shown in Fig. 4–P-3, both capacitors are initially discharged. S_1 is closed first, and 0.03 sec later S_2 is closed. Find the charge on the 8-µf capacitor 0.02 sec after S_2 is closed.

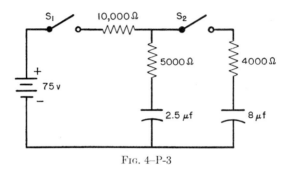

FIG. 4–P-3

4–11. In the circuit of Fig. 4–P-4 the switch S is thrown to position 1 until steady-state conditions are reached and, at $t = 0$, S is thrown to position 2. Find the equation for the voltage from point A to point B.

$$e_{ab} = 0.0908 + 1.051 \, e^{-3640t} \sin 7630 \, t$$

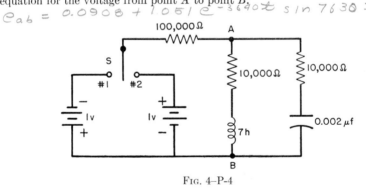

FIG. 4–P-4

4–12. In the circuit of Fig. 4–P-5 S is open until steady-state conditions are reached and closed at $t = 0$. Find the equation for the voltage across the 5-µf capacitor.

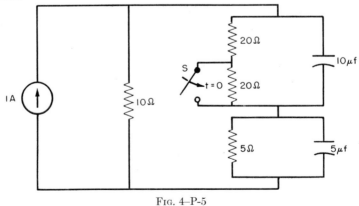

FIG. 4–P-5

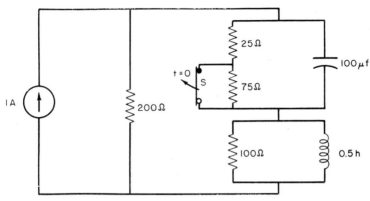

FIG. 4–P-6

4-13. In the circuit of Fig. 4–P-6 S is closed until steady-state conditions are reached, and S is opened at $t = 0$. Find the equation for the current through the 100-μf capacitor.

$i_c = 0.667 e^{-113t} \cos 47.4t$

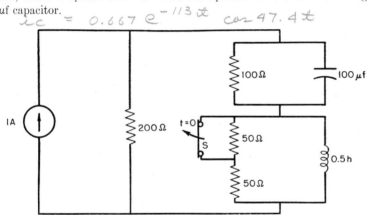

FIG. 4–P-7

4-14. In the circuit of Fig. 4–P-7 S is closed until steady-state conditions are reached, and S is opened at $t = 0$. Find the equation for current in the 0.5-henry inductor.

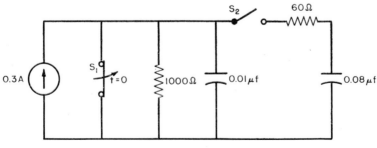

FIG. 4–P-8

4-15. In the circuit of Fig. 4–P-8 the switch S_1 is opened at $t = 0$ and S_2 is closed 5 μsec later. Find the current in the 60-ohm resistor.

4-16. The circuit of Fig. 4–P-9 is assumed to be in the steady state before time $t = 0$. Determine the voltage across the capacitor after the switch S is opened at $t = 0$.

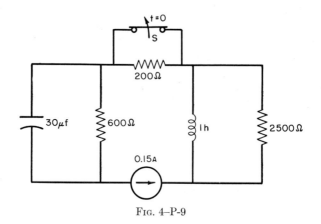

FIG. 4–P-9

4-17. In the circuit of Fig. 4–P-10 S is closed until the steady state is reached and, at $t = 0$, S is opened. Find the current i in the direction shown.

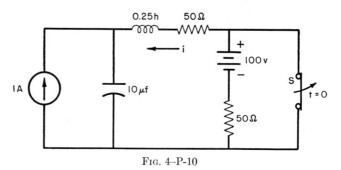

FIG. 4–P-10

$$i = -1 + e^{-200t} \sin 600t$$

CHAPTER 5

INTRODUCTION TO LAPLACE TRANSFORMS AND
THEIR APPLICATIONS

5–1. Introduction. In Chapters 2, 3, and 4 the classical method of solving first- and second-order differential equations was explained. This method consists of the following steps:

(a) Set up the integro-differential equations for the circuit, and differentiate to remove the integral sign.

(b) If simultaneous equations are involved, solve these equations for an equation in the one unknown that is desired.

(c) Obtain the characteristic equation from the equation of step (b).

(d) Factor the characteristic equation.

(e) Put the solution in the desired form with the number of constants of integration corresponding to the order of the differential equations.

(f) By use of the equations of step (a) obtain the number of initial conditions necessary to determine the constants of integration.

(g) Impose the initial conditions of step (f) on the equation of step (e), thus obtaining a set of simultaneous equations involving only the constants of integration.

(h) Solve the equations of step (g) for the constants.

(i) Put the constants into the form of step (e), thus obtaining the final solution.

Although circuits involving three storage elements have not been analyzed, the solution would follow exactly the same steps. Step (b) now gives a third-order differential equation. The characteristic equation is an algebraic equation of the third degree in s which, when factored, gives three roots, $-s_1$, $-s_2$, and $-s_3$. Step (e) can put the solution in the form

$$i = i_{ss} + A_1\epsilon^{-s_1 t} + A_2\epsilon^{-s_2 t} + A_3\epsilon^{-s_3 t} \qquad (5\text{--}1\text{--}1)$$

Three initial conditions must be determined in step (f), and step (g) yields three equations in three unknowns from which A_1, A_2, and A_3 can be determined. To solve a fourth-order differential equation, four initial conditions are required and four equations in four unknowns must be solved for the four constants of integration, etc. As can be seen, a variety of different operations must be performed in obtaining a solution in this manner. Also, as the order of the equation increases, the labor involved in finding the initial conditions and solving for the constants of integration becomes more tedious.

For these reasons many attempts have been made to develop a method of solution where the initial conditions are worked into the original equations and the final solution is obtained directly without using a group of auxiliary steps to evaluate the constants of integration.

One of these methods, widely used a few years ago, is Heaviside's operational calculus method. The Heaviside method, as originally developed, could be used directly only for systems that were initially at rest. This restriction was later removed, but the extended method is less flexible in use than the method now to be described. Also, in the Heaviside method for each new driving function a new method of procedure must be developed for that particular function.

Another method, which is similar in many points of analysis to the Heaviside method but does not suffer the mentioned limitations, is based on use of the Laplace transform. The Laplace transform method has almost entirely replaced Heaviside's method in modern circuit analysis. For this reason the Laplace transform method is utilized in this book.

5–2. The Laplace Transformation Method. Use of logarithms, in a sense, involves the idea of a transformation. By logarithms the process of multiplication is transformed into addition, the process of raising to a power is transformed into multiplication. The Laplace transform method, in an entirely different manner, transforms a differential equation from the realm of time into the realm of a function of a complex variable. The complex variable s has a real part σ and an imaginary part $j\omega$, so that s is given by

$$s = \sigma + j\omega \qquad (5\text{-}2\text{-}1)$$

By carrying out a number of mathematical manipulations that put the function in a desired form, an inverse transformation back to the time realm can be made, thus giving the solution to the differential equation with all the constants of integration evaluated.

The mathematics necessary for a complete understanding of inversion in the Laplace transform method involves the function of a complex variable, which is beyond the scope of this book. However, if a table of transform pairs is developed, this table may be used for inversion and most linear circuit problems involving lumped elements can be solved without need of recourse to the mentioned analysis.

5–3. The Direct Transform Integral. If a function of time, $f(t)$, is multiplied by ϵ^{-st} and then integrated between the limits of zero and infinity, the result is a function of s which is denoted by $F(s)$ and is termed the Laplace transform of $f(t)$. The transform integral is denoted by the symbol $\mathcal{L}$; thus

$$\mathcal{L}[f(t)] = \int_0^\infty f(t)\epsilon^{-st}\, dt = F(s) \qquad (5\text{-}3\text{-}1)$$

It should be noted that by virtue of the upper limit this is an improper integral, and the conditions for convergence necessary for this integral to exist impose certain limitations under which it is valid. Fortunately, the conditions for convergence are satisfied in nearly all circuit problems.

Additional comments are made regarding this aspect as the presentation proceeds.

The following group of examples illustrates the use of the direct integral in determining the direct transform. The function of time and its corresponding direct transform are referred to as a transform pair.

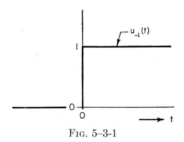

FIG. 5–3-1

EXAMPLE 5–3-1. The unit step function $u_{-1}(t)$, shown in Fig. 5–3-1, is taken as the first example. This function is defined by

$$u_{-1}(t) = 0, \quad t < 0$$
$$u_{-1}(t) = 1, \quad t > 0 \qquad\qquad (5\text{-}3\text{-}2)$$

The function $u_{-1}(t)$ is functionally that of the voltage impressed at $t = 0$ by closing a switch on a 1-volt battery. The direct transform of this function is

$$F(s) = \int_0^\infty 1 \, \epsilon^{-st} \, dt = \left[-\frac{1}{s} \epsilon^{-st} \right]_0^\infty = -\frac{1}{s} [\epsilon^{-s\infty} - \epsilon^0] = \frac{1}{s} \quad (5\text{-}3\text{-}3)$$

As the $\lim_{t \to \infty} \epsilon^{-st}$ is assumed to be zero, $F(s)$ is valid only if σ (the real part of s) is greater than zero. This thus defines the abscissa of convergence $\sigma_0 = 0$, indicating $F(s)$ is valid only if σ is greater than σ_0. This result is entered in Table 5–1, a short table of transform pairs.

EXAMPLE 5–3-2. The second example is $f(t) = \epsilon^{-at}$, wherein a is a real number. The direct transform is

$$F(s) = \int_0^\infty \epsilon^{-at} \epsilon^{-st} \, dt = \int_0^\infty \epsilon^{-(s+a)t} \, dt$$
$$= \left[-\frac{1}{s+a} \epsilon^{-(s+a)t} \right]_0^\infty = -\frac{1}{s+a} [\epsilon^{-(s+a)\infty} - \epsilon^0] = \frac{1}{s+a} \quad (5\text{-}3\text{-}4)$$

As the $\lim_{t \to \infty} \epsilon^{-st}$ is assumed to be zero, $F(s)$ is valid only if σ (the real part of s) is greater than $-a$. Hence $\sigma_0 = -a$. This result is entered in Table 5–1.

EXAMPLE 5–3-3. The third example is $f(t) = \cosh bt$. In this example the direct transform can be found either by using the transform integral or by expanding $\cosh bt$ in its exponential form and using the transform

TABLE 5–1

A Short Table of Transform Pairs

No.	$f(t)$	$F(s)$
1	$u_{-1}(t)$	$\dfrac{1}{s}$
2	$\epsilon^{-at}u_{-1}(t)$	$\dfrac{1}{s+a}$
3	$\cosh bt$	$\dfrac{s}{s^2-b^2}$
4	$\sinh bt$	$\dfrac{b}{s^2-b^2}$
5	$\cos \beta t$	$\dfrac{s}{s^2+\beta^2}$
6	$\sin \beta t$	$\dfrac{\beta}{s^2+\beta^2}$
7	t	$\dfrac{1}{s^2}$
8	$Kf(t)$	$K\mathcal{L}[f(t)]$
9	$f_1(t)+f_2(t)+f_3(t)+\cdots$	$\mathcal{L}[f_1(t)]+\mathcal{L}[f_2(t)]+\mathcal{L}[f_3(t)]+\cdots$
10	$\dfrac{df(t)}{dt}$	$s\mathcal{L}[f(t)]-f(0)$
11	$\displaystyle\int f(t)\,dt$	$\dfrac{\mathcal{L}[f(t)]}{s}+\dfrac{f^{-1}(0)}{s}$
12	$\displaystyle\int_0^t f(t)\,dt$	$\dfrac{\mathcal{L}[f(t)]}{s}$
13	$\epsilon^{-at}\cosh bt$	$\dfrac{s+a}{(s+a)^2-b^2}$
14	$\epsilon^{-at}\sinh bt$	$\dfrac{b}{(s+a)^2-b^2}$
15	$\epsilon^{-at}\cos \beta t$	$\dfrac{s+a}{(s+a)^2+\beta^2}$
16	$\epsilon^{-at}\sin \beta t$	$\dfrac{\beta}{(s+a)^2+\beta^2}$
17	$\epsilon^{-at}t$	$\dfrac{1}{(s+a)^2}$
18	t^n	$\dfrac{n!}{s^{n+1}}$
19	$\epsilon^{-at}t^n$	$\dfrac{n!}{(s+a)^{n+1}}$

determined in Ex. 5–3-2. The latter approach is demonstrated in the following steps:

$$F(s) = \mathcal{L}[\cosh bt] = \mathcal{L}\left[\frac{\epsilon^{+bt} + \epsilon^{-bt}}{2}\right] = \frac{1}{2}\{\mathcal{L}(\epsilon^{+bt}) + \mathcal{L}(\epsilon^{-bt})\}$$

$$F(s) = \frac{1}{2}\left[\frac{1}{s-b} + \frac{1}{s+b}\right] = \frac{1}{2}\left[\frac{(s+b)+(s-b)}{s^2-b^2}\right] = \frac{s}{s^2-b^2} \qquad (5\text{–}3\text{-}5)$$

Therefore, in order that the integral converges, $\sigma_0 = |b|$.

EXAMPLE 5–3-4. The fourth example is $f(t) = \cos \beta t$. For this example $\cos \beta t$ is written as $\cosh j\beta t$; therefore the transform can be found from that of Ex. 5–3-3:

$$\mathcal{L}[\cos \beta t] = \mathcal{L}[\cosh j\beta t] = \frac{s}{s^2 - (j\beta)^2} = \frac{s}{s^2 + \beta^2} \qquad (5\text{–}3\text{-}6)$$

Therefore, σ_0 is easily established as $\sigma_0 = 0$.

EXAMPLE 5–3-5. The last example to be considered at this time is $f(t) = t$. The transform integral can be set up as $F(s) = \int_0^\infty t\epsilon^{-st}\, dt$. Integration by parts gives

$$\int_0^\infty u\, dv = \left[uv\right]_0^\infty - \int_0^\infty v\, du$$

with the identifications
$$u = t \qquad dv = \epsilon^{-st}\, dt$$
$$du = dt \qquad v = -\frac{1}{s}\epsilon^{-st}$$

Upon substitution $F(s)$ is found to be

$$F(s) = \left[t\left(-\frac{1}{s}\epsilon^{-st}\right)\right]_0^\infty - \int_0^\infty -\frac{1}{s}\epsilon^{-st}\, dt = \left[-\frac{1}{s^2}\epsilon^{-st}\right]_0^\infty = \frac{1}{s^2} \qquad (5\text{–}3\text{-}7)$$

Therefore $\sigma_0 = 0$.

The proofs of other transform pairs shown in Table 5–1 are left as problems at the end of the chapter.

5–4. Transform Operations. A number of the following operations, used in the examples worked out in the preceding article, are now examined in detail.

OPERATION 5–1. The Laplace transform of a constant multiplying a function is equal to the constant multiplying the Laplace transform of the function; that is,
$$\mathcal{L}[kf(t)] = k\mathcal{L}[f(t)] \qquad (5\text{–}4\text{-}1)$$

This relationship is true because the transform is in the nature of an integral and the constant can be moved outside the integral sign.

OPERATION 5–2. The Laplace transform of a sum of functions can usually be expressed as the sum of the transforms of the individual functions; that is, $\mathcal{L}[f_1(t) + f_2(t) + f_3(t) + \cdots] = \mathcal{L}[f_1(t)] + \mathcal{L}[f_2(t)] + \cdots \qquad (5\text{–}4\text{-}2)$

This relationship is true if each of the individual integrals exists and equals the integral of the sum of the functions.

OPERATION 5-3. The Laplace transform of a derivative of a function is examined in detail.

$$\mathcal{L}\left[\frac{df(t)}{dt}\right] = \mathcal{L}[f'(t)] = \int_0^\infty f'(t)\epsilon^{-st}\, dt \tag{5-4-3}$$

This integral can be evaluated through integration by parts

$$\int_0^\infty u\, dv = \left[uv\right]_0^\infty - \int_0^\infty v\, du$$

by making the following identifications:

$$dv = f'(t)\, dt \qquad u = \epsilon^{-st}$$
$$v = f(t) \qquad du = -\, s\epsilon^{-st}\, dt$$

Upon substitution, the integral is found to be

$$\int_0^\infty u\, dv = \left[\epsilon^{-st}f(t)\right]_0^\infty - \int_0^\infty f(t)(-\, s\epsilon^{-st})\, dt$$

$$= \epsilon^{-\infty}f(\infty) - \epsilon^0 f(0) + s\int_0^\infty f(t)\epsilon^{-st}\, dt \tag{5-4-4}$$

$$\mathcal{L}[f'(t)] = s\mathcal{L}[f(t)] - f(0)$$

where $f(0)$ is the limit of $f(t)$ as t approaches zero through positive values. It should be noted that in deriving Eq. 5-4-4 it was assumed that

$$\lim_{t\to\infty} \epsilon^{-st}f(t) = 0 \tag{5-4-5}$$

This condition imposes limitations on $f(t)$ which, fortunately, are met by nearly all problems encountered in circuit analysis.

OPERATION 5-4. The Laplace transform of the integral of a function can be found by starting with the direct transform integral

$$\mathcal{L}[f(t)] = \int_0^\infty f(t)\epsilon^{-st}\, dt = F(s)$$

and by using integration by parts

$$\int_0^\infty u\, dv = \left[uv\right]_0^\infty - \int_0^\infty v\, du$$

as follows. The following identifications are made:

$$u = \epsilon^{-st} \qquad\qquad dv = f(t)\, dt$$
$$du = -\, s\epsilon^{-st}\, dt \qquad v = \int f(t)\, dt$$

Upon substitution the integral is found to be

$$\mathcal{L}[f(t)] = \left[\epsilon^{-st}\int f(t)\, dt\right]_0^\infty - \int_0^\infty \left[\int f(t)\, dt\right][-\, s\epsilon^{-st}\, dt]$$

$$= \epsilon^{-\infty}\int f(\infty)\, dt - \epsilon^0 \int f(0)\, dt + s\int_0^\infty \left[\int f(t)\, dt\right]\epsilon^{-st}\, dt$$

$$\mathcal{L}[f(t)] = -f^{-1}(0) + s\mathcal{L}\left[\int f(t)\, dt\right] \tag{5-4-6}$$

Therefore the transform of the integral of a function is given by

$$\mathcal{L}\left[\int f(t)\, dt\right] = \frac{\mathcal{L}[f(t)]}{s} + \frac{f^{-1}(0)}{s} \tag{5-4-7}$$

The term $f^{-1}(0)$ is the limit of $\int f(t)\, dt$ as t approaches zero through positive values. It should be noted that in deriving Eq. 5–4–6 it was assumed that

$$\lim_{t \to \infty} \epsilon^{-st} \int f(t)\, dt = 0 \tag{5-4-8}$$

This condition imposes limitations of $f(t)$ which, fortunately, are met by nearly all problems encountered in circuit analysis.

The Laplace transform of a definite integral is

$$\mathcal{L}\left[\int_0^t f(t)\, dt\right] = \frac{\mathcal{L}[f(t)]}{s} \tag{5-4-9}$$

5–5. Discussion of the Function $F(s)$. The following remarks are an extremely simplified presentation of a few topics from the field of function of a complex variable. This treatment does not pretend to be rigorous, but rather is intended only to acquaint the student with some of the terminology from this area of mathematics.

The type of function $F(s)$ obtained in solving circuits containing lumped elements is a ratio of two polynomials in s. A typical $F(s)$ is the following, given in factored form,

$$F(s) = \frac{K(s + Z_1)(s + Z_2)(s + Z_3)}{s^2(s + P_1)(s + a + j\beta)(s + a - j\beta)} \tag{5-5-1}$$

As the variable s is complex, as given by

$$s = \sigma + j\omega \tag{5-5-2}$$

it is convenient to refer to the complex s-plane as shown in Fig. 5–5–1. The location of the zeros of the numerator of $F(s)$ is shown by circles in

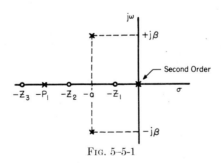

FIG. 5–5–1

this plane. (A zero of a polynomial in s is any value of s for which the polynomial is equal to zero.) The location of the zeros of the denominator of $F(s)$ is shown by the crosses in this plane.

If the magnitude of $F(s)$ at a point in the s-plane is considered equal to the distance perpendicular to the s-plane, then as s takes on all possible values $|F(s)|$ forms a three-dimensional surface. This surface behaves in a regular manner (analytic) except at those points where s takes on the values that are the zeros of the denominator. At these points $|F(s)|$ behaves in a rather singular manner in that it increases in magnitude without bound as s approaches one of the zeros of the denominator. For this reason zeros of the denominator are termed singular points of the function $F(s)$.

Actually the zeros of the denominator of $F(s)$ of Eq. 5–5–1 are a special type of singular points termed poles because of the steeply pointed shape of the surface of $|F(s)|$ in the vicinity of the zeros of the denominator. A pole is defined in the following manner. If $F(s)$ increases without bound as s approaches some $s = -s_0$ in such a manner that $|G(s)|$ of a new function $G(s)$ has a finite nonzero value at this point, where $G(s)$ is defined as

$$G(s) = (s + s_0)^n F(s) \qquad (5\text{–}5\text{–}3)$$

then $F(s)$ is said to have a pole of order n at this point. Applying this definition to the $F(s)$ of Eq. 5–5–1 reveals that this $F(s)$ has a second-order pole at $s = 0$, and first-order poles (a simple pole) at $s = -P_1$, $s = -a - j\beta$, and $s = -a + j\beta$.

A value of s that makes $F(s)$ equal to zero is termed a zero of the function. Therefore the zeros of $F(s)$ are the zeros of its numerator. A zero is either of simple or of multiple order, depending on whether the $(s + z)$ factor is raised to the first or some higher power. Referring back to the $F(s)$ of Eq. 5–5–1, the zeros of the function are shown in Fig. 5–5–1 by circles and the poles of the functions by crosses.

Let it be supposed that some $f(t)$ is given and the corresponding $F(s)$ is found through use of the direct Laplace integral. As discussed in connection with some of the examples in Art. 5–3, the Laplace integral is an improper integral and converges only under certain conditions as indicated. For the general $F(s)$ the integral will converge only if σ (the real part of s) is larger than σ_0 (the largest value of the real part associated with any of the poles). Stated in another way, if the poles and zeros of $F(s)$ are plotted on the complex s-plane (as in Fig. 5–5–1), the integral will converge only in that region of the s-plane to the right of the pole that is the farthest to the right. Once the $F(s)$ is established in this limited region of the s-plane, the function can be extended to the remainder of the s-plane, except at the poles, by a device known as analytic continuation.

5–6. The Inverse Transformation. By the methods already outlined, and as demonstrated by the examples that follow, a differential equation can be transformed into $F(s)$, a function of s. The process of going from this $F(s)$ back to $f(t)$ in the realm of time is known as inversion. The inverse transform operation is written symbolically:

$$\mathcal{L}^{-1}[F(s)] = f(t) \qquad (5\text{–}6\text{–}1)$$

The inverse transform can be performed by using the complex inversion integral given by

$$\mathcal{L}^{-1}[F(s)] = \frac{1}{2\,\pi j} \int_{c-j\infty}^{c+j\infty} F(s)\epsilon^{st}\,ds = f(t) \qquad (5\text{-}6\text{-}2)$$

This equation indicates that integration in the complex s-plane is taken along a path parallel to the $j\omega$-axis and c units from the $j\omega$-axis, as shown in Fig. 5–6-1. Also the quantity c must be so chosen that the path of

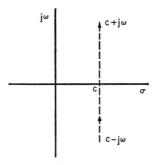

FIG. 5–6-1

integration is to the right of the pole of $F(s)$ farthest to the right. Although the inverse Laplace transform can be found by using the complex integral 5–6-2, evaluation is effected by use of the theory of function of a complex variable and is beyond the scope of this book. The method used here is to put $F(s)$ into a certain desired form and then to use a table such as Table 5–1, picking therefrom the $f(t)$ that corresponds to the known $F(s)$. This procedure is demonstrated in the following examples.

5–7. Examples. EXAMPLE 5–7-1. The circuit shown in Fig. 5–7-1 is in

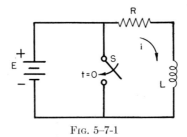

FIG. 5–7-1

the steady state at $t = 0$ when the switch S is closed. After $t = 0$ the circuit equation is

$$0 = Ri + L\frac{di}{dt} \qquad (5\text{-}7\text{-}1)$$

The Laplace transform of this equation is

$$0 = R\mathcal{L}(i) + L\left[s\mathcal{L}(i) - \frac{E}{R}\right] \qquad (5\text{-}7\text{-}2)$$

The initial condition $i(0) = E/R$ is worked into the transformed equation. This equation can be solved for the $\mathcal{L}(i)$:

$$\mathcal{L}(i) = \frac{EL}{R[Ls + R]} = \frac{E}{R[s + R/L]} \qquad (5\text{--}7\text{--}3)$$

This transform is a constant E/R multiplying an $F(s)$ of the form $1/(s + a)$ where a is equal to R/L. By using item 2 in Table 5–1, the inverse transform is

$$i = \frac{E}{R} \epsilon^{-Rt/L} \qquad (5\text{--}7\text{--}4)$$

EXAMPLE 5–7–2. The E-R-C series circuit and the assumed polarity for $q(0)$ are shown in Fig. 5–7–2. The current i in this circuit is found by two different methods to demonstrate the procedure. First, the circuit equation is written using an indefinite integral, and Eq. 5–4–7 is used for the transform. Second, the circuit equation is written as a definite integral, and Eq. 5–4–9 is used as the transform.

When the first of these procedures is followed, the circuit equation uses

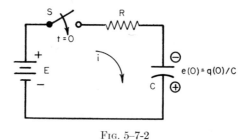

FIG. 5–7–2

an indefinite integral:

$$E = \frac{1}{C} \int i \, dt + Ri \qquad (5\text{--}7\text{--}5)$$

The transform of this equation is taken by using Eq. 5–4–7:

$$\frac{E}{S} = \frac{1}{C}\left[\frac{\mathcal{L}(i)}{s} - \frac{q(0)}{s}\right] + R\mathcal{L}(i) \qquad (5\text{--}7\text{--}6)$$

This equation can be solved for $\mathcal{L}(i)$:

$$\mathcal{L}(i) = \frac{E + e(0)}{s[R + 1/Cs]} = \frac{E + e(0)}{R} \frac{1}{[s + 1/RC]} \qquad (5\text{--}7\text{--}7)$$

The inverse transform is obtained from Table 5–1:

$$i = \frac{E + e(0)}{R} \epsilon^{-t/RC} \qquad (5\text{--}7\text{--}8)$$

As can be seen, Eq. 5–7–8 agrees with the corresponding equation obtained in Chapter 2.

For the second part of the procedure mentioned above, this circuit is analyzed again. This time the definite integral is used:

$$E = Ri + \frac{1}{C} \int_0^t i\, dt - e(0) \qquad (5\text{-}7\text{-}9)$$

The Laplace transform of both sides is taken by using Eq. 5–4–9:

$$\frac{E}{S} = R\mathcal{L}(i) + \frac{1}{C}\frac{\mathcal{L}(i)}{s} - \frac{e(0)}{s} \qquad (5\text{-}7\text{-}10)$$

The $e(0)$ term is treated as a constant. This equation is solved for $\mathcal{L}(i)$:

$$\mathcal{L}(i) = \frac{E + e(0)}{s[R + 1/sC]} = \frac{E + e(0)}{R}\left[\frac{1}{s + 1/RC}\right] \qquad (5\text{-}7\text{-}11)$$

The inverse transform is obtained as

$$i = \frac{E + e(0)}{R}\epsilon^{-t/RC} \qquad (5\text{-}7\text{-}12)$$

Eq. 5–7–12, of course, is the same solution as in Eq. 5–7–8.

All equations involving an integral can be handled by either of the two procedures just demonstrated. However, it is argued by some mathematicians that the indefinite integral is meaningless because the integral is indeterminate to an arbitrary value. This line of argument also states that the equation

$$\mathcal{L}\left[\int f(t)at\right] = \frac{\mathcal{L}[f(t)]}{s} + \frac{f^{-1}(0)}{s}$$

is incorrect and that the term "initial value of the integral" is meaningless. This transform and its use are presented here because it is found in many books; however, the Laplace transform of the definite integral is used throughout this text.

EXAMPLE 5–7–3. The E-R-L series circuit shown in Fig. 5–7–3 is used as the next example. It is assumed that some previous switching operation

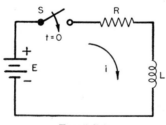

FIG. 5–7–3

has produced an initial current $i(0)$ in the reference direction chosen for the current. The equation for this circuit is

$$E = L\frac{di}{dt} + Ri \qquad (5\text{-}7\text{-}13)$$

The Laplace transform of this equation is

$$\frac{E}{s} = L[s\mathcal{L}(i) - i(0)] + R\mathcal{L}(i) \tag{5-7-14}$$

from which the $\mathcal{L}(i)$ follows:

$$\mathcal{L}(i) = \frac{E}{L}\left[\frac{1}{s(s+R/L)}\right] + \frac{i(0)}{s+R/L} \tag{5-7-15}$$

The second of these two terms is of the form $1/(s+a)$ and can be found in Table 5–1. The first term is of the form $1/[s(s+a)]$ and cannot be found in Table 5–1; however, this term can be separated into two terms which are in Table 5–1 by using partial fractions; thus

$$\frac{1}{s(s+a)} = \frac{1}{as} - \frac{1}{a(s+a)} \tag{5-7-16}$$

The method used for obtaining this partial fraction expansion is explained in the next article.

When the expansion of Eq. 5–7–16 is used in Eq. 5–7–15, the result is

$$\mathcal{L}(i) = \frac{E}{R}\frac{1}{s} + \frac{i(0) - E/R}{s+R/L} \tag{5-7-17}$$

The inverse transform yields the solution

$$i = \frac{E}{R} + [i(0) - E/R]\,\epsilon^{-Rt/L} \tag{5-7-18}$$

which agrees with the equation obtained in Chapter 2.

5–8. Partial Fraction Expansion. The example of the E-R-L circuit demonstrates the need for a partial fraction expansion. If $F(s)$ is more complicated than any entry in a table of Laplace transforms, the need exists for expanding $F(s)$ in simpler terms than are in the table. Let it be supposed that $F(s)$ has the following form and is to be expanded in simpler terms as shown:

$$F(s) = \frac{b_2 s^2 + b_1 s + b_0}{(s+P_1)(s+P_2)(s+P_3)} = \frac{K_{-P_1}}{s+P_1} + \frac{K_{-P_2}}{s+P_2} + \frac{K_{-P_3}}{s+P_3} \tag{5-8-1}$$

Let it be supposed that s moves around a contour in the s-plane that encloses one of the poles of $F(s)$, and let the contour shrink until it becomes smaller and smaller, but still encloses the pole. If the pole in question is $s = -P_1$, in Eq. 5–8–1, then, as the contour shrinks, the term $K_{-P_1}/(s+P_1)$ becomes so large that in comparison the other two terms can be neglected. The term K_{-P_1} is referred to as the residue in the pole at $s = -P_1$. As s takes on this restricted set of values, the left side of Eq. 5–8–1 must also behave in this same manner. The variations in s are so small that, as far as the other poles and the numerator are concerned, s behaves as if it were a constant equal to $-P_1$. Therefore, the residue K_{-P_1} can be found as

$$K_{-P_1} = \frac{b_2 P_1{}^2 - b_1 P_1 + b_0}{(P_2 - P_1)(P_3 - P_1)} \tag{5-8-2}$$

An alternative procedure for obtaining Eq. 5–8-2 follows. When Eq. 5–8-1 is multiplied by $(s + P_1)$, the result is

$$\frac{b_2 s^2 + b_1 s + b_0}{(s + P_2)(s + P_3)} = K_{-P_1} + \frac{K_{-P_2}(s + P_1)}{(s + P_2)} + \frac{K_{-P_3}(s + P_1)}{(s + P_3)} \quad (5\text{–}8\text{-}3)$$

This equation holds for all values of s; therefore, if s is assigned the value $s = -P_1$, the residue K_{-P_1} can be found to agree with Eq. 5–8-2.

The residue K_{-P_2} in the pole at $s = -P_2$ can be found by multiplying Eq. 5–8-1 by $(s + P_2)$. The resulting equation is

$$\frac{b_2 s^2 + b_1 s + b_0}{(s + P_1)(s + P_3)} = \frac{K_{-P_1}(s + P_2)}{(s + P_1)} + K_{-P_2} + \frac{K_{-P_3}(s + P_2)}{(s + P_3)} \quad (5\text{–}8\text{-}4)$$

When s is assigned the value $s = -P_2$, the residue K_{-P_2} results:

$$K_{-P_2} = \frac{b_2 P_2^2 - b_1 P_2 + b_0}{(P_1 - P_2)(P_3 - P_2)} \quad (5\text{–}8\text{-}5)$$

In a similar manner, K_{-P_3} can be found:

$$K_{-P_3} = \frac{b_2 P_3^2 - b_1 P_3 + b_0}{(P_1 - P_3)(P_2 - P_3)} \quad (5\text{–}8\text{-}6)$$

When these residues are substituted in Eq. 5–8-1, the resulting partial fraction expansion is

$$\frac{b_2 s^2 + b_1 s + b_0}{(s + P_1)(s + P_2)(s + P_3)} = \frac{b_2 P_1^2 - b_1 P_1 + b_0}{(P_2 - P_1)(P_3 - P_1)(s + P_1)}$$
$$+ \frac{b_2 P_2^2 - b_1 P_2 + b_0}{(P_1 - P_2)(P_3 - P_2)(s + P_2)} + \frac{b_2 P_3^2 - b_1 P_3 + b_0}{(P_1 - P_3)(P_2 - P_3)(s + P_3)} \quad (5\text{–}8\text{-}7)$$

A rule of thumb that can be remembered is the following: When a residue such as K_{-P_2} in a pole at $s = -P_2$ is to be evaluated, the factor $(s + P_2)$ is "covered-up" and s throughout the remainder of the expression is assigned the value that makes the "covered-up" term equal to zero. By applying this "cover-up" technique, an expansion such as Eq. 5–8-7 can be written by inspection. This "cover-up" technique is a "shorthand" procedure for multiplying both sides of an equation by a factor.

The expansion of an $F(s)$ with a second-order pole is now presented. $F(s)$ and its expansion are

$$F(s) = \frac{b_2 s^2 + b_1 s + b_0}{(s + P_1)(s + P_2)^2} = \frac{K_{-P_1}}{(s + P_1)} + \frac{A}{(s + P_2)^2} + \frac{K_{-P_2}}{(s + P_2)} \quad (5\text{–}8\text{-}8)$$

The K_{-P_1} coefficient can be evaluated exactly as before. To evaluate the A coefficient, both sides of the equation are multiplied by the factor $(s + P_2)^2$:

$$\frac{b_2 s^2 + b_1 s + b_0}{(s + P_1)} = \frac{K_{-P_1}(s + P_2)^2}{s + P_1} + A + K_{-P_2}(s + P_2) \quad (5\text{–}8\text{-}9)$$

When s is assigned the value $s = -P_2$, A can be evaluated:

$$A = \frac{b_2 P_2^2 - b_1 P_2 + b_0}{P_1 - P_2} \tag{5-8-10}$$

Before the K_{-P_2} term is evaluated, Eq. 5-8-9 is differentiated with respect to s:

$$\frac{d}{ds}\left[\frac{b_2 s^2 + b_1 s + b_0}{(s + P_1)}\right] = K_{-P_1}\frac{d}{ds}\left[\frac{(s + P_2)^2}{(s + P_1)}\right] + K_{-P_2} \tag{5-8-11}$$

which becomes

$$\frac{(s + P_1)(2\,b_2 s + b_1) - (b_2 s^2 + b_1 s + b_0)}{(s + P_1)^2}$$

$$= K_{-P_1}\left[\frac{(s + P_1)2(s + P_2) - (s + P_2)^2}{(s + P_1)^2}\right] + K_{-P_2} \tag{5-8-12}$$

The coefficient K_{-P_2} can be found by setting $s = -P_2$:

$$K_{-P_2} = \frac{(P_1 - P_2)(b_1 - 2\,b_2 P_2) - (b_2 P_2^2 - b_1 P_2 + b_0)}{(P_1 - P_2)^2} \tag{5-8-13}$$

The three coefficients of Eq. 5-8-8 are, therefore, determined and the expansion is completed. It should be noted that it has not yet been shown how the inverse transform for the term $1/(s + P)^2$ term can be obtained. This is done in a succeeding article.

5-9. Heaviside Expansion Theorem. Another method of obtaining the partial fraction expansion is to use the Heaviside expansion theorem. The function $F(s)$ is a ratio of polynomials in s:

$$F(s) = \frac{N(s)}{D(s)} \tag{5-9-1}$$

Let it be supposed that $(s + P_1)$ is one of the factors of $D(s)$ and that $G(s)$ is the product of the remaining factors. In other words, $D(s)$ can be written

$$D(s) = (s + P_1)G(s) \tag{5-9-2}$$

With this notation Eq. 5-9-1 becomes

$$F(s) = \frac{N(s)}{(s + P_1)G(s)} \tag{5-9-3}$$

If $F(s)$ is expanded in partial fractions, under assumption of first-order poles, as

$$F(s) = \frac{K_{-P_1}}{(s + P_1)} + \cdots \tag{5-9-4}$$

the residue in the pole at $s = -P_1$ can be determined by covering up the $(s + P_1)$ factor in the right side of Eq. 5-9-3 and substituting $s = -P_1$ in the remaining portion of the function; this yields

$$K_{-P_1} = \frac{N(-P_1)}{G(-P_1)} \tag{5-9-5}$$

The Heaviside expansion theorem achieves the same result in a different way. The denominator of $F(s)$ is differentiated with respect to s and $s = -P_1$ is substituted in the result. The differentiation is performed as follows:

$$\frac{N(s)}{(d/ds)[D(s)]} = \frac{N(s)}{(d/ds)(s + P_1)G(s)} = \frac{N(s)}{(s + P_1)G'(s) + G(s)} \qquad (5\text{-}9\text{-}6)$$

and with the substitution $s = -P_1$ the result is

$$\frac{N(-P_1)}{G(-P_1)} = K_{-P_1} \qquad (5\text{-}9\text{-}7)$$

By this procedure any $F(s)$ with simple poles can be expanded in partial fractions.

The following simple numerical example demonstrates the method:

$$F(s) = \frac{s + 2}{(s + 1)(s + 4)} = \frac{K_{-1}}{s + 1} + \frac{K_{-4}}{s + 4} \qquad (5\text{-}9\text{-}8)$$

The residue in the pole at $s = -1$ is found to be

$$K_{-1} = \frac{s + 2}{(d/ds)[s^2 + 5s + 4]}\bigg|_{s = -1} = \frac{s + 2}{2s + 5}\bigg|_{s = -1} = \frac{1}{3} \qquad (5\text{-}9\text{-}9)$$

The residue in the pole at $s = -4$ is found:

$$K_{-4} = \frac{s + 2}{2s + 5}\bigg|_{s = -4} = \frac{2}{3} \qquad (5\text{-}9\text{-}10)$$

The expansion is completed as

$$\frac{s + 2}{(s + 1)(s + 4)} = \frac{1/3}{s + 1} + \frac{2/3}{s + 4} \qquad (5\text{-}9\text{-}11)$$

5–10. Transform of $\epsilon^{-at}f(t)$. The transform of $\epsilon^{-at}f(t)$ is extremely useful. To develop this transform the following procedure is employed.

Let it be assumed that $f(t)$ is given and that this $f(t)$ has a transform $F(s)$; that is,

$$\int_0^\infty f(t)\epsilon^{-st}\, dt = F(s) \qquad (5\text{-}10\text{-}1)$$

If $f(t)$ is multiplied by ϵ^{-at}, the transform of the product $[\epsilon^{-at}f(t)]$ is

$$\mathcal{L}[\epsilon^{-at}f(t)] = \int_0^\infty \epsilon^{-at}f(t)\epsilon^{-st}\, dt = \int_0^\infty f(t)\epsilon^{-(s+a)t}\, dt \qquad (5\text{-}10\text{-}2)$$

Letting $s' = s + a$ in Eq. 5–10-2 gives

$$\mathcal{L}[\epsilon^{-at}f(t)] = \int_0^\infty f(t)\epsilon^{-s't}\, dt = F(s') = F(s + a) \qquad (5\text{-}10\text{-}3)$$

This step follows because the integral form of Eq. 5–10-3 is that of Eq. 5–10-1, except that s has been replaced by s'.

The significance of Eq. 5–10-3 is that, if $f(t)$ has a transform $F(s)$, the transform of the product $\epsilon^{-at}f(t)$ is that derived from $F(s)$ by replacing s

by $(s + a)$. For example, the transform of the unit step function $u_{-1}(t)$ is $1/s$. The transform of $\epsilon^{-at}u_{-1}(t)$ is of the same form except that s is replaced by $s + a$; thus the transform is $F(s) = 1/(s + a)$. This is shown as entry 2 in Table 5–1. Also, entries 13 through 17 in this table can be obtained by replacing s by $s + a$ in entries 3 through 7.

5–11. Transforms for Higher-Order Derivatives. The transform for the first derivative $f'(t)$ is

$$\mathcal{L}[f'(t)] = s\mathcal{L}[f(t)] - f(0) \qquad (5\text{–}11\text{-}1)$$

To find the transform for $f''(t)$ the following substitution is made:

$$g(t) = f'(t) \qquad (5\text{–}11\text{-}2)$$

Therefore

$$f''(t) = g'(t) \qquad (5\text{–}11\text{-}3)$$

By use of Eq. 5–11-1 the $\mathcal{L}[f''(t)]$ can be written

$$\mathcal{L}[f''(t)] = \mathcal{L}[g'(t)] = s\mathcal{L}[g(t)] - g(0) \qquad (5\text{–}11\text{-}4)$$

This can be rewritten

$$\mathcal{L}[f''(t)] = s\{\mathcal{L}[f'(t)]\} - f'(0) \qquad (5\text{–}11\text{-}5)$$

or

$$\mathcal{L}[f''(t)] = s\{s\mathcal{L}[f(t)] - f(0)\} - f'(0)$$
$$= s^2\mathcal{L}[f(t)] - sf(0) - f'(0) \qquad (5\text{–}11\text{-}6)$$

In a similar manner it can be shown that

$$\mathcal{L}[f'''(t)] = s^3\mathcal{L}[f(t)] - s^2f(0) - sf'(0) - f''(0) \qquad (5\text{–}11\text{-}7)$$

This method can be extended to obtain the transform of a derivative of any order.

5–12. Another Method for Obtaining Transforms. The method to be shown is of help in a number of situations for obtaining transforms. As an example of this method assume that the $\mathcal{L}[1] = 1/s$ is known and that it is desired to find $\mathcal{L}[t]$.

Let $f(t) = t$, whence $f'(t) = 1$; on substitution in Eq. 5–11-1 this becomes

$$\mathcal{L}[1] = s\mathcal{L}[t] - 0 \qquad (5\text{–}12\text{-}1)$$

or

$$\mathcal{L}[t] = \frac{\mathcal{L}[1]}{s} = \frac{1}{s^2} \qquad (5\text{–}12\text{-}2)$$

As a second example the $\mathcal{L}[t^2]$ can be found by repeating this process. Let $f(t) = t^2$; then $f'(t) = 2t$ and Eq. 5–11-1 gives

$$2\mathcal{L}[t] = s\mathcal{L}[t^2] - 0 \qquad (5\text{–}12\text{-}3)$$

or

$$\mathcal{L}[t^2] = \frac{2}{s}\mathcal{L}[t] = \frac{2}{s^3} \qquad (5\text{–}12\text{-}4)$$

By inspection it can be seen that

$$\mathcal{L}[t^n] = \frac{n!}{s^{n+1}} \qquad (5\text{–}12\text{-}5)$$

As a last example to demonstrate this method, the $\mathcal{L}[\sin \beta t]$ is found in the following steps. Let

$$f(t) = \sin \beta t$$

Then

$$f'(t) = \beta \cos \beta t \qquad (5\text{-}12\text{-}6)$$

and thus

$$f''(t) = -\beta^2 \sin \beta t$$

Upon substituting these expressions in Eq. 5-11-6,

$$-\beta^2 \mathcal{L}[\sin \beta t] = s^2 \mathcal{L}[\sin \beta t] - s[0] - \beta \qquad (5\text{-}12\text{-}7)$$

This equation can be factored:

$$\mathcal{L}[\sin \beta t]\{s^2 + \beta^2\} = \beta \qquad (5\text{-}12\text{-}8)$$

giving

$$\mathcal{L}[\sin \beta t] = \frac{\beta}{s^2 + \beta^2} \qquad (5\text{-}12\text{-}9)$$

5-13. Final-Value Theorem. The final value of the function of time can be obtained from the transform by use of the final-value theorem. This theorem can be developed in the following way, using the following transform and its partial fraction as an example:

$$\frac{b_2 s^2 + b_1 s + b_0}{s(s + P_1)(s + P_2)} = \frac{K_0}{s} + \frac{K_{-P_1}}{s + P_1} + \frac{K_{-P_2}}{s + P_2} \qquad (5\text{-}13\text{-}1)$$

The inverse transform of Eq. 5-13-1 is

$$\mathcal{L}^{-1}\left[\frac{b_2 s^2 + b_1 s + b_0}{s(s + P_1)(s + P_2)}\right] = K_0 + K_{-P_1}\epsilon^{-P_1 t} + K_{-P_2}\epsilon^{-P_2 t} \qquad (5\text{-}13\text{-}2)$$

The final value of Eq. 5-13-2 is K_0, as can be seen by letting $t \to \infty$. The K_0 coefficient in the partial fraction expansion of Eq. 5-13-1 is obtained by multiplying both sides of the equation by s and letting s take on the value of zero. The coefficient K_0 is, therefore,

$$K_0 = \lim_{s \to 0} \left\{ s\left[\frac{b_2 s^2 + b_1 s + b_0}{s(s + P_1)(s + P_2)}\right]\right\} \qquad (5\text{-}13\text{-}3)$$

When this theorem is stated in more general terms, it becomes:

$$\lim_{t \to \infty}[f(t)] = \lim_{s \to 0} s[F(s)] \qquad (5\text{-}13\text{-}4)$$

where $F(s)$ is the transform of $f(t)$. If there is no s factor in the denominator of $F(s)$, it follows that the final value of $f(t)$ is zero.

The final-value theorem can be used invalidly, if qualifying statements are not made. That is, the $\lim_{t \to \infty} f(t)$ must exist before the theorem can be properly used. An examination of Eq. 5-13-2 shows that, if P_1 or P_2 were negative, the final value of $f(t)$ would be infinite. Therefore the theorem can be applied only to an $F(s)$ function that has all its poles in the left-half s-plane, except that a single pole may lie at the origin.

5–14. Initial-Value Theorem. The initial-value theorem is stated without proof. If $f(t)$ has the transform $F(s)$, and $f(0+)$ exists, this initial value of $f(t)$ can be found from $F(s)$:

$$\lim_{t \to 0} f(t) = \lim_{s \to \infty} s[F(s)] \qquad (5\text{-}14\text{-}1)$$

5–15. Transform Tables. All the inverse transforms used up to this point have been developed as needed by using partial fractions and the short Table 5–1. In the rest of the text the table of transforms in the Appendix is used as needed. Just as integral tables are used in calculus, transform tables can be developed and used. The forms of some of the transform pairs in the Appendix differ from any used to this point; thus they need to be explained. To do so, a few sample inverse transforms found in the table in the Appendix are derived. The first example is item 13 in the table:

$$\left[\frac{a_1 s + a_0}{(s + a)^2 + \omega^2} \right] \qquad (5\text{-}15\text{-}1)$$

The inverse transform is first put in the form that has been used up to this point:

$$\left[\frac{a_1 s + a_0}{(s + a)^2 + \omega^2} \right] = \frac{a_1 (s + a)}{(s + a)^2 + \omega^2} + \frac{(a_0 - a_1 a)}{\omega} \frac{\omega}{[(s + a)^2 + \omega^2]} \qquad (5\text{-}15\text{-}2)$$

$$\mathcal{L}^{-1} \left[\frac{a_1 s + a_0}{(s + a)^2 + \omega^2} \right] = \epsilon^{-at} \left[a_1 \cos \omega t + \frac{a_0 - a_1 a}{\omega} \sin \omega t \right] \qquad (5\text{-}15\text{-}3)$$

The sine term can be represented by a phasor that is drawn horizontally, and the cosine term by another phasor leading this sine phasor by 90

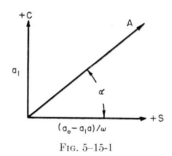

FIG. 5–15-1

degrees as shown in Fig. 5–15-1. The resultant phasor has a magnitude A and leads the sine term by an angle α, where

$$A \epsilon^{j\alpha} = \frac{a_0 - a_1 a}{\omega} + j a_1 \qquad (5\text{-}15\text{-}4)$$

Eq. 5–15-3 can then be written

$$A \epsilon^{-at} \sin (\omega t + \alpha) \qquad (5\text{-}15\text{-}5)$$

This is in more compact form and is easier to plot when a curve for the solution as a function of time is required.

Another method of obtaining an inverse transform in the form of Eq. 5-15-5 is demonstrated to show how many of the transforms in the Appendix are obtained. The transform as expanded in partial fractions is

$$\left[\frac{a_1 s + a_0}{(s+a)^2 + \omega^2} \right] = \frac{a_1(-a+j\omega) + a_0}{(2\,j\omega)(s+a-j\omega)} + \frac{a_1(-a-j\omega) + a_0}{-2\,j\omega(s+a+j\omega)} \quad (5\text{-}15\text{-}6)$$

The inverse transform can be put into the form

$$\mathcal{L}^{-1}\left[\frac{a_1 s + a_0}{(s+a)^2 + \omega^2} \right] = \frac{1}{2\,j}\,\epsilon^{-at}\left\{ \left[\frac{a_1}{\omega}(-a+j\omega) + \frac{a_0}{\omega} \right]\epsilon^{+j\omega t} \right.$$

$$\left. - \left[\frac{a_1}{\omega}(-a-j\omega) + \frac{a_0}{\omega} \right]\epsilon^{-j\omega t} \right\} \quad (5\text{-}15\text{-}7)$$

In order to simplify writing the equation, $A\epsilon^{j\alpha}$ is defined as

$$A\epsilon^{j\alpha} = \frac{a_1}{\omega}(-a+j\omega) + \frac{a_0}{\omega} \quad (5\text{-}15\text{-}8)$$

Examination of the term multiplying $\epsilon^{-j\omega t}$ shows that it is the conjugate of the term multiplying $\epsilon^{+j\omega t}$; thus this term can be written $A\epsilon^{-j\alpha}$. Therefore Eq. 5-15-7 can be written

$$A\epsilon^{-at}\left[\frac{\epsilon^{j(\omega t+\alpha)} - \epsilon^{-j(\omega t+\alpha)}}{2\,j} \right] \quad (5\text{-}15\text{-}9)$$

or

$$A\epsilon^{-at}\sin{(\omega t + \alpha)} \quad (5\text{-}15\text{-}10)$$

As a second example, item 19 in the transform table in the Appendix is developed. This can be expanded as indicated:

$$\left\{ \frac{a_2 s^2 + a_1 s + a_0}{[(s+a)^2 + \omega^2](s+b)} \right\} = \left\{ \frac{a_2 s^2 + a_1 s + a_0}{(s+a-j\omega)(s+a+j\omega)(s+b)} \right\}$$

$$= \frac{K-b}{s+b} + \frac{K_{-a+j\omega}}{s+a-j\omega} + \frac{K_{-a-j\omega}}{s+a-j\omega} \quad (5\text{-}15\text{-}11)$$

Each of the residues can be determined by using the "covered-up" technique as explained before. Since $K_{-a+j\omega}$ is obtained by substituting $s = -a+j\omega$ in a portion of the transform and $K_{-a-j\omega}$ is obtained by substituting $s = -a-j\omega$ in a corresponding portion of the same transform, these two residues are related in a very specific manner. This relationship can best be understood by observing the common portion of the transform into which both $s = -a+j\omega$ and $s = -a-j\omega$ are substituted. This common portion is

$$\frac{a_2 s^2 + a_1 s + a_0}{s+b} \quad (5\text{-}15\text{-}12)$$

When $s = -a+j\omega$ is substituted, the result is

$$\frac{a_2(-a+j\omega)^2 + a_1(-a+j\omega) + a_0}{(-a+j\omega+b)} = B\epsilon^{j\alpha} \quad (5\text{-}15\text{-}13)$$

When $s = -a - j\omega$ is substituted, the result is

$$\frac{a_2(-a-j\omega)^2 + a_1(-a-j\omega) + a_0}{(-a-j\omega+b)} = B\epsilon^{-j\alpha} \qquad (5\text{-}15\text{-}14)$$

The resulting terms $B\epsilon^{+j\alpha}$ and $B\epsilon^{-j\alpha}$ are conjugates because wherever $+j\omega$ appears in Eq. 5-15-13, $-j\omega$ appears in Eq. 5-15-14. Eq. 5-15-11 can now be written

$$\left\{ \frac{a_2 s^2 + a_1 s + a_0}{[(s+a)^2 + \omega^2](s+b)} \right\} = \frac{K_{-b}}{s+b} + \frac{B\epsilon^{j\alpha}}{+(j2)(\omega)(s+a-j\omega)}$$
$$+ \frac{B\epsilon^{-j\alpha}}{-(j2)\omega(s+a+j\omega)} \qquad (5\text{-}15\text{-}15)$$

In the transform table in the Appendix, B/ω is defined as A and the inverse transform can be written

$$\mathcal{L}^{-1}[\ ] = K_{-b}\epsilon^{-bt} + A\epsilon^{-at}\sin(\omega t + \alpha) \qquad (5\text{-}15\text{-}16)$$

It is to be noted that the $+j2$ and $-j2$ factors in the denominator of Eq. 5-15-15 are enveloped in the transition from the exponential form to the trigonometric form.

With this perspective, most of the terms in the table can be obtained with a minimum of difficulty.

5–16. Discussion of the Laplace Transform Method. Although the transform method has been discussed as presented, it may be well to summarize the statements.

The transform method provides a systematic method whereby the solution to a problem can be found by following a definite procedure. The initial conditions are worked into the transformed equation, and no set of auxiliary steps is required to find arbitrary constants. Also, the initial conditions that are worked in the transformed equation are those already known in the circuit problems. That is, the initial conditions needed in the transform method are the $e(0)$'s on the capacitors and $i(0)$'s in the inductors. No matter how many storage elements are present, these are all the initial conditions needed. In the classical method, not only are the $e(0)$'s and $i(0)$'s needed, but also the proper number of $(di/dt)(0)$, $(d^2i/dt^2)(0)$, etc., for a given problem.

5–17. Examples. A number of examples are presented to show the use of the Laplace transform method in solving circuit problems. The first two of these examples are taken from Chapters 3 and 4 so that the results from the transform method can be compared with those obtained previously. These first two examples also make use of the short table of transforms.

EXAMPLE 5–17-1. Same as Ex. 3–9-3. The circuit for Ex. 3–9-3 is redrawn as Fig. 5–17-1 after S has been opened. As obtained before, $e(0)$

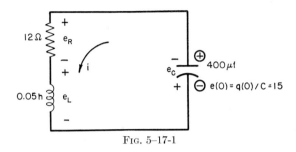

FIG. 5–17-1

is 15 volts in the polarity shown and $i(0)$ is 1.25 amp. The circuit equation is

$$0.05 \frac{di}{dt} + 12\, i + \frac{1}{400 \times 10^{-6}} \int_0^t i\, dt - 15 = 0$$

$$0.05 \frac{di}{dt} + 12\, i + \frac{1}{400 \times 10^{-6}} \int_0^t i\, dt = 15 \qquad (5\text{–}17\text{-}1)$$

When the Laplace transform of both sides of Eq. 5–17-1 is taken, it becomes

$$0.05[s\mathcal{L}(i) - 1.25] + 12\, \mathcal{L}(i) + \frac{\mathcal{L}(i)}{400 \times 10^{-6}\, s} = \frac{15}{s} \qquad (5\text{–}17\text{-}2)$$

$\mathcal{L}(i)$ is

$$\mathcal{L}(i) = \frac{15/s + 0.0625}{0.05\, s + 12 + (2.5 \times 10^3)/s}$$

or

$$\mathcal{L}(i) = 1.25 \left[\frac{s + 240}{s^2 + 240\, s + 5 \times 10^4} \right] \qquad (5\text{–}17\text{-}3)$$

One way of writing the denominator of Eq. 5–17-3 is to put it in the factored form, as in items 15 and 16 of Table 5–1. To do this the first two terms are taken, and to them is added what is necessary to complete the square; thus

$$s^2 + 2\left(\frac{240}{2}\right)s + (120)^2 + 5.0 \times 10^4 - (120)^2 \qquad (5\text{–}17\text{-}4)$$

Of course, this same term has to be subtracted in order not to change the denominator. The denominator can be written

$$(s + 120)^2 + (\sqrt{5.0 \times 10^4 - 1.44 \times 10^4})^2$$

or as $(s + 120)^2 + (189)^2$. Eq. 5–17-3 can then be written

$$\mathcal{L}(i) = 1.25 \left[\frac{s + 240}{(s + 120)^2 + (189)^2} \right] \qquad (5\text{–}17\text{-}5)$$

An examination of Table 5–1 reveals no identity from which the inverse transform can be taken directly. However, Eq. 5–17-5 can be written as two terms, both of which are in the table; thus

$$\mathcal{L}(i) = 1.25 \left\{ \frac{s+120}{(s+120)^2 + (189)^2} + \frac{120}{189}\left[\frac{189}{(s+120)^2 + (189)^2} \right] \right\} \quad (5\text{-}17\text{-}6)$$

The first term of Eq. 5–17-6 is now in the form of item 15 of Table 5–1, and the second term is in the form of item 16 of the table. Therefore the inverse transform is

$$i = \epsilon^{-120t}[1.25 \cos 189\, t + 0.739 \sin 189\, t] \quad (5\text{-}17\text{-}7)$$

This agrees with Eq. 3–9-28. It is to be noted that the constants of integration were found without any group of auxiliary steps. Also, it is to be noted that, although in the classical method of solution $(di/dt)(0)$ must be found, in the Laplace method only $i(0)$ and $e(0)$ are needed.

EXAMPLE 5–17-2. Same as Ex. 4–3-4. The circuit for this example is redrawn as Fig. 5–17-2, after S_1 and S_2 have been closed. The initial

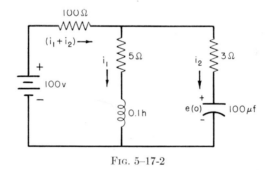

FIG. 5–17-2

conditions are $i_1(0) = 0.681$ and $e(0) = 0$. The circuit equations are rewritten

$$100 = 105\, i_1 + 0.1 \frac{di_1}{dt} + 100\, i_2$$

$$100 = 100\, i_1 + 103\, i_2 + 10^4 \int_0^t i_2\, dt \quad (5\text{-}17\text{-}8)$$

The Laplace transforms are

$$\frac{100}{s} = 105\, \mathcal{L}(i_1) + 0.1[s\mathcal{L}(i_1) - 0.681] + 100\, \mathcal{L}(i_2)$$

$$\frac{100}{s} = 100\, \mathcal{L}(i_1) + 103\, \mathcal{L}(i_2) + \frac{10^4\, \mathcal{L}(i_2)}{s} \quad (5\text{-}17\text{-}9)$$

which can be rewritten

$$\frac{0.0681\, s + 100}{s} = \mathcal{L}(i_1)[0.1\, s + 105] + \mathcal{L}(i_2)\, 100$$

$$\frac{100}{s} = \mathcal{L}(i_1)\, 100 + \mathcal{L}(i_2)\left[103 + \frac{10^4}{s} \right] \quad (5\text{-}17\text{-}10)$$

These equations can be solved in a number of different ways; however, a convenient method is to use determinants:

$$\mathcal{L}(i_2) = \frac{\begin{vmatrix} 0.1\,s + 105 & \dfrac{100 + 0.0681\,s}{s} \\[2mm] 100 & \dfrac{100}{s} \end{vmatrix}}{\begin{vmatrix} 0.1\,s + 105 & 100 \\[2mm] 100 & 103 + \dfrac{10^4}{s} \end{vmatrix}}$$

$$= \frac{10 + \dfrac{10{,}500}{s} - \dfrac{10{,}000}{s} - 6.81}{10.3\,s + 10{,}815 + 1000 + \dfrac{1.05 \times 10^6}{s} - 10{,}000} \qquad (5\text{-}17\text{-}11)$$

whence

$$\mathcal{L}(i_2) = \frac{3.19\,s + 500}{10.3[s^2 + 176\,s + 1.02 \times 10^5]} = \frac{0.309[s + 156]}{(s + 88)^2 + (307)^2} \qquad (5\text{-}17\text{-}12)$$

This equation can be put into forms found in Table 5–1:

$$\mathcal{L}(i_2) = \frac{0.309[s + 88]}{[(s + 88)^2 + (307)^2]} + \frac{0.309 \times 68[307]}{307[(s + 88)^2 + (307)^2]} \qquad (5\text{-}17\text{-}13)$$

The inverse transform is

$$i_2 = \epsilon^{-88t}[0.309 \cos 307\,t + 0.0685 \sin 307\,t] \qquad (5\text{-}17\text{-}14)$$

This solution agrees with that of Eq. 4–3-52. The coefficients of the sine term differ slightly because of slide rule accuracy.

A good deal of work is done in the classical method in finding $i_2(0)$ and $(di_2/dt)(0)$. It is to be noted that none of this work is needed in the Laplace method.

EXAMPLE 5–17-3. Sometimes a circuit is such that there are fewer unknown voltages than there are unknown currents. For example, in the circuit in Fig. 5–17-3 there are three unknown currents, i_1, i_2, and i_3, but

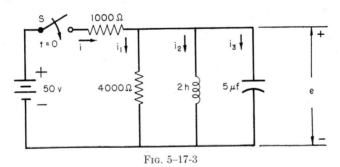

FIG. 5–17-3

only one unknown voltage, e. If voltage equations are written around three loops, the resulting three equations must be solved simultaneously. This work can be saved by writing a current equation that contains only one unknown voltage. Let it be assumed that initially no energy is stored in the inductor or in the capacitor. The circuit equation

$$i = i_1 + i_2 + i_3 \tag{5-17-15}$$

gives

$$\frac{50 - e}{1000} = \frac{e}{4000} + \frac{1}{2}\int_0^t e\, dt + 5 \times 10^{-6}\frac{de}{dt} \tag{5-17-16}$$

Thus

$$0.05 = (0.001 + 0.00025)\, e + 0.5\int_0^t e\, dt + 5 \times 10^{-6}\frac{de}{dt} \tag{5-17-17}$$

The transform is

$$\frac{0.05}{s} = 0.00125\,\mathcal{L}(e) + 0.5\frac{\mathcal{L}(e)}{s} + 5 \times 10^{-6}[s\mathcal{L}(e) - 0] \tag{5-17-18}$$

This can be solved for $\mathcal{L}(e)$:

$$\mathcal{L}(e) = \frac{0.05}{5 \times 10^{-6}\, s^2 + 1.25 \times 10^{-3}\, s + 0.5} = \frac{10{,}000}{s^2 + 250\, s + 10^5} \tag{5-17-19}$$

The denominator can be factored and the equation written

$$\mathcal{L}(e) = \frac{34.4(291)}{[(s + 125)^2 + (291)^2]} \tag{5-17-20}$$

The inverse transform is

$$e = 34.4\,\epsilon^{-125t}\sin 291\, t \tag{5-17-21}$$

If one of the currents is desired, it can be obtained from the voltage e. For example, suppose that i_3 is desired; then

$$i_3 = C\frac{de}{dt} = 5 \times 10^{-6} \times 34.4[\epsilon^{-125t}(291\cos 291\, t - 125\sin 291\, t)]$$

which becomes

$$i_3 = \epsilon^{-125t}[0.05\cos 291\, t - 0.0215\sin 291\, t] \tag{5-17-22}$$

If the current i_2 is sought, the voltage solution yields

$$i_2 = \frac{1}{L}\int_0^t e\, dt \tag{5-17-23}$$

If integration is performed without integral tables, the procedure involves integration by parts, a fairly complicated procedure for equations of this type. However, with Laplace transform tables available, this current can be found without difficulty by writing the transform of Eq. 5-17-23:

$$\mathcal{L}(i_2) = \frac{1}{2}\frac{\mathcal{L}(e)}{s} \tag{5-17-24}$$

When $\mathcal{L}(e)$ from Eq. 5-17-20 is substituted in Eq. 5-17-24, the result is

$$\mathcal{L}(i_2) = \frac{5000}{s[(s + 125)^2 + (291)^2]} \tag{5-17-25}$$

Item 19 in the transform tables in the Appendix can be used with the following identifications: $a_0 = 5000$; $a = 125$; $\omega = 291$; and

$a_2 = a_1 = b = 0$. The term $A \underline{/\alpha}$ is

$$A \underline{/\alpha} = \frac{5000}{291[-125 + j\,291]} = 0.0543 \underline{/-113.25°} \qquad (5\text{-}17\text{-}26)$$

The inverse transform is

$$i_2 = 0.0543\,\epsilon^{-125t}\sin(291\,t - 113.25°) + \frac{5000}{10^5}$$

or

$$i_2 = 0.05 + 0.054\,\epsilon^{-125t}\sin(291\,t - 113.25°) \qquad (5\text{-}17\text{-}27)$$

EXAMPLE 5-17-4. The circuit shown in Fig. 5-17-4 has reached steady-state conditions with S open and, at $t = 0$, S is closed. In the steady state

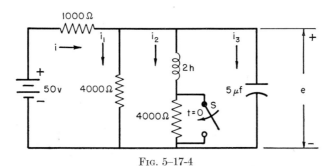

FIG. 5-17-4

the inductor becomes a short circuit and the capacitor an open circuit. Therefore, before $t = 0$,

$$i_1 = i_2 = \tfrac{50}{3000} \times \tfrac{1}{2} = 0.00833 \qquad i_3 = 0$$

the voltage on the capacitor is equal to the voltage across the 4000-ohm resistor, $e_c = 0.00833 \times 4000 = 33.3$ volts. At $t = 0$ the inductor maintains the current i_2 at the same value as before $t = 0$, and the capacitor maintains the voltage on it. After $t = 0$ the circuit equation is

$$i = i_1 + i_2 + i_3 \qquad (5\text{-}17\text{-}28)$$

which can be written

$$\frac{50 - e}{1000} = \frac{e}{4000} + \frac{1}{2}\int_0^t (e)\,dt + 0.00833 + 5 \times 10^{-6}\frac{de}{dt} \qquad (5\text{-}17\text{-}29)$$

or

$$0.05 - 0.00833 = 0.00125\,e + 0.5\int_0^t e\,dt + 5 \times 10^{-6}\frac{de}{dt} \qquad (5\text{-}17\text{-}30)$$

Taking the transform and simplifying give

$$\frac{0.04166}{s} = 0.00125\,\mathcal{L}(e) + \frac{0.5\,\mathcal{L}(e)}{s} + 5 \times 10^{-6}[s\mathcal{L}(e) - 33.3] \qquad (5\text{-}17\text{-}31)$$

Hence

$$\mathcal{L}(e) = \frac{0.04116/s + 1.66 \times 10^{-4}}{5 \times 10^{-6}\,s + 0.00125 + 0.5/s} = \frac{1.66 \times 10^{-4}\,s + 0.04166}{5 \times 10^{-6}\,s^2 + 0.00125\,s + 0.5}$$

$$(5\text{-}17\text{-}32)$$

or
$$\mathcal{L}(e) = \frac{33.3\,s + 8333}{s^2 + 250\,s + 10^5} = \frac{33.3[s + 250]}{[(s + 125)^2 + (291)^2]} \qquad (5\text{--}17\text{--}33)$$

and, finally,
$$\mathcal{L}(e) = 33.3 \left\{ \frac{s + 125}{[(s + 125)^2 + (291)^2]} + \frac{125(291)}{291[(s + 125)^2 + (291)^2]} \right\} \qquad (5\text{--}17\text{--}34)$$

The inverse transform is
$$e = \epsilon^{-125t}[33.3 \cos 291\,t + 14.3 \sin 291\,t] \qquad (5\text{--}17\text{--}35)$$

The current i_2 can be found by writing the equation

$$i_2 = \frac{1}{2} \int_0^t e\,dt + 0.00833 \qquad (5\text{--}17\text{--}36)$$

and transforming:
$$\mathcal{L}(i_2) = \frac{1}{2}\frac{\mathcal{L}(e)}{s} + \frac{0.00833}{s} \qquad (5\text{--}17\text{--}37)$$

With $\mathcal{L}(e)$ substituted into this equation, it becomes

$$\mathcal{L}(i_2) = \frac{16.6\,s + 4166}{s[(s + 125)^2 + (291)^2]} + \frac{0.00833}{s} \qquad (5\text{ }17\text{--}38)$$

Again item 19 of the table in the Appendix can be used with the following identifications: $a_0 = 4166$; $a_1 = 16.6$; $a = 125$; $\omega = 291$; and $a_2 = b = 0$. The term $A\,\underline{/\alpha}$ is

$$A\,\underline{/\alpha} = \frac{4166 - 16.6(125 - j\,291)}{291(-123 + j\,291)} = 0.0570\underline{/-46.5°} \qquad (5\text{--}17\text{--}39)$$

The inverse transform is
$$i_2 = 0.0570\,\epsilon^{-125t} \sin(291\,t - 46.5°) + \frac{4166}{10^5} + 0.00833 \qquad (5\text{--}17\text{--}40)$$

which becomes
$$i_2 = 0.05 + 0.0570\,\epsilon^{-125t} \sin(291\,t - 46.5°) \qquad (5\text{--}17\text{--}41)$$

PROBLEMS

5–1. Solve by Laplace transforms the problems of Chapters 1, 2, 3, or 4 as assigned.

5–2. Verify the following items in Table 5–1: items 4, 6, 18, 19

5–3. Find the inverse transform $f(t)$ corresponding to each of the following $F(s)$.

(a)
$$F(s) = \frac{s + 3}{(s + 2)(s + 4)}$$

(b)
$$F(s) = \frac{s + 6}{(s + 1)(s + 3)(s + 7)}$$

(c)
$$F(s) = \frac{s + 6}{(s + 1)(s + 3)^2}$$

(d)
$$F(s) = \frac{s}{(s + a)^2 + b^2}$$

(e)
$$F(s) = \frac{s + \alpha}{(s + a)^2 + b^2}$$

5–4. In the circuit shown in Fig. 5–P-1, S_1 is closed and 0.0015 sec later S_2 is closed at $t = 0$. Find the equation for i_3 after $t = 0$.

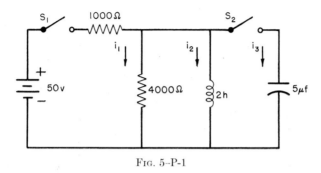

Fig. 5–P-1

5–5. In the circuit shown in Fig. 5–P-2, S_1 is closed and 0.006 sec later S_2 is closed at $t = 0$. Find the equation for i_3 after $t = 0$.

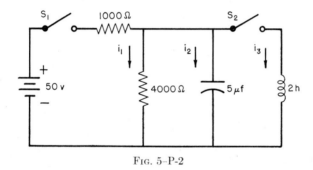

Fig. 5–P-2

5–6. In the circuit shown in Fig. 5–P-3, S is open until steady-state conditions are reached. At $t = 0$, S is closed. Find the equation for current i_1 in the 800-ohm resistor after $t = 0$

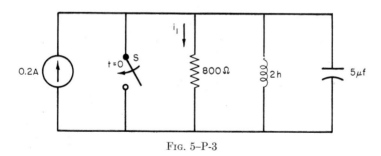

Fig. 5–P-3

5–7. In the circuit in Fig. 5–P-4, S_1 is opened and 0.007 sec later S_2 is closed at $t = 0$. Find the equation for q on the 50-μf capacitor after $t = 0$.

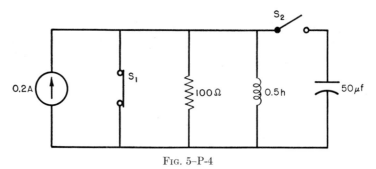

Fig. 5–P-4

5–8. In the circuit in Fig. 5–P-5, S_1 is opened and 0.004 sec later S_2 is closed at $t = 0$. Find the equation for q on the 50-μf capacitor after $t = 0$.

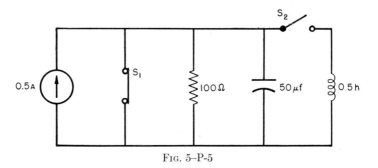

Fig. 5–P-5

5–9. Verify Eq. 5–11-7.

5–10. Verify Eq. 5–12-5.

5–11. By the methods of Art. 5–12, find

(a) $\mathcal{L}[\cos \beta t]$.

(b) $\mathcal{L}[\sinh bt]$.

(c) $\mathcal{L}[\cosh bt]$.

5–12. Check the items in the transform table in the Appendix as assigned.

5–13. By the methods outlined in Ex. 5–17-3 and Ex. 5–17-4 obtain the following:

(a) e_c in Ex. 5–17-1.

(b) e_c in Ex. 5–17-2.

(c) i_3 in Ex. 5–17-4.

5–14. Use the final-value theorem and the initial-value theorem with the transforms in the examples in this chapter as assigned, and check through use of the given solutions.

CHAPTER 6

FACTORING ALGEBRAIC POLYNOMIALS FOR THEIR ZEROS

6-1. Introduction. When a circuit problem is solved either by classical methods or by the Laplace transform method, an algebraic polynomial is obtained which has to be factored. In classical methods, this polynomial set equal to zero is the characteristic equation; in the Laplace transform method, this polynomial is a factor of the denominator of the transformed function

$$F(s) = \frac{Y(s)A(s)}{Z(s)B(s)}$$

This denominator of the Laplace transform is the product of a term $B(s)$ stemming from the driving function and a second term $Z(s)$, which is the characteristic polynomial.

Up to this point only circuits containing two storage elements have been studied. These circuits yielded characteristic polynomials in s of the 2nd degree, and knowledge of the quadratic formula made factoring a relatively simple matter. As soon as the solution of more complicated circuits is attempted, the polynomial in s may be of 3rd, 4th, 5th, or higher degree. Therefore some knowledge of methods of factoring polynomials is necessary. Polynomials of 3rd, 4th, and 5th degree can be factored explicitly by formula; that is, by expressing the zeros in terms of the coefficients. At present, there is no known method of factoring polynomials of higher than the 5th degree by formula. There are, however, many methods of approximating the zeros of polynomials. Because the nature of the approach may well be varied to meet different types of equations, a knowledge of several of these is most useful.

The subject of factoring is a part of the general field of theory of equations. It is not intended to present rigorous proofs, but rather to show the procedures to be followed, as illustrated by simple examples.

6-2. Background Considerations. The $Z(s)$ being considered is a polynomial of the form

$$Z(s) = s^n + a_{n-1}s^{n-1} + \cdots + a_2s^2 + a_1s + a_0 \qquad (6\text{-}2\text{-}1)$$

where, as is commonly the case in circuit analysis, all coefficients are positive and real. A value of s for which the polynomial is zero is termed a zero of the polynomial. If the polynomial is equated to zero, yielding the equation

$$Z(s) = s^n + a_{n-1}s^{n-1} + \cdots + a_2s^2 + a_1s + a_0 = 0 \qquad (6\text{-}2\text{-}2)$$

a value of s that satisfies the equation is termed a root of the equation. Thus the zeros of polynomial 6–2-1 and the roots of Eq. 6–2-2 are identical.

It is convenient to consider the zeros of a polynomial as located in the complex s-plane as shown in Fig. 6–2-1. Thus two complex conjugate

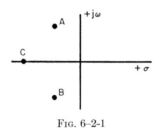

Fig. 6–2-1

zeros A and B and one real zero are shown in Fig. 6–2-1. The portion of the s-plane to the left of the $j\omega$-axis is termed the left-half s-plane; likewise the portion to the right of the $j\omega$-axis is termed the right-half s-plane. If the real part of a zero is negative, the zero is in the left-half s-plane; similarly, if the real part is positive, the zero is in the right-half s-plane. Polynomials with all zeros in the left-half s-plane are termed Hurwitz polynomials.

By the fundamental theorem of algebra each polynomial of the nth degree (such as polynomial 6–2-1) has n, and only n, zeros. If complex zeros are present, they exist as conjugate pairs; that is, if $s_1 = -\sigma + j\omega$ is one zero, there is another zero $s_2 = -\sigma - j\omega$.

As can be seen by inspection, if all coefficients are postulated as positive, the polynomial cannot take on the value zero for a real positive value of s. Therefore this equation can have no positive real zeros. A more general statement concerning the nature of the zeros is afforded by Descartes' rule of signs, which can be stated as follows: A polynomial $Z(s)$ cannot have a greater number of positive real zeros than the number of changes of signs in the coefficients in the polynomial; nor can $Z(s)$ have a greater number of negative real zeros than the number of changes of signs in the coefficients of the equation $Z(-s)$. It is to be noted that in both cases the number of zeros may be less than that determined by this rule, as when complex zeros are present.

Often a polynomial is such that a simple transformation of the variable yields coefficients that are easier to handle. For example, if in the polynomial

$$s^4 + 2 \times 10^4 \, s^3 + 9.5 \times 10^8 \, s^2 + 1.05 \times 10^{13} \, s + 1.8 \times 10^{17} \quad (6\text{–}2\text{-}3)$$

the substitution $s = 10^4 \, y$ is made, the polynomial is transformed into

$$10^{16} \, y^4 + 2 \times 10^4 \times 10^{12} \, y^3 + 9.5 \times 10^8 \times 10^8 \, y^2$$
$$+ 1.05 \times 10^{13} \times 10^4 \, y + 1.8 \times 10^{17} \quad (6\text{–}2\text{-}4)$$

which can be written

$$10^{16}\left[y^4 + 2\,y^3 + 9.5\,y^2 + 10.5\,y + 18\right] \qquad (6\text{-}2\text{-}5)$$

The 10^{16} factor does not affect the values of the zeros; hence they can be ignored. The polynomial in y inside the brackets can be treated more easily than polynomial 6–2–3; when the zeros of polynomial 6–2–5 are obtained, they can be multiplied by 10^4 to yield the zeros of the original polynomial, 6–2–3.

6–3. Geometric Interpretation of $Z(s)$. If s takes on real values (that is, $s = \sigma$) and is allowed to vary from minus infinity to plus infinity, $Z(\sigma)$ can be plotted against σ. For an example, let $Z(s)$ be a cubic:

$$Z(s) = s^3 + a_2 s^2 + a_1 s + a_0 \qquad (6\text{-}3\text{-}1)$$

where the coefficients are all real. Inspection yields $Z(-\infty) \doteq (-\infty)^3$ and $Z(+\infty) \doteq (+\infty)^3$. Therefore the curve starts at minus infinity and ends at plus infinity and must cross the $Z(\sigma) = 0$ axis at least once. Fig. 6–3–1

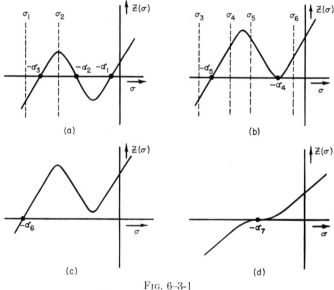

(a) (b) (c) (d)

Fig. 6–3–1

shows four possible curves for the cubic. The polynomial for the curve of Fig. 6–3–1a has three real simple negative zeros, and the polynomial can be written in factored form:

$$(s + \alpha_1)(s + \alpha_2)(s + \alpha_3) \qquad (6\text{-}3\text{-}2)$$

The polynomial for the curve of Fig. 6–3–1b has three real negative zeros; one $(-\alpha_5)$ is simple, the other two comprise a double zero, whence the polynomial can be written in factored form:

$$(s + \alpha_4)^2(s + \alpha_5) \qquad (6\text{-}3\text{-}3)$$

The polynomial for the curve of Fig. 6–3-1c has one negative real zero and two complex zeros. The polynomial for the curve of Fig. 6–3-1d has three negative real zeros, a triple zero, and hence can be written in factored form:

$$(s + \alpha_7)^3 \tag{6-3-4}$$

The entire curve of $Z(\sigma)$ versus σ need not be plotted because the only points required are those sufficient to find the approximate location of the real zeros. The value of $Z(\sigma)$ for a certain σ can be found by synthetic division, as explained in a subsequent article. For example, in Fig. 6–3-1a, if $Z(\sigma_1)$ is negative and $Z(\sigma_2)$ is positive, there is a zero between σ_1 and σ_2. Likewise, in Fig. 6–3-1b, if $Z(\sigma_3)$ is negative and $Z(\sigma_4)$ is positive, there is a zero between σ_3 and σ_4. In the case of the double zero at $\sigma = -\alpha_4$, $Z(\sigma_5)$ and $Z(\sigma_6)$ both have the same sign, but the shape of the curve indicates a minimum between σ_5 and σ_6, and the possibility that the curve is tangent to the axis can be investigated.

Although the above discussion applies to a polynomial of the 3rd degree, the same type of investigation can be made for a polynomial of any degree. Any $Z(s)$ that is of an odd degree n has a value of $Z(-\infty) \doteq (-\infty)^n$ and $Z(+\infty) \doteq (+\infty)^n$, and the plot of it must cross the $Z(\sigma) = 0$ axis at least once; therefore the polynomial has at least one real zero. Any polynomial that is of an even degree n has $Z(-\infty) \doteq (+\infty)^n$ and $Z(+\infty) \doteq (+\infty)^n$, and the plot of it may not cross the $Z(\sigma) = 0$ axis at all. In any case, if the $Z(\sigma) = 0$ axis is crossed, it is crossed an even number of times.

6–4. Synthetic Division. Synthetic division is a procedure that speeds the evaluation of $Z(s)$ for a given value of s. For example, if it is desired to evaluate the polynomial

$$s^3 + 13.45\, s^2 + 63.6\, s + 109 \tag{6-4-1}$$

at $s = -6$, the value of -6 can be substituted for s in the polynomial:

$$(-6)^3 + 13.45(-6)^2 + 63.6(-6) + 109 = -4.4 \tag{6-4-2}$$

The same result can be reached more quickly by using synthetic division. This is done by forming the table

$$
\begin{array}{ccccc}
1 & 13.45 & 63.6 & 109 & /-6 \\
 & -6 & -44.7 & -113.4 & \\
\hline
1 & 7.45 & 18.9 & -\quad 4.4^* &
\end{array}
\tag{6-4-3}
$$

The 1 is brought down and multiplied by -6 and the product entered in the table. The -6 and 13.45 are added algebraically and the result 7.45 then multiplied by -6, etc. The coefficient designated by the asterisk is the value of $Z(s)$ as evaluated at $s = -6$.

That synthetic division gives the correct results can be seen by the following development on the polynomial written with lettered coefficients:

$$s^3 + a_2 s^2 + a_1 s + a_0 \tag{6-4-4}$$

If this polynomial is evaluated at $s = \beta$ by direct substitution, the result is

$$\beta^3 + a_2\beta^2 + a_1\beta + a_0 \qquad (6\text{–}4\text{–}5)$$

This polynomial is evaluated by synthetic division by setting up the table

$$
\begin{array}{cccc|c}
1 & a_2 & a_1 & a_0 & \underline{\;\;\beta} \\
 & \beta & \beta^2 + a_2\beta & \beta^3 + a_2\beta^2 + a_1\beta & \\
\hline
1 & \beta + a_2 & \beta^2 + a_2\beta + a_1 & \beta^3 + a_2\beta^2 + a_1\beta + a_0 &
\end{array}
\qquad (6\text{–}4\text{–}6)
$$

Comparison of the final term obtained by synthetic division with the polynomial 6–4–5 in β shows that identical results have been obtained.

The polynomial 6–4-1 is evaluated at $s = -5$ by setting up the table

$$
\begin{array}{cccc|c}
1 & 13.45 & 63.6 & 109 & \underline{\;\;/-5} \\
 & -5 & -42.25 & -106.75 & \\
\hline
1 & 8.45 & 21.35 & 2.25 &
\end{array}
\qquad (6\text{–}4\text{–}7)
$$

Calculation 6–4-3 shows that $Z(-6)$ is equal to -4.4, and calculation 6–4-7 shows that $Z(-5)$ is equal to 2.25. Therefore the polynomial has at least one zero between $s = -5$ and $s = -6$. This procedure is used as one of the steps of Horner's method.

6–5. Relation between Zeros and Coefficients. Let it be supposed that the following are the zeros of a 5th-degree equation:

$$
\begin{array}{lll}
s_1 = -\sigma_1 + j\omega_1 & s_3 = -\sigma_2 + j\omega_2 & \\
s_2 = -\sigma_1 - j\omega_1 & s_4 = -\sigma_2 - j\omega_2 & s_5 = -\sigma_3
\end{array}
\qquad (6\text{–}5\text{–}1)
$$

The corresponding 5th-degree polynomial is

$$(s + \sigma_1 - j\omega_1)(s + \sigma_1 + j\omega_1)(s + \sigma_2 - j\omega_2)(s + \sigma_2 + j\omega_2)(s + \sigma_3) \qquad (6\text{–}5\text{–}2)$$

which can be written

$$(s^2 + 2\,\sigma_1 s + \sigma_1{}^2 + \omega_1{}^2)(s^2 + 2\,\sigma_2 s + \sigma_2{}^2 + \omega_2{}^2)(s + \sigma_3) \qquad (6\text{–}5\text{–}3)$$

Let $\quad b_1 = 2\,\sigma_1 \qquad b_0 = \sigma_1{}^2 + \omega_1{}^2 \qquad c_1 = 2\,\sigma_2 \qquad c_0 = \sigma_2{}^2 + \omega_2{}^2$

Then the polynomial can be written

$$(s^2 + b_1 s + b_0)(s^2 + c_1 s + c_0)(s + \sigma_3) \qquad (6\text{–}5\text{–}4)$$

When this is multiplied out, the result is

$$
\begin{aligned}
s^5 &+ (b_1 + c_1 + \sigma_3)s^4 + (b_0 + c_0 + b_1c_1 + b_1\sigma_3 + c_1\sigma_3)s^3 \\
&+ (b_0c_1 + b_1c_0 + b_0\sigma_3 + c_0\sigma_3 + b_1c_1\sigma_3)s^2 \\
&+ (b_0c_0 + b_0c_1\sigma_3 + b_1c_0\sigma_3)s + b_0c_0\sigma_3
\end{aligned}
\qquad (6\text{–}5\text{–}5)
$$

Let

$$
\begin{aligned}
a_4 &= b_1 + c_1 + \sigma_3 \qquad a_3 = b_0 + c_0 + b_1c_1 + b_1\sigma_3 + c_1\sigma_3 \\
a_2 &= b_0c_1 + b_1c_0 + b_0\sigma_3 + c_0\sigma_3 + b_1c_1\sigma_3 \qquad a_1 = b_0c_0 + b_0c_1\sigma_3 + b_1c_0\sigma_3 \\
a_0 &= b_0c_0\sigma_3
\end{aligned}
$$

Upon substitution of these coefficients, the polynomial becomes

$$s^5 + a_4 s^4 + a_3 s^3 + a_2 s^2 + a_1 s + a_0 \qquad (6\text{–}5\text{–}6)$$

In circuit work the polynomial to be factored is usually in the form of the polynomial 6–5-6, and the zeros are desired. In other words, the steps outlined above must be performed in reverse. The point that this discussion is demonstrating is seen by inspection of the polynomial 6–5-4, which shows that a 5th-degree polynomial can be expressed as the product of two quadratic terms and one linear term, each of which has real coefficients, even though some of the zeros are complex. Since the zeros of the two quadratic factors can be obtained by use of the quadratic formula, once a polynomial is put into this partially factored form, obtaining the zeros is a simple matter even though they may be complex.

Even though the polynomial in the above example is of 5th degree, a similar separation of a polynomial of any degree into simpler factors is theoretically possible. If the polynomial is of even degree, the partially factored form contains the appropriate number of quadratic terms. If the polynomial is of odd degree, the partially factored form contains one linear term and the appropriate number of quadratic terms.

6–6. Lin's Method. As discussed in Art. 6–5, once a polynomial is partially factored into the proper number of quadratic terms and one linear term if needed, obtaining the zeros is simply a matter of using the quadratic formula. However, there still remains the problem of getting the polynomial into the partially factored form. Many procedures have been effected to do this; however, Lin's method is among the simpler to remember and to use. Lin's method starts by obtaining a trial division from two or three terms of the polynomial; a division therewith yields another trial divisor; by repeating this process as necessary, a linear term (or quadratic term) is obtained to within any desired degree of accuracy.

The details of this procedure can be explained most easily by obtaining the factors of the polynomial

$$s^3 + 16 s^2 + 569 s + 3060 \qquad (6\text{–}6\text{-}1)$$

In this example a linear trial divisor can be obtained from the last two terms, or a quadratic trial divisor can be obtained from the last three terms. In this example the last two terms

$$569 s + 3060 \qquad (6\text{–}6\text{-}2)$$

are used to obtain the linear trial divisor

$$\frac{569 s + 3060}{569} \doteq s + 5.4 \qquad (6\text{–}6\text{-}3)$$

This trial divisor is then divided into the polynomial:

$$
\begin{array}{r}
s^2 + 10.6\ s\ + 511.76 \\
s + 5.4 \overline{)s^3 + 16\ s^2\ + 569\ s + 3060} \\
\underline{s^3 + \ 5.4\ s^2} \\
10.6\ s^2 + 569\ s \\
\underline{10.6\ s^2 + \ 57.24\ s} \\
511.76\ s + 3060 \\
\underline{511.76\ s + 2763.5} \\
296.5
\end{array}
\qquad (6\text{–}6\text{-}4)
$$

Second trial divisor:

If the $(s + 5.4)$ term were an exact factor of the polynomial, the remainder would be zero. The remainder, 296.5, shows that the $(s + 5.4)$ term is not a factor. A rough indication of the accuracy of the $(s + 5.4)$ term is to be obtained by comparing the remainder with the coefficients from which it is obtained. In this example the remainder 296.5 is compared with the coefficients 3060 and 2763.5; since the remainder is approximately 10 percent of these coefficients, the $(s + 5.4)$ term is not a good approximation of the actual factor. Therefore a second trial divisor is obtained from the location indicated in the division 6–6-4 by taking the term

$$511.76 \, s + 3060 \tag{6-6-5}$$

and obtaining the linear trial divisor:

$$\frac{511.76 \, s + 3060}{511.76} \doteq s + 6 \tag{6-6-6}$$

The division process is again repeated:

$$
\begin{array}{r}
s^2 + 10\,s\ + 509 \\
s + 6\overline{)s^3 + 16\,s^2 + 569\,s + 3060} \\
\underline{s^3 +\ \ 6\,s^2} \\
10\,s^2 + 569\,s \\
\underline{10\,s^2 +\ \ 60\,s} \\
509\,s + 3060 \\
\underline{509\,s + 3054} \\
6
\end{array}
\tag{6-6-7}
$$

Since the remainder is small compared with 3060, the cubic has been broken into the approximate factors

$$(s + 6)(s^2 + 10\,s + 509) \tag{6-6-8}$$

and with the use of the quadratic formula the approximate zeros of the polynomial are

$$s_1 = -6 \qquad s_2 = -5 + j\,22 \qquad s_3 = -5 - j\,22 \tag{6-6-9}$$

In the general case the process is continued until the remainder can be neglected, as compared with the coefficients from which it is obtained. The meaning of the expression "can be neglected" depends on the accuracy desired. Perhaps in engineering work, if the remainder is within 1 to 2 percent of the coefficients from which it is obtained, the results are satisfactory. Usually the process must be repeated several times before the remainder can be neglected.

In certain cases the sequence of trial divisors converges very slowly. If so, instead of taking the last two terms of the cubic and forming a linear trial divisor, it may be helpful to take the last three terms and form a quadratic trial divisor. This procedure of dividing by a quadratic is demonstrated below with a 4th-degree polynomial and is not shown for the cubic. At other times, if the sequence of trial divisors is converging slowly, a judicious forecast may save many divisions.

To demonstrate Lin's method on a 4th-degree polynomial, the following example is used:

$$s^4 + 11.7\,s^3 + 93\,s^2 + 14.2\,s + 26 \qquad (6\text{-}6\text{-}10)$$

If it is known that a 4th-degree polynomial has at least two real zeros, a linear term may be used as a trial divisor, as in the above example, rendering the quartic as the product of a linear term and a cubic, whence the cubic can be factored. However, if the quartic has four complex zeros, dividing by a linear term is of no avail. Therefore, in general, it is best to divide by a quadratic, which can be obtained from the last three terms:

$$\frac{93\,s^2 + 14.2\,s + 26}{93} \doteq s^2 + 0.153\,s + 0.28 \qquad (6\text{-}6\text{-}11)$$

The trial divisor is divided into the polynomial:

$$
\begin{array}{r}
s^2 + 11.55\,s\ \ + 90.95 \\[2pt]
s^2 + 0.153\,s + 0.28 \overline{)\,s^4 + 11.7\,s^3\ \ + 93\,s^2 + 14.2\,s + 26} \\
\underline{s^4 + \ \ 0.153\,s^3 + \ \ 0.28\,s^2} \\
11.55\,s^3\ \ + 92.72\,s^2 + 14.2\,s \\
\underline{11.55\,s^3\ \ + \ \ 1.77\,s^2 + \ \ 3.23\,s} \\
90.95\,s^2 + 10.97\,s + 26 \\
\underline{90.95\,s^2 + 10.5\,s\ \ + 25.42} \\
0.47\,s + \ \ 0.58
\end{array}
\qquad (6\text{-}6\text{-}12)
$$

Second trial divisor:

Since the coefficient of the s term in the remainder is approximately 5 percent of the coefficients from which it is obtained, a second trial divisor is taken from the location indicated:

$$\frac{90.95\,s^2 + 10.97\,s + 26}{90.95} \doteq s^2 + 0.121\,s + 0.286 \qquad (6\text{-}6\text{-}13)$$

Division with the second trial divisor yields

$$
\begin{array}{r}
s^2 + 11.58\,s\ \ + 91.31 \\[2pt]
s^2 + 0.121\,s + 0.286 \overline{)\,s^4 + 11.7\,s^3\ \ + 93\,s^2\ \ \ \ + 14.2\,s\ \ + 26} \\
\underline{s^4 + \ \ 0.12\,s^3 + \ \ 0.29\,s^2} \\
11.58\,s^3 + 92.71\,s^2 + 14.2\,s \\
\underline{11.58\,s^3 + \ \ 1.4\,s^2\ \ + \ \ 3.31\,s} \\
91.31\,s^2 + 10.89\,s + 26 \\
\underline{91.31\,s^2 + 11.65\,s + 26.1} \\
-\ \ 0.16\,s - \ \ 0.1
\end{array}
\qquad (6\text{-}6\text{-}14)
$$

The coefficient of each term in the remainder is less than 2 percent of the coefficients from which it is obtained; therefore the original polynomial has been factored into two quadratic factors:

$$(s^2 + 0.121\,s + 0.286)(s^2 + 11.58\,s + 91.31) \qquad (6\text{-}6\text{-}15)$$

Use of the quadratic formula gives the zeros:

$$s_1 = -0.0605 + j\,0.531 \qquad s_3 = -5.79 + j\,7.6$$
$$s_2 = -0.0605 - j\,0.531 \qquad s_4 = -5.79 - j\,7.6 \qquad (6\text{-}6\text{-}16)$$

Theoretically, Lin's method can be used to factor a polynomial of any degree. If the degree is odd, one linear term can be factored out first and thereafter the appropriate number of quadratic terms one by one. If the degree is even, the quadratic terms are factored out one by one.

The two examples just presented demonstrate Lin's method to advantage. That is, only two divisions are necessary to obtain the desired accuracy. Perhaps the main reason for the rapid convergence of the sequence of trial divisors is that the magnitudes of the zeros differ considerably in each of these two examples. The ratio of the magnitudes of the zeros in the first example is greater than 3.5 to 1, and in the second example it is greater than 15 to 1. However, if the magnitudes of the zeros are approximately the same, many trial divisors may be necessary. To demonstrate this fact the following polynomial is manufactured, starting with the zeros:

$$(s + 5.45)(s + 4 - j\,2)(s + 4 + j\,2) \qquad (6\text{-}6\text{-}17)$$

which, when multiplied out, yields

$$s^3 + 13.45\,s^2 + 63.6\,s + 109 \qquad (6\text{-}6\text{-}18)$$

The details of the division are not shown, but when it was attempted to factor out the linear terms the following sequence of trial divisors resulted:

$$\begin{array}{ll} s + 1.716 & s + 3.7 \\ s + 2.5 & s + 3.96 \\ s + 3 & s + 4.2 \\ s + 3.4 & \end{array} \qquad (6\text{-}6\text{-}19)$$

The factor being approached by this sequence is $(s + 5.45)$. If it is noted that the difference between successive trial divisors gets smaller the more closely $(s + 5.45)$ is approached, it can be inferred that perhaps as many as 20 divisions may be necessary before the correct value is approximated.

When the zeros of a 4th- or higher-degree polynomial lie close together in the s-plane, the coefficients of the quadratic trial divisor behave even more erratically. Under some circumstances the coefficients may seem to be approaching a limit, then they deviate widely and seem to go into an oscillatory pattern, making the final evaluation an impossibility. Although special techniques have been developed to circumvent these difficulties, these procedures do not have the essential simplicity of Lin's original method. Therefore the remaining articles develop several alternative approaches which can be useful.

6-7. Horner's Method. Horner's method approximates the value of a real zero of a polynomial to within any desired degree of accuracy. The method is best shown by an example using the polynomial

$$s^3 + 13.45\,s^2 + 63.6\,s + 109 \qquad (6\text{-}7\text{-}1)$$

which was used in Art. 6-4 on synthetic division, where it is demonstrated that the polynomial has a zero between $s = -5$ and $s = -6$. Horner's method proceeds by shifting the $j\omega$-axis to $s = -5$ so that the zero now lies between $\sigma = 0$ and $\sigma = -1$. This is done as indicated in the following table:

1	13.45	63.6	109	/— 5
	— 5	— 42.25	— 106.75	
1	8.45	21.35	*2.25	(6–7-2)
	— 5	— 17.25		
1	3.45	*4.1		
	— 5.00			
*1	*— 1.55			

The arrangement of this table is similar to that for synthetic division; however, the process is carried further. The new polynomial whose zeros are increased by 5 over the zeros of the original polynomial is obtained from the coefficients marked with the asterisk:

$$s^3 - 1.55\, s^2 + 4.1\, s + 2.25 \qquad (6\text{-}7\text{-}3)$$

By use of synthetic division, $Z(-0.4)$ is found to be positive and $Z(-0.5)$ negative; therefore there is a zero between $\sigma = -0.4$ and $\sigma = -0.5$. The process of shifting the $j\omega$-axis is repeated; this time to $\sigma = -0.4$, so that the zeros of the polynomial 6-7-3 are increased by 0.4. This is done as indicated in the following table:

1	— 1.55	4.1	2.25	/— 0.4
	— 0.4	0.78	— 1.952	
1	— 1.95	4.88	+ 0.298	
	— 0.4	0.940		(6–7-4)
1	— 2.35	5.820		
	— 0.4			
1	— 2.75			

The new polynomial is

$$s^3 - 2.75\, s^2 + 5.82\, s + 0.298 \qquad (6\text{-}7\text{-}5)$$

Synthetic division shows that $s = -0.05$ is a zero of this polynomial since $Z(-0.05) = 0$.

1	— 2.75	5.82	0.298	/— 0.05
	— 0.05	0.14	— 0.298	(6–7-6)
1	— 2.8	5.96	0	

Polynomial 6–7-5 can now be expressed as

$$(s + .05)(s^2 - 2.8\, s + 5.96) \qquad (6\text{-}7\text{-}7)$$

When the quadratic term is factored by use of the quadratic formula, the three zeros of the cubic are

$$s_1 = -0.05 \qquad s_2 = 1.4 + j\,2 \qquad s_3 = 1.4 - j\,2 \qquad (6\text{-}7\text{-}8)$$

In order to obtain the zeros of the original polynomial 6–7–1 the zeros of 6–7–8 must be decreased by 5.4 because of the shifts made in the $j\omega$-axis. Therefore the zeros of the original polynomial are

$$s_1 = -5.45 \qquad s_2 = -4 + j\,2 \qquad s_3 = -4 - j\,2 \qquad (6\text{–}7\text{–}9)$$

If $s = 0.05$ had not been a zero of polynomial 6–7–5, the process of locating the zero and shifting the $j\omega$-axis would be repeated until the desired accuracy is obtained.

The main advantage of Horner's method is that a real zero can be found to any desired degree of accuracy, no matter where the other zeros are located in the s-plane. If Lin's method gives trouble on a real zero, Horner's method will always work. The main limitation of Horner's method is that complex zeros cannot be obtained. If a 4th-degree polynomial has four complex zeros, use of Horner's method is of no avail. However, with a combination of Routh's test and a procedure similar to Horner's method, complex zeros can be handled. For this reason Routh's test is presented next.

6–8. Routh's Test. Descartes' rule of signs gives a method by which the maximum number of positive (or negative) real zeros of a polynomial can be determined. However, if a zero is complex, this rule of signs gives no knowledge of the sign of the real part of the complex zero. In fact, all the coefficients of a polynomial can be positive and it can yet have zeros in the right-half s-plane; that is, the real parts of some of the zeros are positive. This can be shown in a simple case by starting with the zeros:

$$s_1 = -a \qquad s_2 = +\sigma - j\omega \qquad s_3 = +\sigma + j\omega \qquad (6\text{–}8\text{–}1)$$

and building up the polynomial

$$(s + a)(s - \sigma + j\omega)(s - \sigma - j\omega) \qquad (6\text{–}8\text{–}2)$$

which gives

$$s^3 + (a - 2\,\sigma)s^2 + (\sigma^2 + \omega^2 - 2\,\sigma a)s^1 + a\sigma^2 + a\omega^2 \qquad (6\text{–}8\text{–}3)$$

The a can certainly be made larger than $2\,\sigma$, so that the coefficient of the s^2 term is positive; likewise, the ω can be made sufficiently large that the coefficient of the s^1 term is positive.

The Routh test is a mechanistic procedure whereby a polynomial can be tested to determine if it has any zeros in the right-half s-plane. The procedure is demonstrated on the polynomial

$$a_6 s^6 + a_5 s^5 + a_4 s^4 + a_3 s^3 + a_2 s^2 + a_1 s + a_0 \qquad (6\text{–}8\text{–}4)$$

The coefficients of the polynomial are placed in two rows as follows:

$$
\begin{array}{cccc}
a_6 & a_4 & a_2 & a_0 \\
a_5 & a_3 & a_1 &
\end{array}
\qquad (6\text{–}8\text{–}5)
$$

The coefficients of the next row are formed from these two rows:

$$b_4 = \frac{a_5 a_4 - a_6 a_3}{a_5}$$

$$b_2 = \frac{a_5 a_2 - a_6 a_1}{a_5} \qquad (6\text{-}8\text{-}6)$$

$$b_0 = \frac{a_5 a_0 - 0 a_6}{a_5} = a_0$$

When these are arrayed below the first two rows, the fourth, fifth rows, etc., are similarly calculated in succession from the previous two rows, resulting in the array

$$
\begin{array}{cccc}
a_6 & a_4 & a_2 & a_0 \\
a_5 & a_3 & a_1 & \\
b_4 & b_2 & b_0 & \\
c_3 & c_1 & & \qquad (6\text{-}8\text{-}7) \\
d_2 & d_0 & & \\
e_1 & & & \\
f_0 & & &
\end{array}
$$

Wherein, to illustrate the procedure further, the coefficients c_3 and d_3 are

$$c_3 = \frac{b_4 a_3 - a_5 b_2}{b_4}$$

$$d_2 = \frac{c_3 b_2 - b_4 c_1}{c_3} \qquad (6\text{-}8\text{-}8)$$

The array for a polynomial of any degree is formed in the same manner. As two additional rows are added, the array has one less column to the right, so the array comprises a finite number of rows, $n + 1$, for a polynomial of finite order n.

Routh's test yields the number of zeros of the polynomial in the right-half s-plane equal to the number of changes of sign in the elements in the first column. Thus, by forming the array and observing the number of changes of sign in the first column, the number of zeros in the right-half s-plane is easily determined.

The Routh test is more commonly termed the Routh criterion for stability, because often the polynomial to which the test is applied is the denominator polynomial obtained in the study of some feedback device. If this denominator polynomial has a zero in the right-half s-plane, the inverse transform contains a corresponding factor such as $\epsilon^{\sigma t}$ and, as σ is positive, the output increases indefinitely with time; hence the system is unstable. Thus the method for determining the stability of an electric circuit, a feedback system, or other device essentially consists of a test of a polynomial to determine if it has zeros in the right-half s-plane.

If there is no change of signs in the first column, the polynomial is Hurwitz since all the zeros lie in the left-half s-plane.

6–9. Horner's Method Extended. Combining Routh's test with the technique of shifting the $j\omega$-axis can be used to find the real part of the complex zeros farthest to the right in the s-plane to any degree of accuracy, in a manner similar to the way in which Horner's method is used for real zeros. Routh's test is first applied to the polynomial as given. If no changes of sign occur in the first column, the $j\omega$-axis is shifted to the left. After a few tries, the zero can be located in a vertical strip in the s-plane between two integral values of σ. Next the field of application of Routh's test is narrowed to locating the zero between, say, $\sigma = -0.2$ and $\sigma = -0.3$. Each successive cycle of testing determines the real part of the complex root to one more decimal place.

To illustrate the method through a simple example, consider the zeros

$$s_1 = -10 \qquad s_2 = -2.5 - j\,2.5 \qquad s_3 = -2.5 + j\,2.5 \qquad \text{(6-9-1)}$$

which yield the polynomial

$$s^3 + 15\,s^2 + 62.5\,s + 125 \qquad \text{(6-9-2)}$$

Routh's array for this polynomial is

$$
\begin{array}{ll}
1 & 62.5 \\
15 & 125 \\
54.2 & \\
125 &
\end{array}
\qquad \text{(6-9-3)}
$$

No change of sign in the first column indicates that all zeros are to the left of the $j\omega$-axis. The $j\omega$-axis is shifted to the old $\sigma = -3$; thus

$$
\begin{array}{cccc}
1 & 15 & 62.5 & 125 \;\underline{/-3} \\
 & -3 & -36 & -79.5 \\
\hline
1 & 12 & 26.5 & 45.5 \\
 & -3 & -27.0 & \\
\hline
1 & 9 & -0.5 & \\
 & -3 & & \\
\hline
1 & 6 & &
\end{array}
\qquad \text{(6-9-4)}
$$

The resulting polynomial

$$s^3 + 6\,s^2 - 0.5\,s + 45.5 \qquad \text{(6-9-5)}$$

is used to establish another array:

$$
\begin{array}{ll}
1 & -0.5 \\
6 & 45.5 \\
-8.05 & \\
45.5 &
\end{array}
\qquad \text{(6-9-6)}
$$

Two changes of sign in the first column indicate that two zeros are to the right of the $j\omega$-axis. With the $j\omega$-axis shifted to $\sigma = -2$, the polynomial is

$$s^3 + 9\,s^2 + 14.5\,s + 52 \qquad \text{(6-9-7)}$$

and Routh's array is

$$
\begin{array}{cc}
1 & 14.5 \\
9 & 52 \\
8.72 & \\
52 &
\end{array}
\qquad (6\text{-}9\text{-}8)
$$

Inspection of the first columns of 6-9-6 and 6-9-8 shows that the two zeros farthest to the right lie between $\sigma = -2$ and $\sigma = -3$. In the following step the real part of the zeros can be determined to an accuracy of the next decimal point. If the $j\omega$-axis of polynomial 6-9-7 is shifted to $\sigma = -0.5$, the polynomial

$$
s^3 + 7.5\, s^2 + 6.25\, s + 46.875 \qquad (6\text{-}9\text{-}9)
$$

results and the new array is

$$
\begin{array}{cc}
1 & 6.25 \\
7.5 & 46.875 \\
0 & \\
46.875 &
\end{array}
\qquad (6\text{-}9\text{-}10)
$$

In this case the zero in the first column shows that the real part of the zero farthest to the right in the s-plane is at $\sigma = -2.5$ for the original polynomial. When a zero appears in the table, the simplest way to complete the table is to assume an arbitrarily small number ϵ in place of the zero and continue.

It is now known that polynomial 6-9-9 has two zeros on the $j\omega$-axis and thus the j-part of the complex zeros is to be determined. This can be done in many ways, particularly in an example as simple as this one. Recalling that, if an exact zero is substituted for s in $Z(s)$, that $Z(s)$ would be zero suggests plotting $|Z(s)|$ versus s as s ranges over the $j\omega$-axis. This can be done by the use of synthetic division. As an illustration $|Z(s)|$ for $s = -j\,2$ can be found through

$$
\begin{array}{ccccc}
1 & 7.5 & 6.25 & 46.875 & \underline{/j\,2} \\
 & +j\,2 & -4+j\,15 & -30 & +j\,4.5 \\
\hline
1 & 7.5+j\,2 & 2.25+j\,15 & 16.875+j\,4.5 & \qquad (6\text{-}9\text{-}11)
\end{array}
$$

The magnitude, $|\,16.875 + j\,4.5\,|$, is approximately equal to 17.45 and is

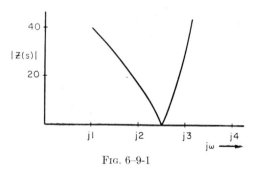

Fig. 6-9-1

plotted as one of the points in Fig. 6–9-1. From this plot and the previous work, it can be seen that

$$s = -2.5 + j\,2.5 \qquad (6\text{–}9\text{–}12)$$

is one of the zeros of the original polynomial. Since complex zeros occur in conjugate pairs,

$$s = -2.5 - j\,2.5 \qquad (6\text{–}9\text{–}13)$$

must also be a zero. From these two zeros the quadratic term

$$s^2 + 5\,s + 12.5 \qquad (6\text{–}9\text{–}14)$$

results. Division into the original polynomial yields the remaining factor

$$s + 10 \qquad (6\text{–}9\text{–}15)$$

It is not proposed that this is the easiest way to factor this particular polynomial; rather, this cubic is used as a simple example to illustrate the general method.

6–10. Factoring a Fourth-Degree Polynomial by Formula. Often reference is made to factoring a 3rd- or 4th-degree polynomial by formula. One method to do so for a 4th-degree polynomial is demonstrated for the sake of completeness. It is believed that the average reader will probably prefer one of the approximate methods presented above, because the same general procedure can be used on a polynomial of any degree. The process to be illustrated is based on Ferrari's solution for the quartic. The equation

$$s^4 + a_3 s^3 + a_2 s^2 + a_1 s + a_0 = 0 \qquad (6\text{–}10\text{–}1)$$

is taken as an example.

By shifting the $j\omega$-axis this equation can be transformed to the form

$$s^4 + b_2 s^2 + b_1 s + b_0 = 0 \qquad (6\text{–}10\text{–}2)$$

which can be rearranged: $s^4 = -b_2 s^2 - b_1 s - b_0 \qquad (6\text{–}10\text{–}3)$

The procedure for shifting the $j\omega$-axis is explained later. Adding $ys^2 + y^2/4$ to both sides gives

$$s^4 + ys^2 + \frac{y^2}{4} = ys^2 + \frac{y^2}{4} - b_2 s^2 - b_1 s - b_0 \qquad (6\text{–}10\text{–}4)$$

whence the left side is a perfect square; thus

$$\left(s^2 + \frac{y}{2}\right)^2 = (y - b_2)s^2 - b_1 s + \frac{y^2}{4} - b_0 \qquad (6\text{–}10\text{–}5)$$

For the right-hand side to be a perfect square, the term $\sqrt{b^2 - 4\,ac}$ of the quadratic formula based on the form $as^2 + bs + c$ must be zero; or, in this case,

$$b_1{}^2 - 4(y - b_2)\left(\frac{y^2}{4} - b_0\right) = 0 \qquad (6\text{–}10\text{–}6)$$

which can be written

$$y^3 - b_2 y^2 - 4\,b_0 y + (4\,b_2 b_0 - b_1{}^2) = 0 \qquad (6\text{–}10\text{–}7)$$

Let it be supposed that y_1 is one of the roots of Eq. 6–10-7. Then from Eq. 6–10-5 the following is obtained:

$$\left(s^2 + \frac{y_1}{2}\right) = \pm \left[\sqrt{y_1 - b_2}\, s - \frac{b_1}{2\sqrt{y_1 - b_2}}\right] \qquad (6\text{–}10\text{-}8)$$

whence two quadratics result:

$$s^2 - \sqrt{y_1 - b_2}\, s + \frac{y_1}{2} + \frac{b_1}{2\sqrt{y_1 - b_2}} = 0 \qquad (6\text{–}10\text{-}9)$$

$$s^2 + \sqrt{y_1 - b_2}\, s + \frac{y_1}{2} - \frac{b_1}{2\sqrt{y_1 - b_2}} = 0 \qquad (6\text{–}10\text{-}10)$$

The value of y_1 satisfies Eq. 6–10-7, since it is a root of this equation; in turn, this means that Eq. 6–10-5 is a perfect square and can be factored into the two quadratic terms, 6–10-9 and 6–10-10, which are both factors of Eq. 6–10-2.

To demonstrate this method, consider the equation

$$s^4 + 2\,s^3 + 9.5\,s^2 + 10.5\,s + 18 = 0 \qquad (6\text{–}10\text{-}11)$$

An examination by the synthetic divisor method of shifting the $j\omega$-axis shows that, if the $j\omega$-axis is shifted to $\sigma = -0.5$, the equation is so transformed that the coefficient of the s^3 term is zero:

1	2	9.5	10.5	18	$\underline{/-0.5}$
	-0.5	-0.75	-4.375	-3.0625	
1	1.5	8.75	6.125	14.9375	
	-0.5	-0.5	4.125		
1	1.0	8.25	2		(6–10-12)
	-0.5	0.25			
1	0.5	8.0			
	-0.5				
1	0				

The equation after the $j\omega$-axis is shifted is

$$s^4 + 8\,s^2 + 2\,s + 14.9375 = 0 \qquad (6\text{–}10\text{-}13)$$

The auxiliary cubic in y is

$$y^3 - 8\,y^2 - 59.75\,y + 474 = 0 \qquad (6\text{–}10\text{-}14)$$

By Horner's method the largest root of this equation is approximately $y_1 = 8.312$. Substituting this value for y_1 in Eqs. 6–10-9 and 6–10-10 gives

$$s^2 - 0.6175\,s + 5.8108 = 0 \qquad (6\text{–}10\text{-}15)$$

and

$$s^2 + 0.6175\,s + 2.5708 = 0 \qquad (6\text{–}10\text{-}16)$$

The four roots of Eq. 6–10-13 are

s_1 and $s_2 = 0.30875 \pm j\, 2.39$ s_3 and $s_4 = -0.30875 \pm j\, 1.572$ (6–10-17)

To obtain the roots to the original equation, 0.5 is subtracted from these roots:

$$s_1 \text{ and } s_2 = -0.19125 \pm j\,2.39 \qquad s_3 \text{ and } s_4 = -0.80875 \pm j\,1.572 \quad (6\text{--}10\text{--}18)$$

Eq. 6–10–14 has two other roots, y_2 and y_3, which could be used instead of y_1. Both of these roots give two quadratics with complex coefficients; this makes the solution for the quadratics a somewhat more complicated procedure, but the results are the same.

6–11. Summary. For factoring polynomials, the easiest method to remember and to apply is Lin's method. Usually this method yields satisfactory results; however, in certain cases the work involved in using Lin's method is excessive, or the method does not yield results. If this is the case, other methods must be used. If real zeros are present, these can be found to any desired degree of accuracy by use of Horner's method. If a polynomial of high degree is to be factored, the real zeros should be removed first. If all real zeros are removed and a high-degree polynomial is left for which Lin's method does not yield results, the extended Horner's method can be used. This multiple attack should enable factoring any polynomial to any desired degree of accuracy. The example of factoring a 4th-degree polynomial by formula was added simply to illustrate such procedures. Since the formula procedure can only be used on low-degree polynomials and since the procedure is difficult to remember, it is believed that discussion of it adds little to the chapter.

6–12. An Example of a Circuit with Three Storage Elements. A circuit with three storage elements is shown in Fig. 6–12–1. It is assumed that

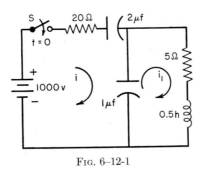

Fig. 6–12–1

the circuit is at rest when the switch is closed at $t = 0$. The loop equations are

$$1000 = 20\,i + \frac{1}{2 \times 10^{-6}} \int_0^t i\,dt + \frac{1}{1 \times 10^{-6}} \int_0^t (i - i_1)\,dt$$

$$0 = \frac{1}{1 \times 10^{-6}} \int_0^t (i_1 - i)\,dt + 5.0\,i_1 + 0.5\frac{di_1}{dt} \qquad (6\text{--}12\text{--}1)$$

These equations can be rewritten

$$1000 = 20\,i + 1.5 \times 10^6 \int_0^t i\,dt - 1 \times 10^6 \int_0^t i_1\,dt$$

$$0 = -1 \times 10^6 \int_0^t i\,dt + 0.5\frac{di_1}{dt} + 5.0\,i_1 + 1 \times 10^6 \int_0^t i_1\,dt \tag{6-12-2}$$

The transforms are

$$\frac{1000}{s} = 20\,\mathcal{L}(i) + 1.5 \times 10^6 \frac{\mathcal{L}(i)}{s} - 1 \times 10^6 \frac{\mathcal{L}(i_1)}{s}$$

$$0 = -1 \times 10^6 \frac{\mathcal{L}(i)}{s} + 0.5\,s\mathcal{L}(i_1) + 5.0\,\mathcal{L}(i_1) + 1 \times 10^6 \frac{\mathcal{L}(i_1)}{s} \tag{6-12-3}$$

These can be rewritten

$$\frac{1000}{s} = \mathcal{L}(i)\left[20 + \frac{1.5 \times 10^6}{s}\right] + \mathcal{L}(i_1)\left[-\frac{1 \times 10^6}{s}\right]$$

$$0 = \mathcal{L}(i)\left[-\frac{1 \times 10^6}{s}\right] + \mathcal{L}(i_1)\left[0.5\,s + 5.0 + \frac{1 \times 10^6}{s}\right] \tag{6-12-4}$$

If the current i is desired, $\mathcal{L}(i)$, in terms of determinants, is

$$\mathcal{L}(i) = \frac{\begin{vmatrix} \dfrac{1000}{s} & -\dfrac{1 \times 10^6}{s} \\[2ex] 0 & 0.5\,s + 5.0 + \dfrac{1 \times 10^6}{s} \end{vmatrix}}{\begin{vmatrix} 20 + \dfrac{1.5 \times 10^6}{s} & -\dfrac{1 \times 10^6}{s} \\[2ex] -\dfrac{1 \times 10^6}{s} & 0.5\,s + 5.0 + \dfrac{1 \times 10^6}{s} \end{vmatrix}} \tag{6-12-5}$$

which upon solution yields

$$\mathcal{L}(i) = \frac{50\,s^2 + 500\,s + 10^8}{s^3 + 7.501 \times 10^4 s^2 + 2.75 \times 10^6\,s + 5 \times 10^{10}} \tag{6-12-6}$$

If the denominator is factored by methods outlined in this chapter, the equation becomes

$$\mathcal{L}(i) = \frac{50\,s^2 + 500\,s + 10^8}{(s + 74{,}980)[(s + 13.9)^2 + (816.5)^2]} \tag{6-12-7}$$

To evaluate this transform, item 19 in the transform table in the Appendix can be used, where:

$$a_2 = 50 \qquad a_1 = 500 \qquad a_0 = 10^8$$
$$a = 13.9 \qquad \omega = 816.5 \qquad b = 74980$$

Thereby

$$A\underline{/\alpha} = \frac{10^8 - 500(13.9 - j\,816.5) + 50(13.9 - j\,816.5)^2}{816.5[(74980 - 13.9) + j\,816.5]}$$

$$= 1.088\underline{/-1.25°} \tag{6-12-8}$$

Hence $\quad i = 1.088\ \epsilon^{-13.9t} \sin (816.5\ t - 1.25°)$

$$+ \frac{10^8 - 500(74{,}980) + 50(74{,}980)^2}{(13.9 - 74980)^2 + (816.5)^2}\ \epsilon^{-74980t} \qquad (6\text{–}12\text{–}9)$$

or $\qquad i = 1.088\ \epsilon^{-13.9t} \sin (816.5\ t - 1.25°) + 50\ \epsilon^{-74980t} \qquad (6\text{–}12\text{–}10)$

Other examples of problems involving polynomials of higher degree than the quadratic occur throughout the remainder of the text.

PROBLEMS

6–1. State what can be determined by using Descartes' rule of signs for the following polynomials:

(a) $s^3 + 4\ s^2 + 12\ s + 30$.

(b) $s^3 - 2\ s^2 - 8\ s + 50$.

(c) $s^3 + 8$.

(d) $s^4 + 3\ s^2 + 7\ s + 16$.

6–2. Transform the polynomials as indicated.

(a) $s^3 + 1.08 \times 10^3 s^2 + 9.8 \times 10^6 s + 1.5 \times 10^{10}$ by dividing the zeros by 10^3.

(b) $s^3 + 3.24 \times 10^{-6} s^2 + 7.5 \times 10^{-12} s + 2.1 \times 10^{-17}$ by multiplying the zeros by 10^6.

6–3. Form the polynomials whose zeros are:

(a) $s_1 = -4.5$; s_2 and $s_3 = -3 \pm j\ 6$.

(b) $s_1 = -2$; $s_2 = -4$; s_3 and $s_4 = -2 \pm j\ 10$.

(c) s_1 and $s_2 = -3 \pm j\ 7$; s_3 and $s_4 = -14 \pm j\ 20$.

6–4. Investigate the plot of $Z(\sigma)$ versus σ for the following polynomials as effected by using synthetic division:

(a) $s^2 + 6\ s + 8$.

(b) $s^2 + 6\ s + 9$.

(c) $s^2 + 6\ s + 10$.

(d) $s^3 + 11\ s^2 + 38\ s + 40$.

(e) $s^3 + 11\ s^2 + 39\ s + 45$.

(f) $s^3 + 11\ s^2 + 40\ s + 50$.

6–5. Factor the following polynomials by using Lin's method and sketch the location of the zeros in the complex s-plane:

(a) $s^3 + 220\ s^2 + 56{,}000\ s + 1{,}400{,}000$.

(b) $s^3 + 10\ s^2 + 55\ s + 120$.

(c) $s^4 + 40\ s^3 + 600\ s^2 + 1200\ s + 2400$.

(d) $s^4 + 6\ s^3 + 17\ s^2 + 31\ s + 24$.

6–6. As polynomials 6–5a and 6–5b are cubics, they must have at least one real zero. In both cases find the real zero by using Horner's method.

6–7. Factor the polynomial formed in Prob. 6–3c by Lin's method.

6–8. Use Routh's test on the following polynomials and therewith determine which of the polynomials are Hurwitz:

(a) $s^2 + 10\ s + 25$.

(b) $s^4 + 6\ s^3 + 16\ s^2 + 20\ s + 12$.

(c) $s^6 + 5\ s^5 + 12\ s^4 + 18\ s^3 + 12\ s^2 + 3\ s + 1$.

(d) $s^7 + 7\ s^6 + 18\ s^5 + 22\ s^4 + 100\ s^3 + 250\ s^2 + 300\ s + 200$.

6–9. Factor the polynomial formed in Prob. 6–3c by using the extended Horner's method.

6–10. Factor the polynomials 6–5c and 6–5d by the extended Horner's method.

6–11. Factor the polynomial formed in Prob. 6–3c by formula.

6–12. The circuit of Fig. 6–P-1 is at rest when S is closed at $t = 0$. Find the equation for the voltage across the 0.2-μf capacitor after $t = 0$.

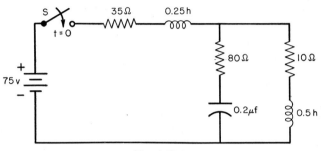

Fig. 6–P-1

6–13. In the circuit of Fig. 6–P-2 the switch S is thrown to position 1 until the steady state is reached; then, at $t = 0$, S is thrown to position 2. Find the equation for the voltage e, located as shown.

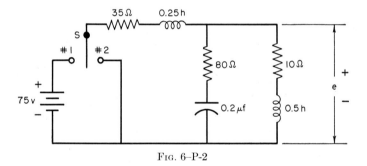

Fig. 6–P-2

6–14. In the circuit of Fig. 6–P-3 the switch S is closed until the steady state is reached; then, at $t = 0$, S is opened. Find the current in the 80-ohm resistor after $t = 0$.

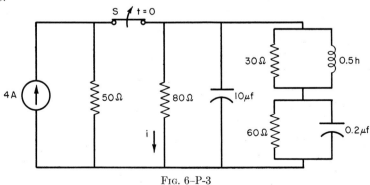

Fig. 6–P-3

CHAPTER 7

CIRCUITS WITH MUTUAL INDUCTANCE BETWEEN TWO COILS

7-1. Mutual Inductance. From Faraday's law, it is known that the voltage e induced in a coil of N turns by a change of flux ϕ is

$$e = N \frac{d\phi}{dt} \qquad (7\text{-}1\text{-}1)$$

Faraday's law stipulates nothing about where the flux originates. If the flux is produced by a current existing in the coil itself, the resulting voltage is due to the effect known as self-inductance. If, on the other hand, the flux is produced by a current existing in a second coil, the resulting voltage is due to the effect known as mutual inductance.

Let it be supposed that the two coils in Fig. 7-1-1 are placed in space and are wound in the manner shown. The current i_1 existing in the assumed

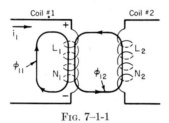

Fig. 7-1-1

direction shown in the figure for coil 1 produces a flux ϕ_1 in the downward direction inside coil 1. The flux ϕ_1 can be considered as comprised of two components. One component, denoted by ϕ_{11}, is the flux that links coil 1 but does not link coil 2. The second component, denoted by ϕ_{12}, is the flux that links both coil 1 and coil 2. These two components of flux add to make ϕ_1, as given by

$$\phi_1 = \phi_{11} + \phi_{12} \qquad (7\text{-}1\text{-}2)$$

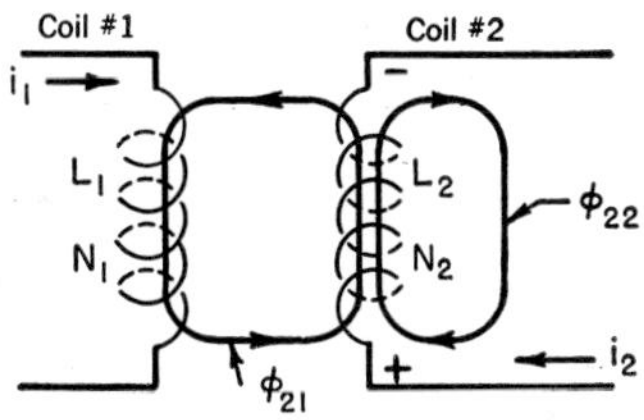

Fig. 7-1-2

The same two coils are shown again in Fig. 7-1-2 with a current i_2 existing in the assumed direction shown in the figure for coil 2. The current i_2 produces a flux ϕ_2 in the upward direction inside coil 2. The flux ϕ_2 can be considered to be comprised of two components in a manner similar to ϕ_1. One component, denoted by ϕ_{22}, is the flux that links coil 2 but does not link coil 1. The second component, denoted by ϕ_{21}, is the flux that links both coil 1 and coil 2. These two components of flux add to make ϕ_2, as given by

$$\phi_2 = \phi_{22} + \phi_{21} \qquad (7\text{-}1\text{-}3)$$

It is to be noted that the method used on the subscript is the following: The first of the two subscripts identifies the coil in which the current exists, the second subscript identifies the coil linked by the flux.

Self-inductance can be defined as flux linkages produced in a coil per unit of current existing in that coil. For coil 1 this definition yields the equation

$$L_1 = \frac{N_1 \phi_1}{i_1} \qquad (7\text{-}1\text{-}4)$$

and for coil 2 the equation

$$L_2 = \frac{N_2 \phi_2}{i_2} \qquad (7\text{-}1\text{-}5)$$

Mutual inductance is defined in a similar manner, except that the flux linkages are in one coil and the current producing the flux is in the other coil. If the current is in coil 2 and the flux linkages are in coil 1, the mutual inductance is

$$M_{21} = \frac{N_1 \phi_{21}}{i_2} \qquad (7\text{-}1\text{-}6)$$

Similarly, if the current is in coil 1 and the flux linkages are in coil 2, the mutual inductance is

$$M_{12} = \frac{N_2 \phi_{12}}{i_1} \qquad (7\text{-}1\text{-}7)$$

If Eq. 7-1-4 is written

$$L_1 i_1 = N_1 \phi_1 \qquad (7\text{-}1\text{-}8)$$

and differentiated with respect to time, the result is

$$L_1 \frac{di_1}{dt} = N_1 \frac{d\phi_1}{dt} \qquad (7\text{-}1\text{-}9)$$

The right side of this equation, by Faraday's law, is an induced voltage e_1. Therefore the left side of the equation is equal to the same voltage; thus

$$e_1 = L_1 \frac{di_1}{dt} \qquad (7\text{-}1\text{-}10)$$

The reference polarity for this voltage is shown in Fig. 7-1-1, as discussed in Chapter 1.

When Eq. 7-1-8 is differentiated to obtain Eq. 7-1-9, it is assumed that the inductance L_1 is a constant. This assumption is correct for an air-core inductor and is approximately correct for an iron-core inductor if the core structure contains a large air gap. For the situation where L_1 is not a constant, differentiation of Eq. 7-1-8 yields

$$L_1 \frac{di_1}{dt} + i_1 \frac{dL_1}{dt} = N_1 \frac{d\phi_1}{dt} \qquad (7\text{-}1\text{-}11)$$

In the remainder of this text it is assumed that L_1 is a constant.

A similar development establishes

$$e_2 = L_2 \frac{di_2}{dt} \qquad (7\text{-}1\text{-}12)$$

with polarity reference for this voltage as shown in Fig. 7-1-2.

If Eq. 7-1-6 is written $\qquad M_{21} i_2 = N_1 \phi_{21} \qquad (7\text{-}1\text{-}13)$

and differentiated with respect to time, the result is

$$M_{21} \frac{di_2}{dt} = N_1 \frac{d\phi_{21}}{dt} \qquad (7\text{-}1\text{-}14)$$

In differentiating, it is assumed that M_{21} is a constant; this is correct for an air-core transformer. The right side of this equation, by Faraday's law, is a voltage induced in coil 1 by a current in coil 2; therefore the voltage equation can be written

$$e_{21} = M_{21} \frac{di_2}{dt} \qquad (7\text{-}1\text{-}15)$$

A similar development establishes

$$e_{12} = M_{12} \frac{di_1}{dt} \qquad (7\text{-}1\text{-}16)$$

as the voltage induced in coil 2 by a current in coil 1.

Next it is shown that $M_{21} = M_{12}$ in an air-core transformer, where both M's are constants. This can be done in several different ways; the method used here is based on energy considerations. The product ei is power, and the time integral of power is energy. The e's involved are the self-induced and mutual-induced voltages. The equation for energy in the field of the coils is established in two different methods which, when equated, show that $M_{21} = M_{12}$. In the circuit shown in Fig. 7-1-2, it is assumed that both i_1 and i_2 are initially zero, and that then current i_1 is increased to a value I_1 in an interval of time T_1 while the value of i_2 is held at zero. The resulting energy stored in the magnetic field is

$$W_1 = \int_0^{T_1} e_1 i_1 \, dt = \int_0^{T_1} L_1 \frac{di_1}{dt} i_1 \, dt = L_1 \int_0^{I_1} i_1 \, di_1 = \left[\frac{L_1 i_1{}^2}{2} \right]_0^{I_1} = \frac{L_1 I_1{}^2}{2} \qquad (7\text{-}1\text{-}17)$$

Now that I_1 has been established in coil 1, the current i_2 is increased from zero to a value of I_2 in an interval of time T_2 while the current I_1 is maintained constant. The total energy W_t stored in the magnetic field is the value of W_1 already stored when i_2 was held at zero plus two other components. The first of these other components, denoted by W_2, is the energy stored due to the time integral of power from the self-induced voltage e_2

and current i_2. The second component, denoted by W_{21}, is due to the time integral of power from the mutual voltage e_{21} and the current I_1. Accordingly, the total energy is

$$W_t = W_1 + W_2 + W_{21} = \frac{L_1 I_1^2}{2} + \int_0^{T_2} e_2 i_2 \, dt + \int_0^{T_2} e_{21} I_1 \, dt \quad (7\text{–}1\text{–}18)$$

The integrals are evaluated in the following steps:

$$\begin{aligned}
W_t &= \frac{L_1 I_1^2}{2} + \int_0^{T_2} L_2 \frac{di_2}{dt} i_2 \, dt + \int_0^{T_2} M_{21} \frac{di_2}{dt} I_1 \, dt \\
&= \frac{L_1 I_1^2}{2} + \int_0^{I_2} L_2 i_2 \, di_2 + \int_0^{I_2} M_{21} I_1 \, di_2 \\
&= \frac{L_1 I_1^2}{2} + \left[\frac{L_2 i_2^2}{2}\right]_0^{I_2} + \left[M_{21} I_1 i_2\right]_0^{I_2} = \frac{L_1 I_1^2}{2} + \frac{L_2 I_2^2}{2} + M_{21} I_1 I_2 \quad (7\text{–}1\text{–}19)
\end{aligned}$$

The same development is repeated, except that i_2 is increased from zero to I_2 while i_1 is held at zero, and then i_1 is increased from zero to I_1 while i_2 is held constant:

$$\begin{aligned}
W_t = W_2 + W_1 + W_{12} &= \int_0^{I_2} L_2 i_2 \, di_2 + \int_0^{I_1} L_1 i_1 \, di_1 + \int_0^{I_1} M_{12} I_2 \, di_1 \\
&= \frac{L_1 I_1^2}{2} + \frac{L_2 I_2^2}{2} + M_{12} I_2 I_1 \quad (7\text{–}1\text{–}20)
\end{aligned}$$

The total energy must be the same in both cases; therefore Eqs. 7–1-19 and 7–1-20 can be equated, yielding

$$M_{21} = M_{12} = M \quad (7\text{–}1\text{–}21)$$

The following constants are defined:

$$K_{12} = \frac{\phi_{12}}{\phi_1} \qquad K_{21} = \frac{\phi_{21}}{\phi_2} \quad (7\text{–}1\text{–}22)$$

and the coefficient of coupling K between the two windings is defined as

$$K = \sqrt{K_{12} K_{21}} = \sqrt{\frac{\phi_{12}}{\phi_1} \frac{\phi_{21}}{\phi_2}} \quad (7\text{–}1\text{–}23)$$

If Eqs. 7–1-6 and 7–1-7 are solved for ϕ_{21} and ϕ_{12}, respectively,

$$\phi_{21} = \frac{M_{21} i_2}{N_1} = \frac{M i_2}{N_1} \quad (7\text{–}1\text{–}24)$$

$$\phi_{12} = \frac{M_{12} i_1}{N_2} = \frac{M i_1}{N_2} \quad (7\text{–}1\text{–}25)$$

and the results are substituted in Eq. 7–1-23, K is

$$K = \sqrt{\frac{M i_2}{N_1 \phi_1} \frac{M i_1}{N_2 \phi_2}} = \sqrt{\frac{i_1}{N_1 \phi_1} \frac{i_2}{N_2 \phi_2} M^2} = \frac{M}{\sqrt{L_1 L_2}} \quad (7\text{–}1\text{–}26)$$

K has a value of 1 as the possible maximum.

The method of determining the polarity reference for the mutual-induced voltages is now taken up.

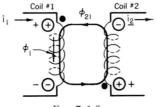

Fig. 7-1-3

The circuit of Fig. 7-1-3 is given and the choice of current directions is made. The polarity reference for the self-induced voltages

$$e_1 = L_1 \frac{di_1}{dt} = N_1 \frac{d\phi_1}{dt} \qquad (7\text{-}1\text{-}27)$$

and

$$e_2 = L_2 \frac{di_2}{dt} = N_2 \frac{d\phi_2}{dt} \qquad (7\text{-}1\text{-}28)$$

are shown by the $+$, $-$ marks. If coil 1 is examined, ϕ_1 is found in the downward direction inside coil 1. If coil 2 is examined, ϕ_2 and hence ϕ_{21} are found in the upward direction inside coil 2. Owing to the physical arrangement of the two coils, ϕ_{21} is in the downward direction inside coil 1, which is in the same direction as ϕ_1. If the time variation of ϕ_1 produces a voltage $e_1 = N_1(d\phi_1/dt)$ with the $+$, $-$ polarity reference as shown, then, since ϕ_{21} is in the same direction as ϕ_1 inside coil 1, the time variation of $e_{21} = N_1(d\phi_{21}/dt)$ produces a voltage whose polarity reference is the same as that for e_1. This polarity reference is shown in Fig. 7-1-3 with the $\oplus$, $\ominus$ marks. A similar inspection of ϕ_2 and ϕ_{12} leads to the $\oplus$, $\ominus$ marks on coil 2.

Instead of showing the actual winding direction and the physical orientation of the windings of a transformer each time one is drawn, a "dot" notation has been devised for the two-winding situation to convey this information. The location of the first dot is arbitrary. Let it be supposed in Fig. 7-1-3 that this is the dot shown on coil 1. The location of the second dot is then determined by the physical arrangement of the transformer. The second dot is placed so that, if both i_1 and i_2 are directed into (or out of) their respective dots, the mutual flux aids the flux of self-induction. This implies that the second dot is to be placed on coil 2 as shown.

If a coil is assembled in such a way that it is impossible to determine the winding directions from inspection, a simple test can be made to determine the location of the dots. With reference to Fig. 7-1-3, if the current i_1 is directed into the dotted end of winding 1, the voltage induced in the secondary winding $e_{12} = M(di_1/dt)$ has the polarity reference shown by the $\oplus$, $\ominus$ marks. It is to be noted that the $\oplus$ mark in the secondary winding is at the dotted end. If the current i_1 increases so that di_1/dt is positive, a d-c voltmeter connected so that it will read upscale has its plus terminal on

the secondary terminal that is dotted. Let it be supposed the transformer
shown in Fig. 7–1-4 has an unknown winding arrangement and it is desired

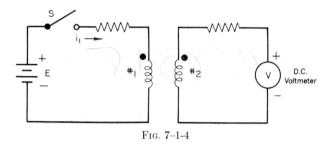

FIG. 7–1-4

to determine the location of the dots. One end of coil 1 can be arbitrarily
dotted, as the one shown is. The switch S is closed, connecting a battery
to winding 1 so that i_1 is directed into the dotted end, thus making di_1/dt
positive. The voltmeter is placed on coil 2 in such a manner as to read
upscale when i_1 is increasing. This is done by experiment. The plus terminal of the voltmeter is then connected to the terminal of coil 2 that
should be dotted. Other simple tests based on a-c measurements can also
be made.

7–2. Parallel Branches with Mutual Inductance. The circuit of Fig. 7–2-1
is considered with a physical orientation of windings as indicated by the

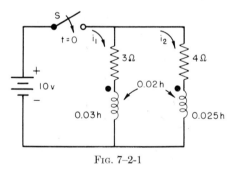

FIG. 7–2-1

dots. Use of numerical values enables the work to be kept in more compact
form, yet all steps of the solution are illustrated. Directions for the currents i_1 and i_2 are arbitrarily chosen as shown. As both i_1 and i_2 are directed
into the dotted ends of their respective coils, the mutually induced voltages
have the same signs as the self-induced voltages, giving the equations

$$10 = 3\,i_1 + 0.03\,\frac{di_1}{dt} + 0.02\,\frac{di_2}{dt}$$

$$10 = 4\,i_2 + 0.025\,\frac{di_2}{dt} + 0.02\,\frac{di_1}{dt}$$

(7–2-1)

It is assumed that i_1 and i_2 were both zero before $t = 0$. Then, since there is an inductor in both current paths, $i_1(0)$ and $i_2(0)$ are both zero. The transformed equations become

$$\frac{10}{s} = \mathcal{L}(i_1)[0.03\ s + 3] + \mathcal{L}(i_2)[0.02\ s]$$

$$\frac{10}{s} = \mathcal{L}(i_1)[0.02\ s] + \mathcal{L}(i_2)[0.025\ s + 4] \qquad (7\text{-}2\text{-}2)$$

Solution of Eq. 7–2–2 for $\mathcal{L}(i_1)$ gives

$$\mathcal{L}(i_1) = \frac{\begin{vmatrix} \dfrac{10}{s} & 0.02\ s \\[2mm] \dfrac{10}{s} & 0.025\ s + 4 \end{vmatrix}}{\begin{vmatrix} 0.03\ s + 3 & 0.02\ s \\ 0.02\ s & 0.025\ s + 4 \end{vmatrix}} = \frac{143\ s + 114{,}200}{s(s + 70.6)(s + 486.5)} \qquad (7\text{-}2\text{-}3)$$

Use of item 16 in the transform table in the Appendix, with $a_2 = 0$, $a_1 = 143$ $a_0 = 114{,}200$, $a = 0$, $b = 70.6$, and $c = 486.5$, yields the desired i_1:

$$i_1 = \frac{114{,}200}{34{,}300} + \left[\frac{143(-70.6) - 114{,}200}{(-70.6)(415.9)}\right]\epsilon^{-70.6t}$$

$$+ \left[\frac{143(-486.5) + 114{,}200}{(-486.5)(-415.9)}\right]\epsilon^{-486.5t} \qquad (7\text{-}2\text{-}4)$$

which simplifies to

$$i_1 = 3.33 - 3.5\ \epsilon^{-70.6t} + 0.22\ \epsilon^{-486.5t} \qquad (7\text{-}2\text{-}5)$$

If the direction of the winding of one coil is reversed, the circuit becomes that of Fig. 7–2–2. As i_1 is directed into the dotted end and i_2 is directed

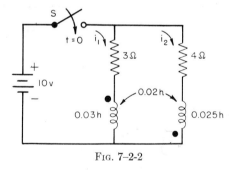

FIG. 7-2-2

into the undotted end of their respective coils, the sign of the mutual-induced voltages has the sign opposite to the self-induced voltages. The circuit equations are

$$10 = 3\ i_1 + 0.03\frac{di_1}{dt} - 0.02\frac{di_2}{dt}$$

$$10 = 4\ i_2 + 0.025\frac{di_2}{dt} - 0.02\frac{di_1}{dt} \qquad (7\text{-}2\text{-}6)$$

The transformed equations are

$$\frac{10}{s} = \mathcal{L}(i_1)[0.03 \, s + 3] + \mathcal{L}(i_2)[- 0.02 \, s]$$

$$\frac{10}{s} = \mathcal{L}(i_1)[- 0.02 \, s] + \mathcal{L}(i_2)[0.025 \, s + 4] \tag{7-2-7}$$

Solution for $\mathcal{L}(i_1)$ yields

$$\mathcal{L}(i_1) = \frac{\begin{vmatrix} \dfrac{10}{s} & - 0.02 \, s \\ \dfrac{10}{s} & 0.025 \, s + 4 \end{vmatrix}}{\begin{vmatrix} 0.03 \, s + 3 & - 0.02 \, s \\ - 0.02 \, s & 0.025 \, s + 4 \end{vmatrix}} = \frac{1286 \, s + 114{,}200}{s(s + 70.6)(s + 486.5)} \tag{7-2-8}$$

Use of item 16 in the transform table gives the desired i_1:

$$i_1 = \frac{114{,}200}{34{,}300} + \left[\frac{1286(- 70.6) + 114{,}200}{(- 70.6)(415.9)}\right] \epsilon^{-70.6t}$$

$$+ \left[\frac{1286(- 486.5) + 114{,}200}{(- 486.5)(- 415.9)}\right] \epsilon^{-486.5t} \tag{7-2-9}$$

which simplifies to

$$i_1 = 3.33 - 0.79 \, \epsilon^{-70.6t} - 2.53 \, \epsilon^{-486.5t} \tag{7-2-10}$$

To illustrate the manner in which initial conditions are included in a problem involving mutual inductance, let it be supposed that in Fig. 7-2-1 the current $i_1(0) = 2$ amp and $i_2(0) = +4$ amp. The transformed equations (7-2-1) become

$$\frac{10}{s} = 3 \, \mathcal{L}(i_1) + 0.03[s\mathcal{L}(i_1) - 2] + 0.02[s\mathcal{L}(i_2) + 4]$$

$$\frac{10}{s} = 4 \, \mathcal{L}(i_2) + 0.025[s\mathcal{L}(i_2) + 4] + 0.02[s\mathcal{L}(i_1) - 2] \tag{7-2-11}$$

When (7-2-11) is solved for $\mathcal{L}(i_1)$ the result is

$$\mathcal{L}(i_1) = \frac{2 \, s^2 - 85.7 \, s + 114{,}200}{s(s + 70.6)(s + 486.5)} \tag{7-2-12}$$

The use of item 16 in the transform table in the Appendix yields

$$i_1 = 3.33 - 4.45 \, \epsilon^{-70.6t} + 3.11 \, \epsilon^{-486.5t} \tag{7-2-13}$$

7-3. Air-Core Transformer. The circuit of Fig. 7-3-1 is considered with the dots as given. Directions for the currents i_1 and i_2 are chosen as shown. Since i_1 and i_2 both are directed into their respective coils at the dotted ends, the mutual fluxes add to the self-fluxes and mutual-voltage terms

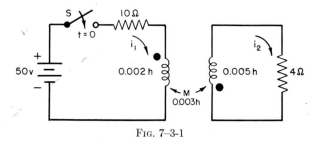

FIG. 7-3-1

can be written with the same sign as the self-induced terms:

$$50 = 10\,i_1 + 0.002\frac{di_1}{dt} + 0.003\frac{di_2}{dt} \qquad (7\text{-}3\text{-}1)$$

$$0 = 0.003\frac{di_1}{dt} + 4\,i_2 + 0.005\frac{di_2}{dt} \qquad (7\text{-}3\text{-}2)$$

If it is assumed that both i_1 and i_2 are zero before $t = 0$, as the inductors keep the currents from jumping, both $i_1(0)$ and $i_2(0)$ are zero.

The transformed equations are

$$\frac{50}{s} = \mathcal{L}(i_1)[0.002\,s + 10] + \mathcal{L}(i_2)[0.003\,s]$$
$$0 = \mathcal{L}(i_1)[0.003\,s] + \mathcal{L}(i_2)[0.005\,s + 4] \qquad (7\text{-}3\text{-}3)$$

Solution of these equations for $\mathcal{L}(i_1)$ gives

$$\mathcal{L}(i_1) = \frac{\begin{vmatrix} \dfrac{50}{s} & 0.003\,s \\[2mm] 0 & 0.005\,s+4 \end{vmatrix}}{\begin{vmatrix} 0.002\,s+10 & 0.003\,s \\[2mm] 0.003\,s & 0.005\,s+4 \end{vmatrix}} = \frac{0.25\times10^6\,s + 2\times10^8}{s(s^2 + 5.8\times10^4\,s + 4\times10^7)} \qquad (7\text{-}3\text{-}4)$$

When the quadratic polynomial is factored, it can be seen that one of the zeros is of very small value compared with the other. As discussed in Chapter 6, the zeros can be approximated by the following technique. If the zeros are $-\alpha_1$, and $-\alpha_2$, the quadratic can be expressed as

$$(s + \alpha_1)(s + \alpha_2) = s^2 + (\alpha_1 + \alpha_2)s + \alpha_1\alpha_2 \qquad (7\text{-}3\text{-}5)$$

When Eqs. 7-3-4 and 7-3-5 are compared, it can be seen that

$$\alpha_1 + \alpha_2 = 5.8\times10^4$$

and

$$\alpha_1\alpha_2 = 4.0\times10^7 \qquad (7\text{-}3\text{-}6)$$

Let it be assumed that α_1 is large compared with α_2. Then α_1 is approximately

$$\alpha_1 \doteq 5.8\times10^4 \qquad (7\text{-}3\text{-}7)$$

and α_2 is approximately

$$\alpha_2 \doteq \frac{4.0\times10^7}{5.8\times10^4} = 690 \qquad (7\text{-}3\text{-}8)$$

Through use of the approximate value of α_2, a more accurate value of α_1 can be found:

$$\alpha_1 \doteq 5.8 \times 10^4 - 690 = 5.73 \times 10^4 \qquad (7\text{-}3\text{-}9)$$

from which, in turn, α_2 can be found:

$$\alpha_2 \doteq \frac{4.0 \times 10^7}{5.73 \times 10^4} = 697 \qquad (7\text{-}3\text{-}10)$$

Eq. 7-3-4 can now be written

$$\mathcal{L}(i_1) = \frac{0.25 \times 10^6\, s + 2 \times 10^8}{s(s + 57{,}310)(s + 697)} \qquad (7\text{-}3\text{-}11)$$

Use of item 16 in the transform table gives

$$i_1 = \frac{2 \times 10^8}{(57{,}300)(697)} + \left[\frac{0.25 \times 10^6(-57{,}300) + 2 \times 10^8}{(-57{,}300)(-57{,}300 + 697)}\right]\epsilon^{-57{,}300t}$$

$$+ \left[\frac{0.25 \times 10^6(-697) + 2 \times 10^8}{(-697)(-697 + 57{,}300)}\right]\epsilon^{-697t} \qquad (7\text{-}3\text{-}12)$$

This simplifies to

$$i_1 = 5 - 4.35\,\epsilon^{-57{,}300t} - 0.65\,\epsilon^{-697t} \qquad (7\text{-}3\text{-}13)$$

7-4. Air-Core Transformer with a Capacitor in the Secondary Mesh.
The circuit of Fig. 7-4-1 is an air-core transformer with a capacitor in the

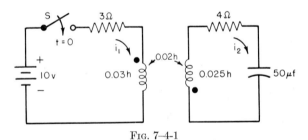

FIG. 7-4-1

secondary mesh. With the currents i_1 and i_2 arbitrarily directed as shown, the voltage equations are

$$10 = 3\,i_1 + 0.03\,\frac{di_1}{dt} + 0.02\,\frac{di_2}{dt}$$

$$0 = 0.02\,\frac{di_1}{dt} + 0.025\,\frac{di_2}{dt} + 4\,i_2 + 2 \times 10^4 \int_0^t i_2\,dt \qquad (7\text{-}4\text{-}1)$$

If it is assumed that the circuit is at rest before $t = 0$, $i_1(0)$ and $i_2(0)$ are zero. The transformed equations are

$$\frac{10}{s} = \mathcal{L}(i_1)[0.03\,s + 3] + \mathcal{L}(i_2)[0.02\,s]$$

$$0 = \mathcal{L}(i_1)[0.02\,s] + \mathcal{L}(i_2)\left[0.025\,s + 4 + \frac{2 \times 10^4}{s}\right] \qquad (7\text{-}4\text{-}2)$$

Solution of these equations for $\mathcal{L}(i_2)$ gives

$$\mathcal{L}(i_2) = \frac{\begin{vmatrix} 0.03\,s+3 & \dfrac{10}{s} \\[2mm] 0.02\,s & 0 \end{vmatrix}}{\begin{vmatrix} 0.03\,s+3 & 0.02\,s \\[2mm] 0.02\,s & 0.025\,s+4+\dfrac{2\times10^4}{s} \end{vmatrix}}$$

$$= \frac{-571\,s}{s^3 + 557.1\,s^2 + 1.745\times10^6\,s + 1.715\times10^8} \qquad (7\text{–}4\text{–}3)$$

When the denominator of this equation is factored by methods explained in Chapter 6, the equation can be written

$$\mathcal{L}(i_2) = \frac{-571\,s}{(s+101)[(s+228)^2+(1283)^2]} \qquad (7\text{–}4\text{–}4)$$

Use of item 19 in the transform table and simplifying the resulting current equation yield

$$i_2 = 0.0347\,\epsilon^{-101t} + 0.455\,\epsilon^{-228t}\sin(1283\,t - 175.6) \qquad (7\text{–}4\text{–}5)$$

7–5. Air-Core Transformer with a Capacitor in the Primary and Secondary Meshes. The circuit of an air-core transformer with a capacitor in the

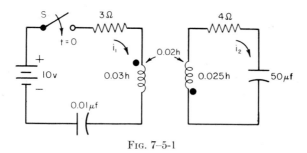

Fig. 7–5–1

primary mesh and another in the secondary mesh is shown in Fig. 7–5–1. With i_1 and i_2 arbitrarily directed as shown, the voltage equations are

$$10 = 3\,i + 0.03\,\frac{di_1}{dt} + 10^8\int_0^t i_1\,dt + 0.02\,\frac{di_2}{dt}$$
$$0 = 0.02\,\frac{di_1}{dt} + 4\,i_2 + 0.025\,\frac{di_2}{dt} + 2\times10^4\int_0^t i_2\,dt \qquad (7\text{–}5\text{–}1)$$

Again it is assumed that the circuit is quiescent at $t=0$; the transformed equations are

$$\frac{10}{s} = \mathcal{L}(i_1)\left[0.03\,s+3+\frac{10^8}{s}\right] + \mathcal{L}(i_2)[0.02\,s]$$
$$0 = \mathcal{L}(i_1)[0.02\,s] + \mathcal{L}(i_2)\left[0.025\,s+4+\frac{2\times10^4}{s}\right] \qquad (7\text{–}5\text{–}2)$$

Solution of these equations for $\mathcal{L}(i_2)$ gives

$$\mathcal{L}(i_2) = \frac{-571\,s^2}{s^4 + 557.1\,s^3 + 71.4 \times 10^8\,s^2 + 114.4 \times 10^{10}\,s + 5.71 \times 10^{14}} \quad (7\text{-}5\text{-}3)$$

When the denominator is factored, the equation becomes

$$\mathcal{L}(i_2) = \frac{-571\,s^2}{[(s+80)^2 + (890)^2][(s+198.5)^2 + (84{,}500)^2]} \quad (7\text{-}5\text{-}4)$$

Use of item 27 in the transform table and simplifying the resulting current equation yield

$$i_2 = 7.25 \times 10^{-5}\,\epsilon^{-80t}\sin{(890\,t + 10.3)}$$
$$+ 6.75 \times 10^{-3}\,\epsilon^{-198.5t}\sin{(84{,}500\,t + 180)} \quad (7\text{-}5\text{-}5)$$

7–6. General Considerations about Air-Core Transformers. The air-core transformer with a capacitor in its secondary mesh shown in Fig. 7–4–1 is characterized by an equation of which the transform has a function of s in the denominator that is a cubic. In general, the circuit parameters can be such that this cubic has three real negative zeros, or one real negative zero and two complex zeros. With three real negative zeros, plots of the currents are of the shapes sketched in Fig. 7–6-1. The current

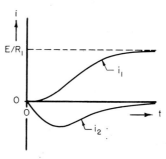

FIG. 7–6-1

i_1 has a steady-state value, as confirmed from inspection of the circuit. The current i_2 is negative because of the choice of current direction in the secondary mesh.

If the cubic has one real negative zero and two complex zeros, plots of the currents are of the shapes sketched in Fig. 7–6-2. Increasing the coupling between the two coils has several effects on this oscillatory case. Both the frequency of oscillation and the damping factor increase as the coefficient of coupling increases; and the current i_2 becomes less symmetric with respect to the time axis.

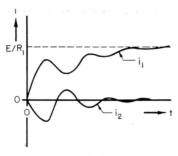

FIG. 7–6-2

If the capacitor is moved from the secondary mesh of the transformer to the primary mesh, as shown in Fig. 7–6-3, three storage elements are

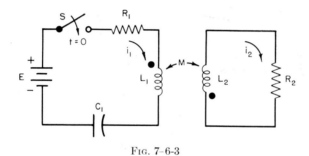

FIG. 7–6-3

still present, and thus the denominator of the transform equation is a cubic function of s. The plots of the currents have shapes quite similar to those of Figs. 7–6-1 and 7–6-2, except that i_{1ss} is equal to zero.

The transformer shown in Fig. 7–5-1 with capacitors in the primary and secondary meshes is characterized by a transform which has a quartic function of s in the denominator. In the general case the circuit parameters can be such that this quartic can have four negative real zeros, two negative real zeros and a pair of complex conjugate zeros, or two pairs of complex conjugate zeros. If the quartic has four real negative zeros, plots of the currents have the shapes of those shown in Fig. 7–6-1 except that i_{1ss} is zero. If the quartic has two real negative zeros and two complex zeros, plots of the currents have shapes similar to those of Fig. 7–6-2 except that again i_{1ss} is zero. If the quartic has two pairs of complex zeros, plots of the currents show two different frequencies of oscillations. Each frequency of oscillation has a particular damping rate associated with it. If the two frequencies differ considerably, the plot of one of the currents approximates that shown in Fig. 7–6-4. The oscillation of higher frequency usually has the larger damping rate, and hence decays most rapidly.

If the two frequencies are nearly the same, beating occurs, as shown by the plot of one of the currents in Fig. 7–6-5. The frequency of the envelope

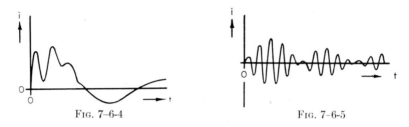

FIG. 7–6-4   FIG. 7–6-5

is the difference between the two frequencies of oscillation. The variation of the frequencies of oscillation is shown in Fig. 7–6-6a and the damping constant in Fig. 7–6-6b as a function of the mutual inductance M. As the

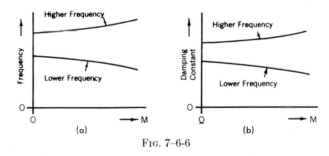

(a)   (b)

FIG. 7–6-6

mutual inductance M is increased, the effect is to separate further the two frequencies of oscillation. The higher frequency increases, the lower frequency decreases. As M increases, the damping constant of the higher frequency of oscillation increases, that of the lower frequency decreases.

PROBLEMS

7–1. In the circuit of Fig. 7–P-1, find the equation for the current i.

$$i = 1.43 - 1.43 e^{-36.8 t}$$

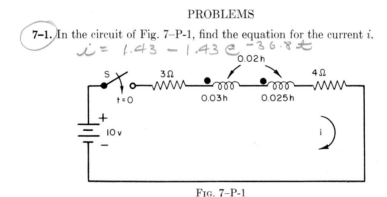

FIG. 7–P-1

7–2. In the circuit of Fig. 7–P-1 the dot on the 0.025-henry inductor is moved to the other end of the coil. Find the equation for i.

7-3. In the circuit of Fig. 7–P-2, find the equation for the current i_2.

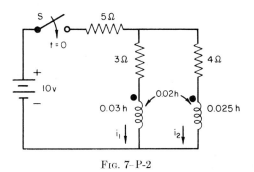

FIG. 7–P-2

7-4. In the circuit of Fig. 7–P-2 the dot on the 0.03-henry inductor is moved to the other end of the coil. Find the equation for i_1.

7-5. In the circuit of Fig. 7–P-3 find the equation for the current i_2.

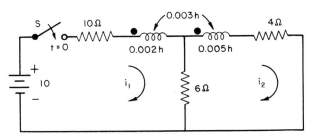

FIG. 7–P-3

7-6. In the circuit of Fig. 7–P-3 the dot on the 0.003-henry inductor is moved to the other end of the coil. Find the equation for i_1.

7-7. In the circuit of Fig. 7–P-4 it is given that S_1 is closed and 0.02 sec later

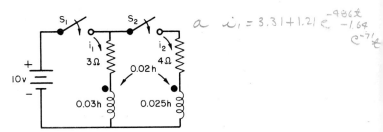

$$a \quad i_1 = 3.31 + 1.21 e^{-486t} - 1.64$$
$$e^{-7/t}$$

FIG. 7–P-4

S_2 is closed at $t = 0$. Find the equation for the following after $t = 0$: (a) i_1; (b) i_2; (c) e across the 0.025-henry inductor.

7–8. In the circuit of Fig. 7–P-5 it is given that the circuit has reached steady-state conditions before S is closed at $t = 0$. Find the equation for i_1 after $t = 0$.

$i_1 = 3.31 - 2.15e^{-7t} - 1.15e^{-486t}$

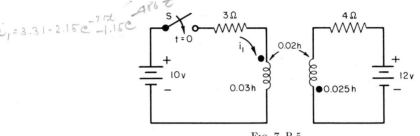

FIG. 7–P-5

7–9. In the circuit of Art. 7–4 find the equation for the current i_1.

7–10. In the circuit of Art. 7–4 find the equation for the voltage on the 50-μf capacitor.

7–11. In the circuit of Art. 7–5 find the equation for the current i_1.

7–12. In the circuit of Art. 7–5 find the equation for the voltage on the 0.01-μf capacitor.

7–13. Remove the 50-μf capacitor in the circuit of Art. 7–5 and solve for i_1.

7–14. Hold all circuit values constant in the circuit of Art. 7–5 except for a decrease of M from 0.02 to 0.01 henry and solve for i_1. Compare the frequencies of oscillation and damping factors with those previously found and thus determine if the results agree with the statements made in Art. 7–6.

CHAPTER 8

TRANSIENTS WITH AN ALTERNATING–CURRENT SOURCE

8–1. Introduction. Until recently it has been customary for universities to teach a-c circuit theory first, and, if time permitted, a course in transients followed. However, even if both courses were offered, they were generally taught from entirely different points of view and the student was left with the impression that somehow a circuit has a certain type of response to an a-c source in the steady state and another response which is quite different when some sort of switching operation produces a transient. In the last few years it has become apparent that a study of transients is not an auxiliary but is equally as important as the study of steady-state a-c circuit theory. Also, the relationship between the transient and the steady-state response plays an important role in control system analysis and network theory. For these reasons an introduction to some of these concepts should be presented at the undergraduate level. These relationships are developed and explained in this chapter and in Chapter 10.

It is not advanced that the following is a complete presentation of a-c circuit theory; rather, it is designed to serve one of two purposes. If the use of this book is preceded by a course in a-c circuit theory, the following is a review. If this book is used in a course that precedes a course in a-c circuit theory, the following is an introduction to a more general treatment of material which comes in the later course.

8–2. Steady-State Alternating-Current Response of a Circuit. The dif-

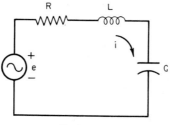

Fig. 8–2–1

ferential equation for the circuit of Fig. 8–2–1 is

$$e = Ri + L\frac{di}{dt} + \frac{1}{C}\int i\,dt \qquad (8\text{–}2\text{–}1)$$

179

The usual procedure for finding the a-c steady-state response tacitly assumes that the circuit is in the steady state through the form of the current (or voltage) generally used:

$$i = I_M \sin \omega t \qquad (8\text{-}2\text{-}2)$$

The differential equation 8–2-1 describes the circuit behavior at all times; accordingly, if the steady-state current is substituted in the right side of Eq. 8–2-1, the steady-state voltage across the circuit results. In order to do this the derivative and integral of the current are needed; thus

$$\frac{di}{dt} = I_M \omega \cos \omega t \qquad (8\text{-}2\text{-}3)$$

$$\int i \, dt = -\frac{I_M}{\omega} \cos \omega t \qquad (8\text{-}2\text{-}4)$$

As the solution sought is the steady-state component, the transient component is ignored. Therefore the initial conditions implied by the integration of Eq. 8–2-4 are neglected. This procedure is in keeping with that used in most books on a-c circuit theory. Once in a while this procedure leads to results that are in error, as demonstrated by some of the examples presented in this chapter. Upon substitution, Eq. 8–2-1 becomes

$$e = I_M \left[R \sin \omega t + \left(\omega L - \frac{1}{\omega C} \right) \cos \omega t \right] \qquad (8\text{-}2\text{-}5)$$

The voltage e is also sinusoidal, because whenever a sine term is added to a cosine term of the same frequency the resultant is also a sinusoidal quantity, as can be found by using trigonometric identities. An inspection of Eq. 8–2-5 suggests an identity based on the sine or the cosine of the sum of two angles. It is customary in a-c circuit theory to use the sine identity, which is

$$\sin (A + B) = \cos A \sin B + \sin A \cos B \qquad (8\text{-}2\text{-}6)$$

If B represents the ωt terms, the identity 8–2-6 is applicable to Eq. 8–2-5 if the following relationships hold:

$$R = K \cos A \qquad (8\text{-}2\text{-}7)$$

$$\omega L - \frac{1}{\omega C} = K \sin A \qquad (8\text{-}2\text{-}8)$$

where, so far, K is just a factor of proportionality. The last two equations suggest the triangle of Fig. 8–2-2, where the hypotenuse is customarily

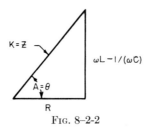

K = Z

$\omega L - 1/(\omega C)$

A = θ

R

FIG. 8–2-2

designated by Z instead of K, and the angle by θ instead of A. In this example, then, Z and θ are given by

$$Z = \sqrt{R^2 + (\omega L - 1/\omega C)^2} \qquad (8\text{-}2\text{-}9)$$

$$\theta = \tan^{-1} \frac{\omega L - 1/\omega C}{R} \qquad (8\text{-}2\text{-}10)$$

Eq. 8-2-5 can be written

$$e = I_M Z[\cos\theta \sin\omega t + \sin\theta \cos\omega t] \qquad (8\text{-}2\text{-}11)$$

Using identity 8-2-6 gives

$$e = I_M Z \sin(\omega t + \theta) \qquad (8\text{-}2\text{-}12)$$

or, finally,

$$e = E_M \sin(\omega t + \theta) \qquad (8\text{-}2\text{-}13)$$

where

$$E_M = I_M Z \qquad (8\text{-}2\text{-}14)$$

The circuit determines two relationships between the voltage and the current. The magnitude of Z determines the ratio between E_M and I_M as

$$Z = \frac{E_M}{I_M} \qquad (8\text{-}2\text{-}15)$$

and the angle θ determines the relative phase between the voltage and current. Eq. 8-2-12 defines θ as positive when the voltage leads the current, or (an equivalent statement) θ is positive when the current lags the voltage. The term impedance, by definition, includes both of these ideas. That is, impedance has a magnitude that determines the relationship between E_M and I_M and an angle that determines the phase between voltage and current. The impedance is denoted by

$$Z\underline{/\theta} \qquad (8\text{-}2\text{-}16)$$

Because of the difficulties in solving circuit problems by manipulating trigonometric functions, other techniques have been developed. One of these is the concept of a rotating phasor or vector. Fig. 8-2-3 helps explain

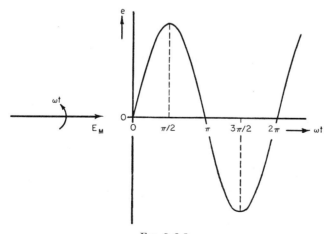

Fig. 8-2-3

this concept. The phasor rotates at the constant angular velocity determined by the frequency of the source. Projection of this phasor on a vertical line establishes a sinusoidal function of time. Thus, instead of drawing sinusoidal curves to represent instantaneous quantities, a phasor can be drawn. The phase relationships between two quantities can be shown very conveniently on a phasor diagram. For example, Fig. 8–2-4

Fig. 8–2-4   Fig. 8–2-5

shows the current leading the voltage by 30°, and Fig. 8–2-5 shows the voltage leading the current by 30°.

Another concept is use of the complex plane. The reason for its use is that it simplifies manipulations of the quantities involved. A point

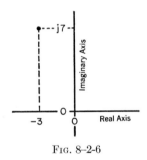

Fig. 8–2-6

is located on this plane by specifying both the real and the imaginary part. For example, the point

$$-3 + j\,7 \qquad\qquad (8\text{–}2\text{–}17)$$

is located 3 units to the left of the j-axis and 7 units above the real axis. The usual implication of a quantity such as $(-3 + j\,7)$ is that it determines a phasor which originates at the origin and terminates at the specified point in the complex plane, as shown in Fig. 8–2-7. Specifying a phasor as $(-3 + j\,7)$ is the rectangular coordinate method of identification. The same phasor can be specified in polar form as a magnitude and an angle. The phasor $-3 + j\,7$ when expressed in polar form is

$$7.6\underline{/113.2°} \qquad\qquad (8\text{–}2\text{–}18)$$

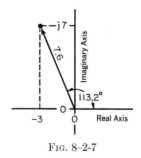

Fɪɢ. 8–2-7

Euler's relations

$$A\epsilon^{j\alpha} = A \cos \alpha + jA \sin \alpha = A\underline{/\alpha}$$
$$A\epsilon^{-j\alpha} = A \cos \alpha - jA \sin \alpha = A\underline{/-\alpha} \qquad (8\text{–}2\text{-}19)$$

give an alternative method for writing the polar form for a complex quantity in what is termed the exponential form.

Multiplication of two phasors follows directly from the rules of mathematics once the phasors are placed in the exponential form, as illustrated by the example

$$A\epsilon^{j\alpha} \cdot B\epsilon^{j\beta} = AB\epsilon^{j(\alpha+\beta)} \qquad (8\text{–}2\text{-}20)$$

In words, this relationship is that the product of two phasors is obtained by multiplying their magnitudes and adding their angles. Division is illustrated by the example

$$\frac{A\epsilon^{j\alpha}}{B\epsilon^{j\beta}} = \frac{A}{B}\epsilon^{+j(\alpha-\beta)} \qquad (8\text{–}2\text{-}21)$$

In words, this relationship is that two phasors are divided by dividing the magnitudes and subtracting the angle of the denominator from the angle of the numerator. Other relationships follow in a similar manner.

In the development from Eq. 8–2-1 through Eq. 8–2-14 the instantaneous current is taken as a sine wave:

$$i = I_M \sin \omega t \qquad (8\text{–}2\text{-}22)$$

This current can be represented by a phasor:

$$I_M\underline{/0°} \qquad (8\text{–}2\text{-}23)$$

The resulting voltage across the $R\text{-}L\text{-}C$ circuit, as

$$e = I_M Z \sin(\omega t + \theta) \qquad (8\text{–}2\text{-}24)$$

can be represented in phasor form by

$$I_M\underline{/0}Z_M\underline{/\theta} = E_M\underline{/\theta} \qquad (8\text{–}2\text{-}25)$$

Eq. 8–2-25 can be written $\qquad \mathbf{E}_M = \mathbf{I}_M\mathbf{Z} \qquad (8\text{–}2\text{-}26)$

where the use of boldface for a quantity indicates that it is a phasor, and includes both magnitude and angle. In other words, this entire development justifies the relationship that, if $\mathbf{I}_M$ and $\mathbf{Z}_M$ are expressed as phasors, when these two are multiplied in accordance with the rules of multiplication of complex quantities the resulting E_M is a phasor. All other operations such as division follow for the same reasons.

When the impedance is written Z/θ, this notation shows the impedance written in a form identical to the polar coordinate form, for example, that of quantity 8–2-18, and suggests that the impedance can also be written in a rectangular coordinate form. For example, the impedance of the circuit of Fig. 8–2-1 is

$$\sqrt{R^2 + (\omega L - 1/\omega C)^2} \Big/ \tan^{-1} \frac{\omega L - 1/\omega C}{R} \qquad (8\text{-}2\text{-}27)$$

If the impedance is written

$$R + j\left(\omega L - \frac{1}{\omega C}\right) \qquad (8\text{-}2\text{-}28)$$

an examination of the second form shows that it contains all of the information of 8–2-27 and hence is an alternative method of expressing the impedance.

The use of the mathematics of complex quantities eliminates the need for treating a circuit problem through a maze of trigonometric identities, for with the concept of the projection of the phasors producing the instantaneous value identically the same results are achieved.

Usually at this point in a-c circuit theory, the rms values (or effective value) of currents and voltages are defined. However, for the purposes for which a-c circuit theory is being developed in this book, rms quantities are not needed.

8–3. Steady-State Equations from the Laplace Transform. The e-R-L-C circuit of Fig. 8–2-1 is again used. Its differential equation is

$$e = Ri + L\frac{di}{dt} + \frac{1}{C} \int i \, dt \qquad (8\text{-}3\text{-}1)$$

In the previous development the current was written in the form

$$i = I_M \sin \omega t \qquad (8\text{-}3\text{-}2)$$

In the present development the phasor concept is used, and the current is written

$$I_M = I_M \epsilon^{j\omega t} \qquad (8\text{-}3\text{-}3)$$

When it is recalled that I_M is a rotating phasor and that the concept of phasors implies that the instantaneous current is the projection of a rotating phasor on a vertical line, it can be seen that Eq. 8–3-3 can be thought of as representing Eq. 8–3-2.

In the previous development the current was differentiated and integrated in order to substitute into the differential equation; thus

$$\frac{di}{dt} = I_M \omega \cos \omega t \qquad (8\text{-}3\text{-}4)$$

and

$$\int i \, dt = -\frac{I_M}{\omega} \cos \omega t \qquad (8\text{-}3\text{-}5)$$

It is reasonable to attempt to perform the same differentiation and integration of the instantaneous current, using the phasor concept:

$$\frac{d\boldsymbol{I}_M}{dt} = jI_M\omega\epsilon^{j\omega t} \tag{8-3-6}$$

and
$$\int \boldsymbol{I}_M \, dt = \frac{I_M}{j\omega} \epsilon^{j\omega t} = -j\frac{I_M}{\omega} \epsilon^{j\omega t} \tag{8-3-7}$$

When these results are compared with the results of Eqs. 8–3-4 and 8–3-5, it is to be seen that they are the same. Eq. 8–3-6 is detailed to show this. The projection of $\epsilon^{j\omega t}$ on a vertical line corresponds to a sine curve and, when $\epsilon^{j\omega t}$ is multiplied by j, this advances the phasor by 90 degrees. Since through the use of trigonometric identities it is known that a sine curve advanced by 90 degrees becomes a cosine curve, Eq. 8–3-6 is an alternative method for representing Eq. 8–3-4. A similar comparison can be made between Eqs. 8–3-7 and 8–3-5.

When the results of using the phasor notation are substituted in the differential equation, it becomes

$$\boldsymbol{E}_M = RI_M\epsilon^{j\omega t} + j\omega LI_M\epsilon^{j\omega t} - j\frac{1}{\omega C} I_M\epsilon^{j\omega t} \tag{8-3-8}$$

and can be written
$$\boldsymbol{E}_M = \left[R + j\left(\omega L - \frac{1}{\omega C}\right)\right]I_M\epsilon^{j\omega t} \tag{8-3-9}$$

or as
$$\boldsymbol{E}_M = \boldsymbol{Z}\boldsymbol{I}_M \tag{8-3-10}$$

Thus use of the phasor concept leads to the same results as obtained before.

Laplace transform methods can also be used to obtain the a-c steady-state solution. Since steady-state a-c circuit theory is independent of initial conditions, the Laplace transform of the differential equation is taken for quiescent initial conditions. As an example, the differential equation 8–3-1 is again used; its transform is

$$\mathcal{L}(e) = \left[R + sL + \frac{1}{sC} \right]\mathcal{L}(i) \tag{8-3-11}$$

Comparison of Eqs. 8–3-9 and 8–3-11 shows that, if

$$s = j\omega \tag{8-3-12}$$

is substituted in Eq. 8–3-11, the result

$$\boldsymbol{E}_M(j\omega) = \left[R + j\left(\omega L - \frac{1}{\omega C}\right)\right]\boldsymbol{I}_M(j\omega) \tag{8-3-13}$$

is the same as Eq. 8–3-9. Therefore, to go from the Laplace transform of a differential equation where all initial conditions are quiescent to the phasor notation, the quantity s is replaced by $j\omega$ and the Laplace transform of the quantity $\mathcal{L}[f(t)] = F(s)$ is replaced by a phasor $\boldsymbol{F}(j\omega)$.

That the substitution $s = j\omega$ can always be made can be seen by a comparison of the phasor method and the Laplace transform method. If a phasor is differentiated, a $j\omega$ appears in front of the original quantity. The Laplace transform of the derivative of a quantity always has an s

before the Laplace transform of that quantity. If the phasor ·is differentiated twice, $(j\omega)^2$ appears in front; similarly, the Laplace transform has an s^2 factor. For integration, the phasor has a factor $1/j\omega$ in front of the original quantity, and the Laplace transform has the factor $1/s$. As this line of reasoning can be extended to a derivative or integral of any order, the correspondence of $j\omega$ and s is complete.

Even though the only example used thus far is the circuit of Fig. 8–2-1, this method of going from the Laplace transform to the steady-state sinusoidal solution can be used for any linear electric circuit and mechanical or electromechanical system. Examples of these systems are taken up in this and later chapters.

8–4. Transients with an Alternating-Current Source. The preceding articles present a summary of certain basic aspects of a-c theory. The methods developed can be used to find the steady-state component of the total solution when a circuit is connected to an a-c source at $t = 0$. For, when a circuit is connected to an a-c source, the total solution can be expressed as the sum of two components, the steady-state component and the transient component:

$$i = i_{ss} + i_{tr} \tag{8-4-1}$$

In form, Eq. 8–4-1 is exactly the same as that used in the earlier chapters. The only difference is that with an a-c source the steady-state component is found by a-c circuit methods. The transient component is found in identically the same manner as before.

When a circuit is connected to an a-c source, not only the magnitude and frequency of the source but also the instant in the cycle at which the circuit is energized have to be considered. For example, if the source is a voltage source of frequency f, the following equation can be written:

$$e = E_M \sin (\omega t + \delta) \tag{8-4-2}$$

Here E_M is the maximum value of the alternating voltage, ω is $2\pi f$, and δ is the phase angle of value depending on the instant in the cycle at which the circuit is energized.

8–5. The R circuit. When the switch is closed in Fig. 8–5-1, the equation is

$$iR = E_M \sin (\omega t + \delta) \tag{8-5-1}$$

or

$$i = \frac{E_M}{R} \sin (\omega t + \delta) \tag{8-5-2}$$

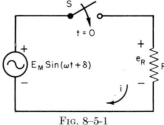

Fig. 8–5-1

In this case the current reaches its steady-state value instantly and the transient term is zero. This is shown in Fig. 8–5-2. The dotted lines before

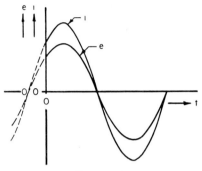

Fig. 8–5-2

the $t = 0$ are a guide showing what the steady-state values in the a-c circuit sense would be if they existed before $t = 0$.

8–6. The L Circuit. When the switch is closed in the circuit of Fig. 8–6-1

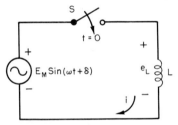

Fig. 8–6-1

on the inductor which has no energy stored in it at $t = 0$, the equation is

$$E_M \sin (\omega t + \delta) = L \frac{di}{dt} \qquad (8\text{-}6\text{-}1)$$

As the inductor prevents the current from jumping, the current at $t = 0+$ is zero. Solution of Eq. 8–6-1 by separation of parts gives

$$i = \frac{E_M}{L} \int_0^t \sin (\omega t + \delta) \, dt = -\frac{E_M}{\omega L} \cos (\omega t + \delta) \Big|_0^t \qquad (8\text{-}6\text{-}2)$$

$$i = \frac{E}{Z_L} \sin (\omega t + \delta - 90°) - \frac{E_M}{Z_L} \sin (\delta - 90°) \qquad (8\text{-}6\text{-}3)$$

where the magnitude of the impedance ωL is written Z_L. Eq. 8–6-1 can also be solved by the differential equation method relying on a-c circuit theory to provide the steady-state component. In this approach the solution comprises a steady-state component and a transient component:

$$i = i_{ss} + i_{tr} \qquad (8\text{-}6\text{-}4)$$

The differential equation for the circuit of Fig. 8–6-1 is

$$e = L\frac{di}{dt} \qquad (8\text{–}6\text{-}5)$$

The Laplace transform of this equation is

$$\mathcal{L}(e) = sL\mathcal{L}(i) \qquad (8\text{–}6\text{-}6)$$

and, with the substitution $s = j\omega$, the phasor equation is

$$\boldsymbol{E}_M = j\omega L \boldsymbol{I}_M \qquad (8\text{–}6\text{-}7)$$

This equation can be solved for $\boldsymbol{I}_M$:

$$\boldsymbol{I}_M = \frac{\boldsymbol{E}_M}{j\omega L} \qquad (8\text{–}6\text{-}8)$$

Interpretation of Eq. 8–6-8 in terms of instantaneous quantities is that the magnitude of $\boldsymbol{I}_M$ is equal to the magnitude of $\boldsymbol{E}_M$ divided by $Z_L = \omega L$, and that the current lags the voltage by 90 degrees. The instantaneous equation stating these same relationships is

$$i_{ss} = \frac{E_M}{Z_L}\sin(\omega t + \delta - 90°) \qquad (8\text{–}6\text{-}9)$$

If Eq. 8–6-9 is substituted in the differential equation 8–6-1, it satisfies the equation because this is the basis upon which a-c circuit theory is based, as shown in Art. 8–2. Therefore, if $i_{ss} + i_{tr}$ is substituted for i in Eq. 8–6-1, the result is

$$E_M \sin(\omega t + \delta) = L\frac{di_{ss}}{dt} + L\frac{di_{tr}}{dt} \qquad (8\text{–}6\text{-}10)$$

and, on the basis of the preceding discussion,

$$L\frac{di_{ss}}{dt} = E_M \sin(\omega t + \delta) \qquad (8\text{–}6\text{-}11)$$

it must be that

$$L\frac{di_{tr}}{dt} = 0 \qquad (8\text{–}6\text{-}12)$$

For di_{tr}/dt to equal zero, i_{tr} must be a constant. Therefore

$$i_{tr} = A \qquad (8\text{–}6\text{-}13)$$

and the total current i is

$$i = \frac{E_M}{Z_L}\sin(\omega t + \delta - 90°) + A \qquad (8\text{–}6\text{-}14)$$

Imposing the condition that $i(0) = 0$ on this equation gives for A

$$0 = \frac{E_M}{Z_L}\sin(\delta - 90°) + A \quad \text{or} \quad A = -\frac{E_M}{Z_L}\sin(\delta - 90°) \qquad (8\text{–}6\text{-}15)$$

When this value for A is substituted in Eq. 8–6-14, the result is

$$i = \frac{E_M}{Z_L}\sin(\omega t + \delta - 90°) - \frac{E_M}{Z_L}\sin(\delta - 90°) \qquad (8\text{–}6\text{-}16)$$

Comparison of Eqs. 8–6-16 and 8–6-3 shows them to be the same. One benefit that comes from presenting the differential equation solution is that it aids in visualization of the manner in which the circuit responds. When $i(0) = 0$, the $i_{tr} = -i_{ss}$ at $t = 0$. This can be seen by setting i equal to zero in the equation $i = i_{ss} + i_{tr}$. The curves of Fig. 8–6-2 show this relationship for several values of δ. In Fig. 8–6-2a the value of δ is approximately 150°, and i_{ss} is a broken line as a guide. At $t = 0$, i_{ss} has a positive value, so i_{tr} must be equal to this in magnitude but have the opposite sign. The current component i_{tr} is sketched; and i, which is the sum of i_{ss} and i_{tr}, is indicated by a heavy line. Fig. 8–6-2b is similar to Fig. 8–6-2a except that $\delta = 0$. At $t = 0$ this means that i_{ss} is of maximum negative value. When i_{tr} is found and added to i_{ss}, the result is that all the i curve is above the axis. It is to be noted that i reaches a value twice the maximum value

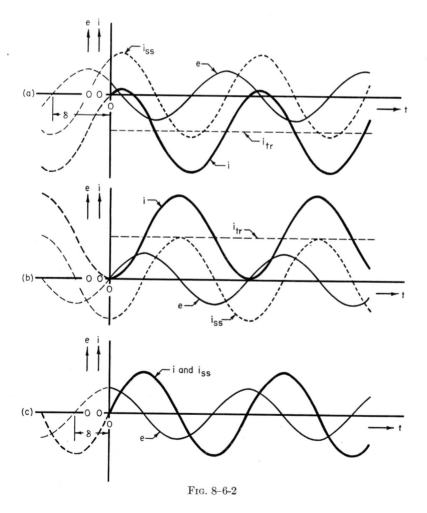

Fig. 8–6-2

of i_{ss}. If the switch S were closed when $\delta = 180°$, all the i curve would be below the axis. In Fig. 8–6-2c the value of δ is $90°$. At $t = 0$ this means that i_{ss} equals zero; therefore i_{tr} is also equal to zero. In this case i_{ss} satisfies not only the differential equation but also the initial condition. If the switch is closed so that $\delta = 270°$, again the transient component is zero.

Fig. 8–6-3 shows a circuit similar to that of Fig. 8–6-1 except that a switching operation previous to $t = 0$ causes the inductor to have energy

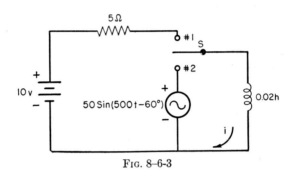

Fig. 8–6-3

stored in it at $t = 0$. In this figure it is assumed that S is thrown to position 1 until steady-state conditions are reached; then, at $t = 0$, S is thrown to position 2. The inductor maintains the current at $t = 0$; therefore the initial current is $i(0) = 10/5 = 2.0$. The solution for the steady-state component of the current is

$$i_{ss} = \tfrac{50}{10} \sin (500\, t - 60° - 90°) \qquad (8\text{–}6\text{-}17)$$

or

$$i_{ss} = 5 \sin (500\, t - 150°) \qquad (8\text{–}6\text{-}18)$$

The total current i is, then,

$$i = 5 \sin (500\, t - 150°) + A \qquad (8\text{–}6\text{-}19)$$

The constant A can be found by imposing the condition $i(0) = 2.0$ on Eq. 8–6-19:

$$2 = 5 \sin (-150°) + A$$

whence $\qquad\qquad\qquad\qquad\qquad\qquad\qquad\qquad (8\text{–}6\text{-}20)$

$$A = 2 + 5 \sin 30° = 2 + 2.5 = 4.5$$

and the final solution is

$$i = 5 \sin (500\, t - 150°) + 4.5 \qquad (8\text{–}6\text{-}21)$$

Fig. 8–6-4 is a sketch of the various quantities for this example.

Let it be supposed that δ is no longer assigned a specific value, such as the $(-60°)$ in the previous example, and that the desired solution is the value of δ such that zero transient component of current is required in the circuit of Fig. 8–6-3. For there to be zero transient component, i_{ss} at $t = 0$ must

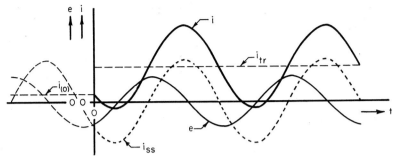

FIG. 8–6–4

have a value equal to $i(0)$. In this example this means that the following equation must be satisfied:

$$2 = 5 \sin (\delta - 90°); \quad \text{thus } \sin (\delta - 90°) = 0.4 \qquad (8\text{-}6\text{-}22)$$

This equation is satisfied by two values of δ:

$$\delta_1 = 23.6° + 90° = 113.6° \qquad \delta_2 = 156.4° + 90° = 246.4° \quad (8\text{-}6\text{-}23)$$

If $i(0)$ is larger in magnitude than I_M, there is no instant in the cycle where the switch can be closed without a transient component of the current being required.

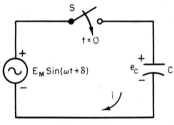

FIG. 8–7–1

8–7. The C Circuit. Fig. 8–7–1 shows a capacitor connected to an a-c source. In the first portion of this discussion it is assumed that no energy is stored on the capacitor before $t = 0$. The voltage equation is

$$E_M \sin (\omega t + \delta) = \frac{q}{C} \qquad (8\text{-}7\text{-}1)$$

The current in the capacitor is

$$i = C \frac{de}{dt} \qquad (8\text{-}7\text{-}2)$$

If the switch is closed at any instant in the cycle other than the instant at which the applied voltage e is equal to zero, the voltage on the capacitor e_c, which is zero before $t = 0$, must jump from zero to the value $E_M \sin \delta$, which is the magnitude of the applied voltage at $t = 0$. As explained in Chapter 1, de/dt is then infinite, and an impulse of current exists at $t = 0$ of sufficient value to charge the capacitor to the proper voltage, given by the equation

$$\frac{q}{C} = E_M \sin \delta \qquad (8\text{--}7\text{--}3)$$

Therefore the current contains an impulse at $t = 0$ and after that assumes

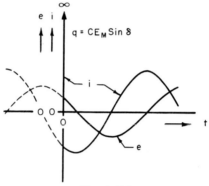

Fig. 8-7-2

the sinusoidal steady-state value which can be obtained by using Eq. 8–7-2. This gives the steady-state component as

$$i_{ss} = \omega C E_M \cos (\omega t + \delta) \qquad (8\text{--}7\text{--}4)$$

This equation can be written

$$i_{ss} = \frac{E_M}{1/\omega C} \sin (\omega t + \delta + 90°) = \frac{E_M}{Z_c} \sin (\omega t + \delta + 90°) \qquad (8\text{--}7\text{--}5)$$

A sketch of the solution is shown in Fig. 8–7-2. Eq. 8–7-5 shows that the steady-state current leads the voltage by 90 degrees, and that the magnitude of the impedance is $Z_c = 1/\omega C$. In order for the switch to be closed so that no impulse of current occurs at $t = 0$, the applied voltage e must

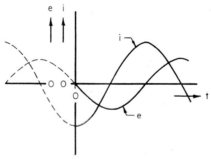

Fig. 8-7-3

be equal to zero at $t = 0$ for the case when the capacitor is initially discharged. Here, then, δ must be either $0°$ or $180°$. Fig. 8-7-3 demonstrates the situation when $\delta = 180°$.

If the capacitor has an initial charge before $t = 0$, then, in order for the switch to be closed so that no impulse of current occurs at $t = 0$, the applied voltage e at $t = 0$ must equal the voltage $e(0)$ already on the capacitor before $t = 0$. This statement is expressed by the equation

$$E_M \sin \delta = e(0) \tag{8-7-6}$$

The circuit of Fig. 8-7-4 provides an example of the type of problem where δ is the variable and it is desired to find δ so that no impulse of current occurs at $t = 0$. Using Eq. 8-7-6 for this example gives

$$50 \sin \delta = 35 \tag{8-7-7}$$

Two values of δ satisfy Eq. 8-7-7:

$$\delta_1 = 44.5° \quad \text{and} \quad \delta_2 = 135.5° \tag{8-7-8}$$

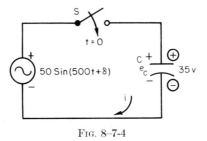

Fɪɢ. 8-7-4

Fig. 8-7-5a illustrates the circuit behavior for $\delta = \delta_1$, and Fig. 8-7-5b that for $\delta = \delta_2$.

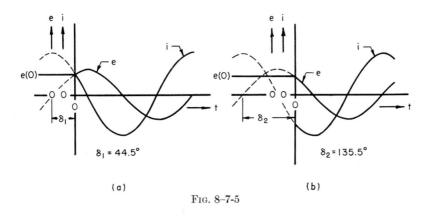

Fɪɢ. 8-7-5

8-8. The R-L Circuit. The work of Art. 8-6 for the L circuit is actually for a hypothetical case, because an inductor cannot be made without some resistance. The R-L circuit of Fig. 8-8-1 more nearly approaches an actual circuit. In the first example it is assumed that $i(0) = 0$. The equation

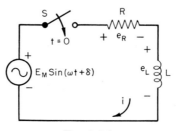

Fig. 8-8-1

for the circuit is

$$E_M \sin (\omega t + \delta) = Ri + L \frac{di}{dt} \qquad (8\text{-}8\text{-}1)$$

Again the current is comprised of two components:

$$i = i_{ss} + i_{tr}$$

The steady-state component is found by starting with the equation

$$e = Ri + L \frac{di}{dt} \qquad (8\text{-}8\text{-}2)$$

and taking the Laplace of this equation:

$$\mathcal{L}(e) = [R + Ls]\mathcal{L}(i) \qquad (8\text{-}8\text{-}3)$$

The phasor equation is obtained from this equation by again letting $s = j\omega$:

$$\mathbf{E}_M = [R + j\omega L]\mathbf{I}_M \qquad (8\text{-}8\text{-}4)$$

which can be written

$$\mathbf{I}_M = \frac{\mathbf{E}_M}{\mathbf{Z}(j\omega)} \qquad (8\text{-}8\text{-}5)$$

where

$$\mathbf{Z}(j\omega) = R + j\omega L = Z\underline{/\theta} \qquad (8\text{-}8\text{-}6)$$

The magnitude of Z is

$$Z = \sqrt{R^2 + (\omega L)^2} \qquad (8\text{-}8\text{-}7)$$

and the angle θ is

$$\theta = \tan^{-1} \frac{\omega L}{R} \qquad (8\text{-}8\text{-}8)$$

Therefore the steady-state current is

$$i_{ss} = \frac{E_M}{Z} \sin (\omega t + \delta - \theta) \qquad (8\text{-}8\text{-}9)$$

Again the steady-state component of the current satisfies the differential equation 8-8-1 because the steady-state component was so derived in

Art. 8–2. However, in general, i_{ss} cannot satisfy the initial condition, which in this example is $i(0) = 0$. Substitution of $i_{ss} + i_{tr}$ for i in Eq. 8–8–1 gives

$$E_M \sin (\omega t + \delta) = R i_{ss} + L \frac{di_{ss}}{dt} + R i_{tr} + L \frac{di_{tr}}{dt} \qquad (8\text{–}8\text{-}10)$$

Since the steady-state component itself satisfies Eq. 8–8–1,

$$E_M \sin (\omega t + \delta) = R i_{ss} + L \frac{di_{ss}}{dt} \qquad (8\text{–}8\text{-}11)$$

and therefore

$$R i_{tr} + L \frac{di_{tr}}{dt} = 0 \qquad (8\text{–}8\text{-}12)$$

Equations identical with Eq. 8–8–12 have been solved previously. The solution of this equation is of the form

$$i_{tr} = A \epsilon^{-Rt/L} \qquad (8\text{–}8\text{-}13)$$

The total current is

$$i = \frac{E}{Z} \sin (\omega t + \delta - \theta) + A \epsilon^{-Rt/L} \qquad (8\text{–}8\text{-}14)$$

The constant A can be evaluated by imposing the condition $i(0) = 0$:

$$0 = \frac{E}{Z} \sin (\omega t + \delta - \theta) - \frac{E}{Z} \sin (\delta - \theta) \epsilon^{-Rt/L} \qquad (8\text{–}8\text{-}15)$$

Physical interpretation of the solution is similar to that for the L circuit, except that here the transient component decays because of the $\epsilon^{-Rt/L}$ factor. Initially i_{tr} is of the same magnitude, but of opposite sign to that of i_{ss} at $t = 0$. Fig. 8–8–2 shows a circuit where $\theta = 70°$ and $\delta = 150°$. The

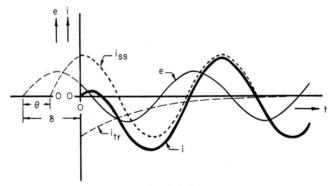

Fig. 8–8–2

current components i_{ss} and i_{tr} are shown as broken lines as a guide; the total current i is shown by the heavy line.

For the switch S to be so closed that the transient component is zero, the switch must be closed when i_{ss} is zero at $t = 0$. This, of course, is true only when $i(0) = 0$, as in this example. This occurs when

$$\sin (\delta - \theta) = 0 \qquad (8\text{-}8\text{-}16)$$

or when $$\delta_1 = \theta \quad \text{or} \quad \delta_2 = \theta + 180° \qquad (8\text{-}8\text{-}17)$$

If S is closed when i_{ss} is a maximum, $i_{tr}(0)$ is a maximum and i has a maximum value somewhat less than twice the maximum value of i_{ss} by an amount determined by the decay factor $\epsilon^{-Rt/L}$.

Fig. 8-8-3 shows a circuit similar to that just discussed, except that S is thrown to position 1 until the steady state is reached; then at $t = 0$ it is

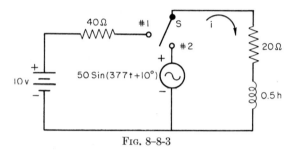

FIG. 8-8-3

thrown to position 2. This means that the inductor has an initial current of

$$i(0) = \tfrac{10}{60} = 0.166 \qquad (8\text{-}8\text{-}18)$$

After $t = 0$ the following quantities can be found:

$$Z(j\omega) = 20 + j\, 377 \times 0.5 = 190\underline{/84°} \qquad (8\text{-}8\text{-}19)$$

and $\quad i_{ss} = \dfrac{50}{190} \sin (377\, t + 10° - 84°) = 0.263 \sin (377\, t - 74°) \qquad (8\text{-}8\text{-}20)$

and $\qquad i = i_{ss} + i_{tr} = 0.263 \sin (377\, t - 74°) + A\epsilon^{-20t/0.5} \qquad (8\text{-}8\text{-}21)$

The constant A can be found by imposing the conditions at $t = 0$ on this equation:
$$0.166 = 0.263 \sin (- 74°) + A \qquad (8\text{-}8\text{-}22)$$

which gives for A $\qquad A = 0.166 + 0.252 = 0.418$

When this value for A is substituted in Eq. 8-8-21, the final solution is

$$i = 0.263 \sin (377\, t - 74°) + 0.418\, \epsilon^{-40t} \qquad (8\text{-}8\text{-}23)$$

Let it be supposed that δ is the variable and that it is desired to find the values of δ such that the transient component is zero. This means that δ must be of such a value that the i_{ss} term at $t = 0$ equals $i(0)$. In this example

$$0.166 = 0.263 \sin (\delta - 84°) \qquad (8\text{-}8\text{-}24)$$

or $$\sin (\delta - 84°) = \frac{0.166}{0.263} = 0.63 \qquad (8\text{-}8\text{-}25)$$

This equation is satisfied by two values of δ:

$$\delta_1 = 39° + 84° = 123° \quad \text{or} \quad \delta_2 = 141° + 84° = 225° \qquad (8\text{-}8\text{-}26)$$

Again, as in the example of the L circuit, if $i(0)$ is larger than the maximum value of i_{ss}, there is no instant in the cycle where S can be closed without a transient component being required.

8–9. The R-C Circuit. The R-C circuit to be analyzed is shown in

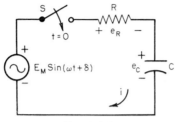

FIG. 8–9-1

Fig. 8–9-1. In the first example it is assumed that $e(0)$ is zero. The voltage equation is

$$E_M \sin (\omega t + \delta) = Ri + \frac{1}{C} \int_0^t i \, dt \tag{8–9-1}$$

The current before $t = 0$ is equal to zero, but, since this is an R-C circuit, the current can jump to a new value at $t = 0$. The value of $i(0)$ can be determined by imposing the conditions at $t = 0$ on Eq. 8–9-1:

$$i(0) = \frac{E_M}{R} \sin \delta \tag{8–9-2}$$

The steady-state component is found by starting with the equation

$$e = Ri + \frac{1}{C} \int_0^t i \, dt \tag{8–9-3}$$

and taking the Laplace of this equation:

$$\mathcal{L}(e) = \left[R + \frac{1}{sC} \right] \mathcal{L}(i) \tag{8–9-4}$$

The phasor equation obtained from this equation by letting $s = j\omega$ is

$$E_M = \left[R - j \frac{1}{\omega C} \right] I_M \tag{8–9-5}$$

which can be written $\quad I_M = \dfrac{E_M}{Z(j\omega)} \tag{8–9-6}$

where $\quad Z(j\omega) = R - j \dfrac{1}{\omega C} = Z \underline{/\theta} \tag{8–9-7}$

The magnitude of Z is $\quad Z = \sqrt{R^2 + \left(\dfrac{1}{\omega C} \right)^2} \tag{8–9-8}$

and the angle θ is $\quad \theta = \tan^{-1} \left(-\dfrac{1/\omega C}{R} \right) \tag{8–9-9}$

The steady-state component of the current is

$$i_{ss} = \frac{E_M}{Z} \sin (\omega t + \delta - \theta) \qquad (8\text{-}9\text{-}10)$$

It is to be noted that θ is a negative angle.

As with the R-L circuit, the i_{ss} satisfies the circuit equation but will not in general satisfy the initial condition. If $i_{ss} + i_{tr}$ is substituted for i, in Eq. 8-9-1 the i_{ss} term gives a voltage term on the right side that exactly cancels the voltage term on the left side, leaving

$$Ri_{tr} + \frac{1}{C} \int i_{tr} \, dt = 0 \qquad (8\text{-}9\text{-}11)$$

This equation has been solved before, and the solution is

$$i_{tr} = A \epsilon^{-t/RC} \qquad (8\text{-}9\text{-}12)$$

It is to be noted that the limits of integration are omitted in these steps because the steady-state solution of a problem of this sort is independent of the initial conditions. The final solution satisfies the proper initial conditions due to the manner in which the constant A is determined. Another way of stating this is to say that Eq. 8-9-1 needs to be differentiated to obtain the differential equation, and it is this equation that is satisfied by i_{ss}. Actually the process of differentiation removes the initial conditions from these steps. Therefore either procedure leads to the same results.

The total current is of the form

$$i = \frac{E_M}{Z} \sin (\omega t + \delta - \theta) + A \epsilon^{-t/RC} \qquad (8\text{-}9\text{-}13)$$

where A can be obtained by imposing the initial condition on the equation:

$$\frac{E_M}{R} \sin \delta = \frac{E_M}{Z} \sin (\delta - \theta) + A \qquad (8\text{-}9\text{-}14)$$

The constant A can be obtained from Eq. 8-9-14, and the final solution is

$$i = \frac{E_M}{Z} \sin (\omega t + \delta - \theta) + \left[\frac{E_M}{R} \sin \delta - \frac{E_M}{Z} \sin (\delta - \theta) \right] \epsilon^{-t/RC} \qquad (8\text{-}9\text{-}15)$$

If this circuit is solved in terms of charge, a better physical interpretation is obtained of the conditions that produce the transient term. With a resistor in series with the capacitor, the charge on the capacitor cannot jump from one value to another without an impulse of voltage occurring across the R-C combination. If no charge is on the capacitor before S is closed, the $q(0) = 0$. The total charge is comprised of two terms:

$$q = q_{ss} + q_{tr} \qquad (8\text{-}9\text{-}16)$$

The q_{ss} term can be obtained by integrating i_{ss}. Again, because the steady-state value of charge is being found, the constant of integration is ignored.

$$q_{ss} = \int \frac{E_M}{Z} \sin (\omega t + \delta - \theta) \, dt = \frac{E_M}{Z\omega} \sin (\omega t + \delta - \theta - 90°) \qquad (8\text{-}9\text{-}17)$$

The q_{tr} component has a form similar to i_{tr} of Eq. 8–9-12, and the total charge then becomes

$$q = \frac{E_M}{Z\omega} \sin (\omega t + \delta - \theta - 90°) + A \epsilon^{-t/RC} \qquad (8\text{–}9\text{-}18)$$

The constant A can be found from the fact that $q(0) = 0$; thus

$$0 = \frac{E_M}{Z\omega} \sin (\delta - \theta - 90°) + A \quad \text{or} \quad A = -\frac{E_M}{Z\omega} \sin (\delta - \theta - 90°) \qquad (8\text{–}9\text{-}19)$$

On substitution for A the charge is found:

$$q = \frac{E_M}{Z\omega} \sin (\omega t + \delta - \theta - 90°) - \frac{E_M}{Z\omega} \sin (\delta - \theta - 90°) \, \epsilon^{-t/RC} \qquad (8\text{–}9\text{-}20)$$

Differentiation of this equation for charge yields, for i,

$$i = \frac{dq}{dt} = \frac{E_M}{Z} \sin (\omega t + \delta - \theta) + \frac{E_M}{Z\omega RC} \sin (\delta - \theta - 90°) \, \epsilon^{-t/RC} \qquad (8\text{–}9\text{-}21)$$

It can be shown that the factors multiplying the $\epsilon^{-t/RC}$ term in Eq. 8–9-15 and Eq. 8–9-21 are equal.

A study of charge on the capacitor in an R-C circuit gives an excellent interpretation of how the steady-state and transient components add together to form total solution. If $q(0)$ is zero, the equation

$$q = q_{ss} + q_{tr} \qquad (8\text{–}9\text{-}22)$$

is evaluated at $t = 0$:

$$q_{tr}(0) = - \, q_{ss}(0) \qquad (8\text{–}9\text{-}23)$$

A sketch of the various quantities for one value of δ is shown in Fig. 8–9-2. The curves of this sketch illustrate the situation where S is closed

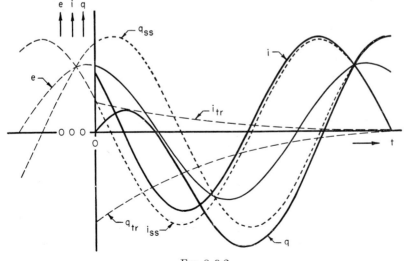

Fig. 8–9-2

with $\delta = 100°$. The current i_{ss} is shown leading e by the angle of the impedance. The component of charge q_{ss} lags i_{ss} by 90 degrees; and, at $t = 0$, $q_{tr}(0) = -q_{ss}(0)$. The current is the derivative of charge.

To find the value of δ so that S can be closed with zero transient term, q_{ss} at $t = 0$ must equal $q(0)$. In this example where $q(0) = 0$, q_{ss} at $t = 0$ must equal zero. This leads to two values of δ:

$$\delta_1 = \theta + 90° \quad \text{or} \quad \delta_2 = \theta + 270° \qquad (8\text{-}9\text{-}24)$$

The circuit of Fig. 8-9-3 is an example similar to the preceding development except that the capacitor has an initial charge. The switch S is

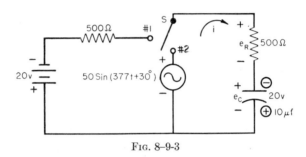

Fig. 8-9-3

thrown to position 1 until steady-state conditions are reached; then, at $t = 0$, S is thrown to position 2. The result of this switching operation is that the capacitor has a charge on it at $t = 0$ that produces 20 volts with the polarity shown on Fig. 8-9-3. The initial charge does not affect the impedance, which is given by Eq. 8-9-8.

$$Z = \sqrt{R^2 + (1/\omega C)^2} = 565 \qquad (8\text{-}9\text{-}25)$$

$$\theta = \tan^{-1}\left(-\frac{1/\omega C}{R}\right) = -28° \qquad (8\text{-}9\text{-}26)$$

The steady-state current is

$$i_{ss} = \tfrac{50}{565}\sin(377\,t + 30° + 28°) = 0.0882\sin(377\,t + 58°) \quad (8\text{-}9\text{-}27)$$

and the steady-state charge is

$$q_{ss} = \frac{0.0882}{377}\sin(377\,t + 58° - 90°) = 0.000233\sin(377\,t - 32°) \quad (8\text{-}9\text{-}28)$$

The transient component of charge has the form

$$q_{tr} = A\epsilon^{-t/RC} = A\epsilon^{-200t} \qquad (8\text{-}9\text{-}29)$$

The equation for the total charge is of the form

$$q = 0.000233\sin(377\,t - 32°) + A\epsilon^{-200t} \qquad (8\text{-}9\text{-}30)$$

The constant A can be found from knowing that $e(0) = -20$ volts; therefore $q(0) = e(0)C = -20 \times 10 \times 10^{-6} = -0.0002 \qquad (8\text{-}9\text{-}31)$

which gives, for A,

$$-0.0002 = 0.000233 \sin(-32°) + A \quad \text{or} \quad A = -0.000077 \quad (8\text{-}9\text{-}32)$$

The final equation for charge is

$$q = 0.000233 \sin(377\,t - 32°) - 0.000077\,\epsilon^{-200t} \quad (8\text{-}9\text{-}33)$$

The current is

$$i = \frac{dq}{dt} = 0.0882 \sin(377\,t + 58°) + 0.0154\,\epsilon^{-200t} \quad (8\text{-}9\text{-}34)$$

Let it be supposed that δ is the variable and that it is desired to find the values of δ such that the transient component is zero. δ must have a value such that the q_{ss} term at $t = 0$ must be equal to $q(0)$. If the preceding example is used, except that δ is now a variable, δ can be found from

$$q_{ss}(0) = 0.000233 \sin(\delta + 28° - 90°) = -0.0002 \quad (8\text{-}9\text{-}35)$$

or

$$\sin(\delta - 62°) = -\frac{0.0002}{0.000233} = -0.86 \quad (8\text{-}9\text{-}36)$$

This equation is satisfied by two values of δ:

$$\delta_1 = -59.3° + 62° = 2.7° \quad \text{or} \quad \delta_2 = -120.7° + 62° = -58.7° \quad (8\text{-}9\text{-}37)$$

If the value of $q(0)$ on the capacitor is larger than the maximum value of q_{ss}, there is no value of δ for which S can be closed without a transient component.

8-10. The R-L-C Circuit. The R-L-C circuit to be analyzed is shown in

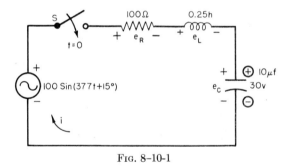

FIG. 8-10-1

Fig. 8-10-1. The voltage equation for this circuit is

$$100 \sin(377\,t + 15°) = 100\,i + 0.25\frac{di}{dt} + \frac{\int_0^t i\,dt}{10 \times 10^{-6}} + 30 \quad (8\text{-}10\text{-}1)$$

The impedance for this circuit is found, in Eqs. 8-2-9 and 8-2-10, to be

$$Z = \sqrt{R^2 + (\omega L - 1/\omega C)^2} = 198 \quad (8\text{-}10\text{-}2)$$

$$\theta = \tan^{-1}\frac{\omega L - 1/\omega C}{R} = -59.6° \quad (8\text{-}10\text{-}3)$$

The steady-state component of the current is

$$i_{ss} = \tfrac{100}{198} \sin (377\,t + 15° + 59.6°) = 0.505 \sin (377\,t + 74.6°) \qquad (8\text{–}10\text{–}4)$$

As explained above, if Eq. 8–10-1 is differentiated, i_{ss} satisfies the resulting equation. If $i_{ss} + i_{tr}$ is substituted in the derivative of Eq. 8–10-1, the following results:

$$0.25 \frac{d^2 i_{tr}}{dt^2} + 100 \frac{d i_{tr}}{dt} + \frac{i_{tr}}{10 \times 10^{-6}} = 0 \qquad (8\text{–}10\text{–}5)$$

Accordingly, the characteristic polynomial is

$$0.25\,s^2 + 100\,s + \frac{1}{10 \times 10^{-6}} \qquad (8\text{–}10\text{–}6)$$

which has the zeros s_1 and $s_2 = -\,200 \pm j\,600$ $\qquad (8\text{–}10\text{–}7)$

The current has the form

$$i = 0.505 \sin (377\,t + 74.6°) + \epsilon^{-200t}[A \cos 600\,t + B \sin 600\,t] \qquad (8\text{–}10\text{–}8)$$

Two initial conditions are needed to determine A and B. It is known that $i(0) = 0$ and $(di/dt)(0)$ can be found by imposing the conditions at $t = 0$ in Eq. 8–10-1:

$$100 \sin (15°) = 0.25 \frac{di}{dt}(0) + 30$$

or $$\frac{di}{dt}(0) = \frac{25.85 - 30}{0.25} = -\,16.6 \qquad (8\text{–}10\text{–}9)$$

When $i(0) = 0$ is imposed on Eq. 8–10-8, the value of A is found:

$$0 = 0.505 \sin (74.6°) + A \quad \text{or} \quad A = -\,0.486 \qquad (8\text{–}10\text{–}10)$$

Substitution of A in Eq. 8–10-8 yields

$$i = 0.505 \sin (377\,t + 74.6°) + \epsilon^{-200t}[-\,0.486 \cos 600\,t + B \sin 600\,t] \qquad (8\text{–}10\text{–}11)$$

which is differentiated to evaluate B:

$$\frac{di}{dt} = 0.505 \times 377 \cos (377\,t + 74.6°)$$
$$+ \epsilon^{-200t}[+\,0.486(600) \sin 600\,t + B\,600 \cos 600\,t]$$
$$+ [-\,0.486 \cos 600\,t + B \sin 600\,t](-\,200)\,\epsilon^{-200t} \qquad (8\text{–}10\text{–}12)$$

When the conditions at $t = 0$ are imposed on this equation, B is obtained from

$$-\,16.6 = 0.505 \times 377 \cos 74.6° + 600\,B + (-\,200)(-\,0.486)$$
$$B = \frac{-\,16.6 - 50.5 - 97.2}{600} = -\,0.274 \qquad (8\text{–}10\text{–}13)$$

The final solution is

$$i = 0.505 \sin (377\,t + 74.6°) + \epsilon^{-200t}[-\,0.486 \cos 600\,t - 0.274 \sin 600\,t] \qquad (8\text{–}10\text{–}14)$$

This can also be written

$$i = 0.505 \sin (377\,t + 74.6°) + 0.558\,\epsilon^{-200t} \sin (600\,t - 119.4°) \qquad (8\text{–}10\text{–}15)$$

Sketches of the various components of the solution are shown in Fig. 8–10-2.

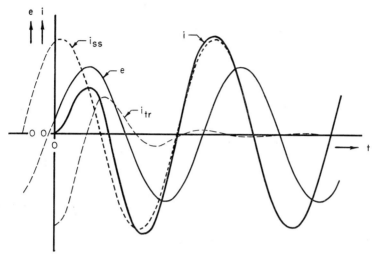

FIG. 8–10-2

The example just considered had values of R, L, and C such that the response of the circuit was oscillatory with frequency:

$$f = \frac{600}{2\,\pi}\ \text{cps} \qquad\qquad (8\text{–}10\text{-}16)$$

No matter what type of input excites this circuit, the response has the same natural frequency, which appears in the transient term. The $f = 60$ cps term of the solution is the steady-state term, and this frequency is determined entirely by the a-c source. If this circuit were connected to a source of 120 cps frequency, the ω of the first term of Eq. 8–10-15 would become $\omega = 754$, whereas the ω of the second term would remain at $\omega = 600$.

If R, L, and C are such that the response of the circuit is nonoscillatory, the current will settle into its steady-state value without oscillating about i_{ss}.

For the switch to be closed so that the transient term is zero, the inductor must have an $i(0)$ which exactly equals i_{ss} at $t = 0$, the capacitor must have on it a $q(0)$ exactly equal to q_{ss} at $t = 0$, and the δ must be such that the switch is closed at the proper instant. If switching is done at random, the chance that $q(0)$, $i(0)$, and δ all have their proper values is very slight.

8–11. Discussion. The preceding articles of this chapter demonstrate the procedure for finding the solution when simple circuits are connected to an a-c source. This same procedure can be extended to as complicated a circuit as desired.

When the circuit is connected to cither an a-c or a d-c source (or any other type for that matter), the solution can always be expressed as the sum of a steady-state component and a transient component. The steady-state component by itself demands that certain conditions be met at $t = 0$. If the actual conditions that exist are not identical with these conditions, the circuit must undergo a transient period before steady-state conditions are reached. No matter how many capacitors or inductors are present, no transient period occurs if all the steady-state components of charge at $t = 0$ are equal to their respective $q(0)$ in the case of capacitors and if all the steady-state components of currents at $t = 0$ are equal to their respective $i(0)$ in the case of inductors.

PROBLEMS

8-1. Given the voltage source shown in Fig. 8–P-1, each of the following cir-

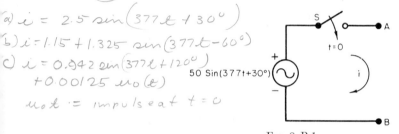

(handwritten)
a) $i = 2.5 \sin(377t + 30^\circ)$
b) $i = 1.15 + 1.325 \sin(377t - 60^\circ)$
c) $i = 0.942 \sin(377t + 120^\circ) + 0.00125 u_0(t)$
  $u_0 \doteq$ impulse at $t = 0$

Fig. 8–P-1

cuit elements is connected in turn to points A–B. In each case find the equation for current and sketch: (a) $R = 20$ ohms; (b) $L = 0.1$ henry; (c) $C = 50$ μf.

8-2. In the circuit of Fig. 8–P-2, S is thrown to position 1 until steady-state conditions are reached; then, at $t = 0$, S is thrown to position 2. Each of the cir-

(handwritten left margin)
b
(a) anything
(b) $\delta = \pm 52.8^\circ$
3 (c) $\frac{\partial i}{\partial i} = -23.6^\circ$
   $\frac{\partial}{\partial 2} = -156.4^\circ$

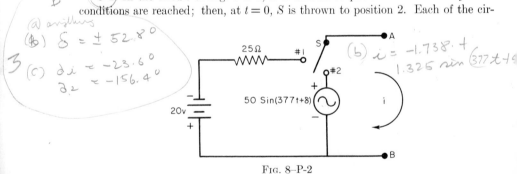

(handwritten)
(b) $i = -1.738 \cdot t$
   $1.325 \sin(377t + 4$

Fig. 8–P-2

cuit elements is connected in turn to points A–B. Find the equations for current in each case and sketch when $\delta = 135^\circ$: (a) $R = 20$ ohms; (b) $L = 0.1$ henry; (c) $C = 50$ μf.

8-3. Consider the circuit and elements of Prob. 8–2. In (a), (b), and (c), find the values of δ such that in each case the transient term is zero.

8-4. In the circuit of Fig. 8–P-3, S is thrown to position 1 until steady-state conditions are reached and, at $t = 0$, S is thrown to position 2. Find the equation for the current and sketch when $\delta = 70^\circ$ and $E = 115$ volts.

(handwritten)
$i = -0.4005 e^{-400t} + 0.557 \sin(1000t + 1.8)$

8-5. For the circuit of Fig. 8-P-3 with $E = 115$ volts, find the values of δ such that the transient component in the solution is zero.

$\partial_1 = 24.9 \quad \partial_2 = -68.5$

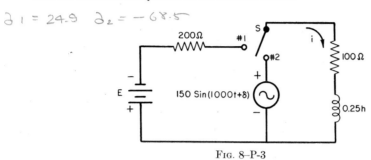

FIG. 8-P-3

8-6. For the circuit of Fig. 8-P-3 find the maximum value of E such that it is still possible to have zero transient component. Find the value of δ corresponding to this E. Sketch the solution.

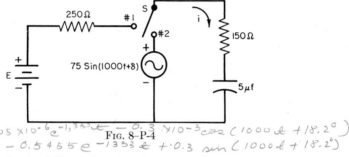

$q = 405 \times 10^{-6} e^{-1,333t} - 0.3 \times 10^{-3} \cos (1000t + 18.2°)$
$i = -0.5455 e^{-1333t} + 0.3 \sin (1000t + 18.2°)$

FIG. 8-P-4

8-7. In the circuit of Fig. 8-P-4, S is thrown to position 1 until steady-state conditions are met; then, at $t = 0$, S is thrown to position 2. Find the equations for q and i and sketch when $\delta = -35°$ and $E = 25$ volts.

8-8. For the circuit of Fig. 8-P-4 with $E = 25$ volts, find the values of δ such that the transient terms are zero.

8-9. For the circuit of Fig. 8-P-4, find the maximum value of E such that the transient term is zero. Find the value of δ corresponding to this E. Sketch the solution.

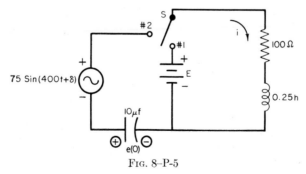

FIG. 8-P-5

$i = 0.417 \sin(400t + 171.3°) + e^{-200t}[0.137 \cos 600 t + 0.638$

8–10. In the circuit of Fig. 8–P-5, S is thrown to position 1 until steady-state conditions are reached; then, at $t = 0$, S is thrown to position 2. Assume that $E = 20$ volts, $e(0) = 0$, and $\delta = 115°$. Find the equation for i after $t = 0$.

8–11. For the circuit of Fig. 8–P-5, $E = 30$ volts, $e(0) = -50$ volts, and $\delta = 35°$, find the equation for voltage across the capacitor and for the current after $t = 0$.

8–12. For the circuit of Fig. 8–P-5, $E = 20$ volts, find the two values of $e(0)$ so that it is possible to close S with a zero transient component. Find the value of δ that corresponds to each $e(0)$.

8–13. For the circuit of Fig. 8–P-5 find the largest value of E such that S can still be closed with zero transient component. Find the values of $e(0)$ and δ that correspond to this E.

CHAPTER 9

ALTERNATING–CURRENT SOURCES AND OTHER WAVE SHAPES USING LAPLACE TRANSFORMS

9–1. Introduction. The method of studying the circuits in Chapter 8 is to use a procedure which may be termed the differential equation method. The solution was expressed as the sum of steady-state and transient components. By this method the steady-state component can be determined by using a-c circuit methods and the form of the transient component determined by setting the driving voltage (or current) equal to zero, just as was done in the earlier chapters. The arbitrary constants are determined by imposing the proper initial conditions on the sum of these two components.

Solutions to all problems studied in Chapter 8 can also be obtained by the Laplace transform method. This is done by writing the differential equation and taking the Laplace transform, as is demonstrated in the following examples. This chapter studies a variety of switching operations when the driving function is a sinusoidal source, after which a variety of other driving functions are considered and a few examples presented.

9–2. Change in Circuit Impedance. EXAMPLE 9–2-1. In the circuit of Fig. 9–2-1, switch S has been closed long enough for steady-state con-

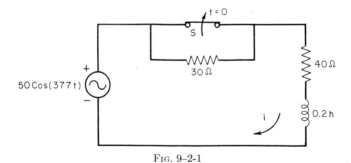

FIG. 9–2-1

ditions to be reached. Thereafter, the switch is opened at $t = 0$. The angle δ in this example indicates the instant in the voltage cycle at which the switch is opened.

Before $t = 0$, the circuit is comprised of a 40-ohm resistor in series with a 0.2-henry inductor and the combination has an impedance

$$\mathbf{Z} = 40 + j\,75.4 = 85.5\underline{/62°} \tag{9–2-1}$$

The steady-state component of the current is

$$i_{ss} = \frac{50}{85.5} \cos (\omega t - 62°) = 0.585 \cos (377\, t - 62°) \qquad (9\text{-}2\text{-}2)$$

The current existing in the circuit at $t = 0$ is

$$\cdot\; i_{ss}(0) = 0.585 \cos (-62°) = 0.274 \qquad (9\text{-}2\text{-}3)$$

and this becomes $i(0)$. The details of the rest of the solution parallel those for the circuits studied in Chapter 8, as the previous history of the circuit contributes nothing but $i(0)$. However, in this example, the solution is determined by using the Laplace transform method. The equation for the circuit is

$$50 \cos (377\, t) = 70\, i + 0.2 \frac{di}{dt} \qquad (9\text{-}2\text{-}4)$$

The transformed equation is

$$\frac{50\, s}{s^2 + (377)^2} = 70\, \mathcal{L}(i) + 0.2[s\mathcal{L}(i) - 0.274] \qquad (9\text{-}2\text{-}5)$$

which, when solved for $\mathcal{L}(i)$, gives

$$\mathcal{L}(i) = \frac{0.274\, s^2 + 250\, s + 38,900}{[s + 350][s^2 + (377)^2]} \qquad (9\text{-}2\text{-}6)$$

Item 19 in the transform tables can be used by letting

$$\begin{array}{lll} a_2 = 0.274 & a_1 = 250 & a_0 = 38,900 \\ b = 350 & a = 0 & \omega = 377 \end{array} \qquad (9\text{-}2\text{-}7)$$

$$A\underline{/\alpha} = \frac{38,900 - 250(-j\,377) + 0.274(-j\,377)^2}{377(350 + j\,377)} = 0.485\underline{/42.9°} \qquad (9\text{-}2\text{-}8)$$

$$i = 0.485\, \epsilon^{0t} \sin (377\, t + 42.9°)$$

$$+ \frac{38,900 - (250)(350) + 0.274(350)^2}{(350)^2 + (377)^2}\, \epsilon^{-350t} \qquad (9\text{-}2\text{-}9)$$

On simplifying, the solution is

$$i = 0.485 \sin (377\, t + 42.9°) - 0.0568\, \epsilon^{-350t} \qquad (9\text{-}2\text{-}10)$$

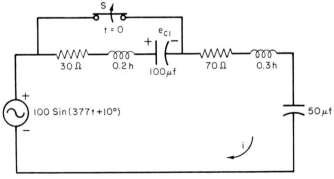

FIG. 9-2-2

EXAMPLE 9–2–2. As the next example, the circuit of Fig. 9–2–2 is considered. The switch S has been closed long enough for the circuit to reach steady-state conditions and, at $t = 0$, S is opened. The solution is the voltage e_{c_1} on the 100-μf capacitor.

The circuit impedance before $t = 0$ is

$$Z = 70 + j\left(377 \times 0.3 - \frac{1}{377 \times 50 \times 10^{-6}}\right) = 92\underline{/40.6°} \quad (9\text{–}2\text{–}11)$$

The steady-state current before $t = 0$ is

$$i_{ss} = \tfrac{100}{92} \sin (377\,t + 10° - 40.6°) \quad (9\text{–}2\text{–}12)$$

and the current in the 0.3-henry inductor at $t = (0-)$ (before the switch is opened) is

$$i(0-) = 1.085 \sin (-30.6°) = -0.553 \quad (9\text{–}2\text{–}13)$$

The current in the 0.2-henry inductor at $t = 0-$ is zero; and at the moment the switch is opened the current i jumps to a new value which, as determined from the concept of conservation of flux linkages, is

$$(L_1 + L_2)i(0+) = L_1 i_1(0-) + L_2 i_2(0-)$$

or

$$i(0+) = \frac{0.3(-0.553) + 0.2(0)}{0.3 + 0.2} = -0.331 \quad (9\text{–}2\text{–}14)$$

The q_{ss} on the 50-μf capacitor can be obtained:

$$q_{ss} = \int i_{ss}\,dt = \frac{1.085}{377} \sin (377\,t - 30.6 - 90) \quad (9\text{–}2\text{–}15)$$

and $q(0)$ is

$$q(0) = 0.00288 \sin (-120.6°) = -0.00248 \quad (9\text{–}2\text{–}16)$$

and $e(0)$ is

$$e(0) = \frac{-0.00248}{50 \times 10^{-6}} = -49.6 \quad (9\text{–}2\text{–}17)$$

At $t = 0+$ the circuit has a current of -0.331 amp in the combined inductor of 0.5 henry and has zero volts on the 100-μf capacitor and -49.6 volts on the 50-μf capacitor.

The circuit equation can be written

$$100 \sin (377\,t + 10°) = 100\,i + 0.5 \frac{di}{dt} + \frac{1}{100 \times 10^{-6}} \int_0^t i\,dt$$

$$+ \frac{1}{50 \times 10^{-6}} \int_0^t i\,dt - 49.6 \quad (9\text{–}2\text{–}18)$$

The driving function can be expanded:

$$98.5 \sin 377\,t + 17.38 \cos 377\,t \quad (9\text{–}2\text{–}19)$$

and the transform of both sides of Eq. 9–2–18 is

$$\frac{98.5 \times 377}{s^2 + (377)^2} + \frac{17.38\,s}{s^2 + (377)^2} = 100\,\mathcal{L}(i) + 0.5[s\mathcal{L}(i) + 0.331]$$

$$+ 3 \times 10^4 \frac{\mathcal{L}(i)}{s} - \frac{49.6}{s} \quad (9\text{–}2\text{–}20)$$

Eq. 9–2-20 can be solved for $\mathcal{L}(i)$ and the denominator factored and put in the form

$$\mathcal{L}(i) = \frac{-0.331\,s^3 + 134\,s^2 + 27.2 \times 10^3\,s + 14.1 \times 10^6}{[s^2 + (377)^2][(s+100)^2 + (223.8)^2]} \qquad (9\text{–}2\text{–}21)$$

The voltage e_{c_1} is the desired solution.

$$e_{c_1} = \frac{1}{100 \times 10^{-6}} \int_0^t i\,dt + 0 \qquad (9\text{–}2\text{–}22)$$

If the inverse transform of $\mathcal{L}(i)$ is taken, the result must be integrated to obtain e_{c_1}. It is easier to find the inverse transform of $\mathcal{L}(e_{c_1})$ directly. The transform of Eq. 9–2-22 is

$$\mathcal{L}(e_{c_1}) = \frac{10^4}{s}\,\mathcal{L}(i)$$

which leads to

$$\mathcal{L}(e_{c_1}) = \frac{-0.331 \times 10^4\,s^3 + 1.34 \times 10^6\,s^2 + 2.72 \times 10^8\,s + 14.1 \times 10^{10}}{s[s^2 + (377)^2][(s+100)^2 + (223.8)^2]} \qquad (9\text{–}2\text{–}23)$$

The inverse transform can be found by using item 32 in the table, leading to

$$A\underline{/\alpha} = \frac{14.1 \times 10^{10} + 2.72 \times 10^8(j\,377) + 1.34 \times 10^6(j\,377)^2 - 0.331 \times 10^4(j\,377)^3}{377[(j\,377 + 100)^2 + 50,000][j\,377]}$$

$$A\underline{/\alpha} = 18\underline{/-127.6°} \qquad (9\text{–}2\text{–}24)$$

and

$$B\underline{/\beta} = \frac{\left\{\begin{array}{l} 14.1 \times 10^{10} - 2.72 \times 10^8[100 - j\,223.8] \\ + 1.34 \times 10^6[100 - j\,223.8]^2 + 0.331 \times 10^4[100 - j\,223.8]^3 \end{array}\right\}}{223.8[(100 - j\,223.8)^2 + (377)^2][-100 + j\,223.8]}$$

$$B\underline{/\beta} = 3.45\underline{/-42.3°} \qquad (9\text{–}2\text{–}25)$$

The final solution is

$$\begin{aligned} e_{c_1} &= 18\sin(377\,t - 127.6°) \\ &\quad + 3.45\,\epsilon^{-100t}\sin(223.8\,t - 42.3°) + 16.5 \qquad (9\text{–}2\text{–}26) \end{aligned}$$

Before leaving this example, it is interesting to observe that the form of the voltage e_{c_1} in the steady state is made up of the usual a-c steady-state response to be expected from a-c circuit theory plus the 16.5-volt term which may appear unexpected. An examination of the circuit shows that the 16.5-volt term is the result of the $q(0)$ on the 50-μf capacitor, which in the steady state redistributes itself between the two capacitors. In the usual a-c circuit theory the 16.5-volt term would not appear. This is true when using actual circuit elements because the leakage resistance of the capacitors would remove the 16.5 volts in the steady state.

9–3. Switching from One Voltage Source to Another. EXAMPLE 9–3-1. In the circuit of Fig. 9–3-1 the switch S has been thrown to position 1 long enough for the circuit to reach steady state. At $t = 0$, S is thrown to position 2 and the equation for i is desired. Use of the angle δ on the two voltages shows the phase of each at $t = 0$. In other words, the voltage con-

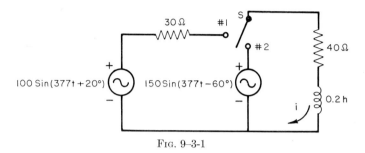

FIG. 9–3-1

nected to position 2 lags the other voltage by 80 degrees. The circuit impedance before $t = 0$ is

$$Z = 70 + j\,377 \times 0.2 = 103\underline{/47.2^\circ} \qquad (9\text{-}3\text{-}1)$$

and the steady-state component of the current is

$$i_{ss} = \tfrac{100}{103} \sin\,(377\,t + 20^\circ - 47.2^\circ) = 0.97 \sin\,(377\,t - 27.2^\circ) \quad (9\text{-}3\text{-}2)$$

At $t = 0$ the current $i(0)$ is

$$i(0) = 0.97 \sin\,(-27.2^\circ) = -0.444 \qquad (9\text{-}3\text{-}3)$$

As in preceding articles, the $i(0)$ in the inductor is the only contribution made to the problem at $t = 0$ through the previous history of the circuit. After $t = 0$ the equation for the circuit is

$$150 \sin\,(377\,t - 60^\circ) = 40\,i + 0.2\,\frac{di}{dt} \qquad (9\text{-}3\text{-}4)$$

$$75 \sin 377\,t - 130 \cos 377\,t = 40\,i + 0.2\,\frac{di}{dt} \qquad (9\text{-}3\text{-}5)$$

The transform of this equation is

$$\frac{75 \times 377}{s^2 + (377)^2} - \frac{130\,s}{s^2 + (377)^2} = 40\,\mathcal{L}(i) + 0.2[s\mathcal{L}(i) + 0.444] \quad (9\text{-}3\text{-}6)$$

which when solved for the $\mathcal{L}(i)$ gives

$$\mathcal{L}(i) = \frac{-0.444\,s^2 - 650\,s + 78{,}250}{(s + 200)[s^2 + (377)^2]} \qquad (9\text{-}3\text{-}7)$$

Use of item 19 in the transform table in the Appendix gives

$$A\underline{/\alpha} = \frac{78{,}250 + 650(-j\,377) - 0.444(-j\,377)^2}{377[200 + j\,377]} = 1.75\underline{/-122^\circ} \quad (9\text{-}3\text{-}8)$$

$$i = 1.75 \sin\,(377\,t - 122^\circ) + \frac{78{,}250 + 650(200) - 0.444(200)^2}{(200)^2 + (377)^2}\,\epsilon^{-200t}$$

$$(9\text{-}3\text{-}9)$$

This simplifies to

$$i = 1.75 \sin\,(377\,t - 122^\circ) + 1.05\,\epsilon^{-200t} \qquad (9\text{-}3\text{-}10)$$

EXAMPLE 9–3–2. A second example of this type is shown in Fig. 9–3–2, where the switching operation is the same as in the previous example.

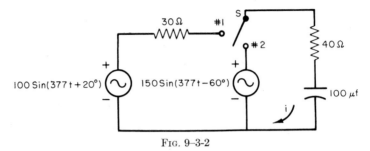

FIG. 9–3–2

The circuit impedance before $t = 0$ is

$$Z = 70 - j\frac{1}{377 \times 100 \times 10^{-6}} = 75\underline{/-20.7°} \qquad (9\text{-}3\text{-}11)$$

The steady-state components of current and charge are

$$i_{ss} = \tfrac{100}{75}[\sin(377\,t + 20° + 20.7°)] = 1.33 \sin(377\,t + 40.7°) \qquad (9\text{-}3\text{-}12)$$

$$q_{ss} = \frac{1.33}{377} \sin(377 + 40.7° - 90°) = 0.00353 \sin(377\,t - 49.3°) \qquad (9\text{-}3\text{-}13)$$

The charge $q(0)$ at $t = 0$ is

$$q(0) = 0.00353 \sin(-49.3°) = -0.00268 \qquad (9\text{-}3\text{-}14)$$

which gives for $e(0)$ $\qquad e(0) = \dfrac{q(0)}{C} = -26.8$ volts

After $t = 0$ the equation for the circuit becomes

$$150 \sin(377\,t - 60°) = 40\,i + \frac{1}{10^{-4}} \int_0^t i\,dt - 26.8 \qquad (9\text{-}3\text{-}15)$$

When transformed, this equation becomes

$$\frac{-130\,s + 28{,}250}{s^2 + (377)^2} = 40\,\mathcal{L}(i) + \frac{\mathcal{L}(i)}{10^{-4}\,s} - \frac{26.8}{s} \qquad (9\text{-}3\text{-}16)$$

which when solved for $\mathcal{L}(i)$ gives

$$\mathcal{L}(i) = \frac{-2.58\,s^2 + 706\,s + 9.52 \times 10^4}{(s + 250)[s^2 + (377)^2]} \qquad (9\text{-}3\text{-}17)$$

Use of item 19 in the transform table gives

$$A\underline{/\alpha} = \frac{9.52 \times 10^4 - 706(-j\,377) - 2.58(-j\,377)^2}{377(250 + j\,377)}$$

$$A\underline{/\alpha} = 3.13\underline{/-26.5°} \qquad (9\text{-}3\text{-}18)$$

$$i = \frac{1180}{377} \sin(377\,t - 26.5°) + \frac{9.52 \times 10^4 - 706(250) - 2.58(250)^2}{(250)^2 + (377)^2}\,\epsilon^{-250t}$$

$$\qquad (9\text{-}3\text{-}19)$$

The final solution is

$$i = 3.13 \sin (377\,t - 26.5°) - 1.19\,\epsilon^{-250t} \qquad (9\text{-}3\text{-}20)$$

9–4. Other Driving Functions. The Laplace transform method has been used thus far on driving functions that are either constant (d-c) or sinusoidal (a-c) functions. When a driving function of other form is applied to the circuit, the solution to the problem can be found by the transform method in the same manner as before. The following examples demonstrate a variety of driving functions.

EXAMPLE 9–4-1. The response of the R-L circuit of Fig. 9–4-1 when it

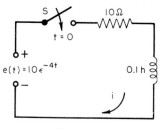

FIG. 9–4-1

is driven by a voltage $10\,\epsilon^{-4t}$ can be found by writing the circuit equation

$$10\,\epsilon^{-4t} = 10\,i + 0.1\,\frac{di}{dt} \qquad (9\text{-}4\text{-}1)$$

It is assumed that the circuit was at rest before $t = 0$; therefore the initial current is zero and the transformed equation is

$$\frac{10}{s+4} = 10\,\mathcal{L}(i) + 0.1\,s\,\mathcal{L}(i) \qquad (9\text{-}4\text{-}2)$$

which can be solved for $\mathcal{L}(i)$:

$$\mathcal{L}(i) = \frac{100}{(s+4)(s+100)} \qquad (9\text{-}4\text{-}3)$$

The inverse transform of this equation is

$$i = 1.04\,\epsilon^{-4t} - 1.04\,\epsilon^{-100t} \qquad (9\text{-}4\text{-}4)$$

It is to be noted in Eq. 9–4-3 that the pole at $s = -4$ comes from the driving function and the pole at $s = -100$ comes from the circuit. In the solution the $1.04\,\epsilon^{-4t}$ term corresponds to what has been referred to as the steady-state component, when using the classical procedure. In differential equation terminology this is termed a particular solution; because of the nature of the exponential decay, this seems to be a better terminology. The $-1.04\,\epsilon^{-100t}$ is the transient component; in differential equation terminology it is termed the complementary solution.

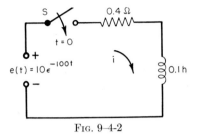

Fig. 9–4-2

EXAMPLE 9–4-2. The circuit of Fig. 9–4-2 is analyzed in order to contrast the results with the preceding example. The circuit equation is

$$10 \, \epsilon^{-100t} = 0.4 \, i + 0.1 \, \frac{di}{dt} \qquad (9\text{–}4\text{–}5)$$

Again it is assumed that $i(0)$ is zero, and the transformed equation is

$$\frac{10}{s + 100} = 0.4 \, \mathcal{L}(i) + 0.1 \, s \, \mathcal{L}(i) \qquad (9\text{–}4\text{–}6)$$

This can be solved for $\mathcal{L}(i)$:

$$\mathcal{L}(i) = \frac{100}{(s + 100)(s + 4)} \qquad (9\text{–}4\text{–}7)$$

The inverse transform of this equation is

$$i = -1.04 \, \epsilon^{-100t} + 1.04 \, \epsilon^{-4t} \qquad (9\text{–}4\text{–}8)$$

When Eqs. 9–4-7 and 9–4-3 are compared, it is seen that they are identical. However, the pole at $s = -4$ now comes from the circuit and the pole at $s = -100$ comes from the driving function. Therefore in the solution the term $1.04 \, \epsilon^{-4t}$ is the complementary function and the term $-1.04 \, \epsilon^{-100t}$ is the particular solution.

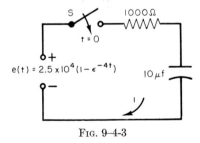

Fig. 9–4-3

EXAMPLE 9–4-3. The circuit of Fig. 9–4-3 has the following circuit equation, assuming $q(0) = 0$.

$$2.5 \times 10^4 (1 - \epsilon^{-4t}) = 1000 \, i + \frac{1}{10 \times 10^{-6}} \int_0^t i \, dt \qquad (9\text{–}4\text{–}9)$$

The transformed equation is

$$2.5 \times 10^4 \left(\frac{1}{s} - \frac{1}{s + 4} \right) = 1000 \, \mathcal{L}(i) + 10^5 \frac{\mathcal{L}(i)}{s} \qquad (9\text{–}4\text{–}10)$$

This can be solved for $\mathcal{L}(i)$:

$$\mathcal{L}(i) = \frac{100}{(s+4)(s+100)} \tag{9-4-11}$$

This equation is the same as Eqs. 9-4-7 and 9-4-3 and hence the solution is the same.

The circuits in the last three examples have exactly the same current response. It is to be pointed out that these circuits are not duals, because in dual circuits the voltage of one circuit responds in a manner similar to the current in its dual. In each of these examples the response is current.

The following two examples demonstrate the method of solution for other driving functions.

EXAMPLE 9-4-4. In this example the voltage $e = 6\,t$ is applied to the R-L circuit as shown in Fig. 9-4-4, where again it is assumed that initially

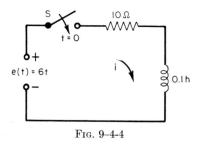

FIG. 9-4-4

no energy is stored in the inductor. The circuit equation is

$$6\,t = 10\,i + 0.1\frac{di}{dt} \tag{9-4-12}$$

The transformed equation is

$$\frac{6}{s^2} = 10\,\mathcal{L}(i) + 0.1[s\mathcal{L}(i) - 0] \tag{9-4-13}$$

$$\mathcal{L}(i) = \frac{6}{s^2(0.1s+10)} = \frac{60}{s^2(s+100)} \tag{9-4-14}$$

The $\mathcal{L}(i)$ is expanded in partial fractions by the following steps:

$$\frac{60}{s^2(s+100)} = \frac{A}{s^2} + \frac{B}{s} + \frac{C}{s+100} \tag{9-4-15}$$

$$A = \frac{60}{s+100}\bigg|_{s=0} = \frac{60}{100} = 0.6$$

$$B = \frac{d}{ds}\left[\frac{60}{s+100}\right]\bigg|_{s=0} = \frac{-60}{(s+100)^2}\bigg|_{s=0} = -0.006$$

$$C = \frac{60}{(-100)^2} = 0.006$$

$$\mathcal{L}(i) = \frac{0.6}{s^2} - \frac{0.006}{s} + \frac{0.006}{s+100} \tag{9-4-16}$$

The inverse transform is

$$i = 0.6\,t - 0.006 + 0.006\;\epsilon^{-100t} \tag{9-4-17}$$

EXAMPLE 9–4-5. The example considered next is the circuit shown in Fig. 9–4-5. The switch S is thrown to position 1 until steady state is

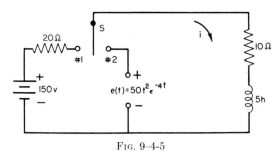

FIG. 9–4-5

reached; then, at $t = 0$, S is thrown to position 2. This gives

$$i(0) = \tfrac{150}{30} = 5$$

and the circuit equation is

$$50\,t^2\epsilon^{-4t} = 10\,i + 5\,\frac{di}{dt} \tag{9-4-18}$$

The transformed equation is

$$\frac{50 \times 2!}{(s+4)^3} = 10\,\mathcal{L}(i) + 5[s\mathcal{L}(i) - 5] \tag{9-4-19}$$

and solution for $\mathcal{L}(i)$ gives

$$\mathcal{L}(i) = \frac{100}{(s+4)^3(5\,s+10)} + \frac{25}{5\,s+10} = \frac{20}{(s+4)^3(s+2)} + \frac{5}{s+2} \tag{9-4-20}$$

The first term of $\mathcal{L}(i)$ can be expanded:

$$\frac{1}{(s+4)^3(s+2)} = \frac{A}{(s+4)^3} + \frac{B}{(s+4)^2} + \frac{C}{(s+4)} + \frac{D}{(s+2)} \tag{9-4-21}$$

To find A, both sides of the equation are multiplied by $(s+4)^3$:

$$\frac{1}{s+2} = A + B(s+4) + C(s+4)^2 + D\,\frac{(s+4)^3}{(s+2)} \tag{9-4-22}$$

and s is set equal to -4. A is

$$A = \frac{1}{2-4} = -0.5$$

To find B both sides of the $F(s) \cdot (s+4)^3$ are differentiated:

$$\frac{d}{ds}\left[\frac{1}{s+2}\right] = B + 2\,C(s+4) + D\,\frac{d}{ds}\left[\frac{(s+4)^3}{s+2}\right] \tag{9-4-23}$$

and in the result $s = -4$; thus

$$B = -\frac{1}{(s+2)^2} = -\frac{1}{(2-4)^2} = -\frac{1}{4} = -0.25$$

To find C, Eq. 9–4-23 is again differentiated:

$$\frac{d^2}{ds^2}\left[\frac{1}{s+2}\right] = 2\,C + D\,\frac{d^2}{ds^2}\left[\frac{(s+4)^3}{s+2}\right]$$

and in the result $s = -4$; thus

$$C = \frac{1}{2}\left[-\frac{-2}{(s+2)^3}\right]\Bigg|_{s=-4} = \frac{1}{(-2)^3} = -\frac{1}{8} = -0.125$$

D is found in the usual manner:

$$D = \frac{1}{(s+4)^3}\Bigg|_{s=-2} = \frac{1}{(2)^3} = \frac{1}{8} = 0.125$$

The expanded equation is written

$$\mathcal{L}(i) = 20\left[-\frac{0.5}{(s+4)^3} - \frac{0.25}{(s+4)^2} - \frac{0.125}{(s+4)} + \frac{0.125}{(s+2)}\right] + \frac{5}{(s+2)} \qquad (9\text{–}4\text{-}24)$$

$$\mathcal{L}(i) = -\frac{10}{(s+4)^3} - \frac{5}{(s+4)^2} - \frac{2.5}{(s+4)} + \frac{7.5}{(s+2)} \qquad (9\text{–}4\text{-}25)$$

The inverse transform is

$$i = -5\,t^2\epsilon^{-4t} - 5\,t\epsilon^{-4t} - 2.5\,\epsilon^{-4t} + 7.5\,\epsilon^{-2t} \qquad (9\text{–}4\text{-}26)$$

9–5. Transform of Dead Time Delay. The Laplace transform of a function $f(t)$ is given by

$$F(s) = \int_0^\infty f(t)\epsilon^{-st}\,dt$$

Suppose that $F(s)$ is multiplied by ϵ^{-Ts} and it is desired to find the function of time $f_T(t)$ corresponding to the new transform

$$\epsilon^{-Ts}F(s) = \epsilon^{-Ts}\int_0^\infty f(t)\epsilon^{-st}\,dt \qquad (9\text{–}5\text{-}1)$$

Since the integration is with respect to t, the term ϵ^{-Ts} is a constant and can be moved inside the integral sign; thus

$$\epsilon^{-Ts}F(s) = \int_0^\infty f(t)\epsilon^{-s(t+T)}\,dt \qquad (9\text{–}5\text{-}2)$$

A change of variable

$$\tau = t + T \qquad (9\text{–}5\text{-}3)$$

leads to the limits of integration and the differential as

$$\begin{aligned} t &= 0 & \tau &= T \\ t &= \infty & \tau &= \infty \\ dt &= d\tau \end{aligned} \qquad (9\text{–}5\text{-}4)$$

so that Eq. 9–5-2 can be written

$$\epsilon^{-Ts}F(s) = \int_0^T (0)\,d\tau + \int_T^\infty f(\tau - T)\epsilon^{-s\tau}\,d\tau \qquad (9\text{–}5\text{-}5)$$

The new function $f_T(t)$ defined from this is

$$f_T(t) = 0 \quad \text{for} \quad 0 < t < T \tag{9-5-6}$$

and $$f_T(t) = f(t - T) \quad \text{for} \quad T < t < \infty$$

In other words, the original $f(t)$ is given a dead time delay of T seconds as illustrated in Fig. 9–5–1.

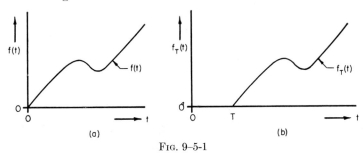

(a)   (b)

FIG. 9–5–1

The properties of this dead time delay make it possible to construct the Laplace transforms of many functions, as demonstrated in the following examples.

EXAMPLE 9–5–1. The square pulse of Fig. 9–5–2a is taken as the first example. By inspection, it is to be seen that when the two components shown in Figs. 9–5–2b and 9–5–2c are added they make up the original square pulse. Therefore the Laplace transform of the square pulse can be obtained by adding the transforms of these two components:

$$F(s) = \frac{1}{s} - \frac{1}{s} \epsilon^{-Ts} = \frac{1 - \epsilon^{-Ts}}{s} \tag{9-5-7}$$

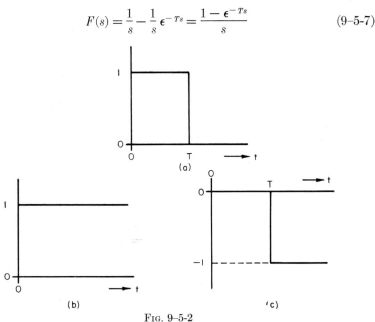

(a)

(b)   (c)

FIG. 9–5–2

EXAMPLE 9–5-2. The Laplace transform for the triangular pulse shown
in Fig. 9–5-3a can be taken by expanding the pulse as the three com-

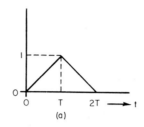

(a)

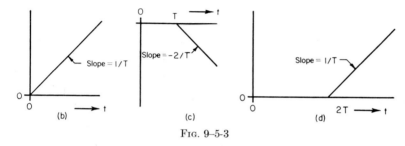

FIG. 9–5-3

ponents shown in Figs. 9–5-3b, c, and d. The sums of Laplace transforms
of the three components is

$$F(s) = \frac{1}{Ts^2} - \frac{2}{Ts^2} \epsilon^{-Ts} + \frac{1}{Ts^2} \epsilon^{-2Ts}$$

$$F(s) = \frac{(1 - \epsilon^{-Ts})^2}{Ts^2} \tag{9-5-8}$$

EXAMPLE 9–5-3. If a wave shape is periodic, the Laplace transform can
be found by the following procedure. Let it be supposed that the transform
for the wave shape in the first period is $F_1(s)$. Since the wave is periodic,
the wave shape in the next period is the same as that in the first, only
being delayed by one period T; therefore it has a transform $F_1(s)\epsilon^{-Ts}$
By an extension of this argument the transform for the periodic wave $F(s)$ is

$$F(s) = F_1(s)[1 + \epsilon^{-Ts} + \epsilon^{-2Ts} + \epsilon^{-3Ts} + \cdots] \tag{9-5-9}$$

The terms inside the brackets are an infinite series that can be summed
such that $F(s)$ is given by

$$F(s) = \frac{F_1(s)}{1 - \epsilon^{-Ts}} \tag{9-5-10}$$

Use is now made of this procedure for the periodic wave of Fig. 9–5-4.
The three components of the wave shape in the first period can be visualized
and the transform taken as

$$F_1(s) = \frac{1}{s} - \frac{2}{s} \epsilon^{-(T/2)s} + \frac{1}{s} \epsilon^{-Ts} = \frac{(1 - \epsilon^{-(T/2)s})^2}{s} \tag{9-5-11}$$

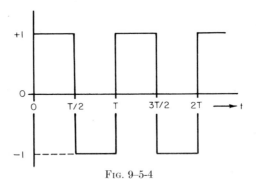

FIG. 9-5-4

Therefore the transform for the periodic wave is

$$F(s) = \frac{F_1(s)}{1 - \epsilon^{-Ts}} = \frac{(1 - \epsilon^{-(T/2)s})^2}{s(1 - \epsilon^{-Ts})} = \frac{1 - \epsilon^{-(T/2)s}}{s(1 + \epsilon^{-(T/2)s})} \qquad (9\text{-}5\text{-}12)$$

This equation can be rewritten

$$F(s) = \frac{(\epsilon^{+(T/4)s} - \epsilon^{-(T/4)s})}{s(\epsilon^{+(T/4)s} + \epsilon^{-(T/4)s})} = \frac{1}{s} \tanh \frac{T}{4} s \qquad (9\text{-}5\text{-}13)$$

EXAMPLE 9-5-4. The transform for the periodic wave shape of Fig. 9-5-5a can be found by first visualizing the two components shown in Figs.

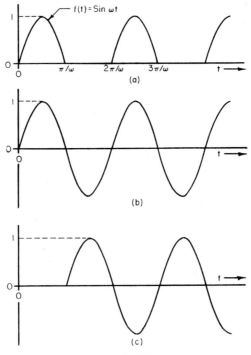

FIG. 9-5-5

9–5-5b and 9–5-5c that make up the $f(t)$ in the first period. The transform for the wave shape in the first period is

$$F_1(s) = \frac{\omega[1 + \epsilon^{-(\pi/\omega)s}]}{s^2 + \omega^2} \qquad (9\text{–}5\text{-}14)$$

Therefore the transform for the periodic wave is

$$F(s) = \frac{F_1(s)}{1 - \epsilon^{-(2\pi/\omega)s}} = \frac{\omega[1 + \epsilon^{-(\pi/\omega)s}]}{[s^2 + \omega^2][1 - \epsilon^{-(2\pi/\omega)s}]}$$

$$= \frac{\omega}{[s^2 + \omega^2][1 - \epsilon^{-(\pi/\omega)s}]} \qquad (9\text{–}5\text{-}15)$$

EXAMPLE 9–5-5. The transform for the periodic wave of Fig. 9–5-6a can be expressed as the two periodic waves shown in Figs. 9–5-6b and

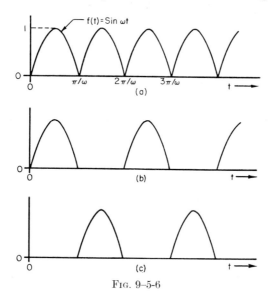

FIG. 9–5-6

9–5-6c. The transform for Fig. 9–5-6b is that given in Eq. 9–5-15, and the transform for that in Fig. 9–5-6c is that of Fig. 9–5-6b delayed by π/ω seconds. The transform for the sum of the two parts is

$$F(s) = \frac{\omega[1 + \epsilon^{-(\pi/\omega)s}]}{[s^2 + \omega^2][1 - \epsilon^{-(\pi/\omega)s}]} = \frac{\omega}{[s^2 + \omega^2]} \coth \frac{\pi}{2\,\omega}\,s \qquad (9\text{–}5\text{-}16)$$

EXAMPLE 9–5-6. The Laplace transform for the square pulse shown in Fig. 9–5-7 can be found:

$$\frac{1}{\delta} \frac{1 - \epsilon^{-\delta s}}{s} \qquad (9\text{–}5\text{-}17)$$

As explained in Chapter 2, if δ approaches zero as a limit, the square pulse approaches the unit impulse. Therefore the Laplace transform of the unit impulse can be obtained from Eq. 9–5-17 by taking the limit as δ approaches zero. If this is done in the equation as it stands, the result is the inde-

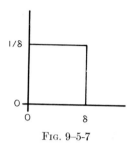

FIG. 9–5-7

terminate form 0/0; however, this can be evaluated by differentiating the numerator and denominator with respect to δ:

$$\mathcal{L}[u_0(t)] = \lim_{\delta \to 0} \frac{1}{\delta} \frac{(1 - \epsilon^{-\delta s})}{s} = \lim_{\delta \to 0} \frac{s\epsilon^{-\delta s}}{s} = 1 \qquad (9\text{–}5\text{-}18)$$

The transform of the unit impulse can also be obtained by taking the

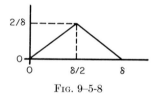

FIG. 9–5-8

limit as δ approaches zero in the triangular pulse of Fig. 9–5-8. The transform of this wave shape is

$$\frac{4}{\delta^2} \frac{(1 - \epsilon^{-\delta s/2})^2}{s^2} \qquad (9\text{–}5\text{-}19)$$

The limit of this as δ approaches zero can be evaluated by taking the derivative of the numerator and denominator the proper number of times and then passing to the limit, as shown in the successive steps:

$$\mathcal{L}[u_0(t)] = \lim_{\delta \to 0} \frac{4[1 - 2\epsilon^{-\delta s/2} + \epsilon^{-\delta s}]}{\delta^2 s^2} = \frac{0}{0}$$

$$\mathcal{L}[u_0(t)] = \lim_{\delta \to 0} \frac{4[s\epsilon^{-\delta s/2} - s\epsilon^{-\delta s}]}{2\delta s^2} = \frac{0}{0}$$

$$\mathcal{L}[u_0(t)] = \lim_{\delta \to 0} \frac{4[-(s^2/2)\epsilon^{-\delta s/2} + s^2\epsilon^{-\delta s}]}{2s^2} = 1 \qquad (9\text{–}5\text{-}20)$$

This final value agrees with the preceding result.

EXAMPLE 9–5-7. It is of interest to attempt to visualize the derivative of the unit impulse. In thinking in terms of the derivative, the function shown in Fig. 9–5-8 is convenient to use; its derivative is shown in Fig. 9–5-9. The limit of this function as δ approaches zero is the unit second-order impulse and is the derivative of the unit first-order impulse, or what has been referred to until now as the unit impulse. The Laplace

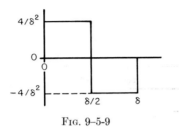

FIG. 9–5-9

transform of the unit second-order impulse can be found by taking the limit as δ approaches zero of the transform of the wave shape of Fig. 9–5-9. The transform before taking the limit is

$$\frac{4(1 - \epsilon^{-\delta s/2})^2}{\delta^2 s} \tag{9–5-21}$$

The limit of this as δ approaches zero can be evaluated by taking the derivative of the numerator and denominator the proper number of times as shown in the successive steps and then letting $\delta \to 0$; thus

$$\mathcal{L}[u_{+1}(t)] = \lim_{\delta \to 0} \frac{4 \cdot s \left[\epsilon^{-\delta s/2} - \epsilon^{-\delta s}\right]}{2 \, s\delta} = \frac{0}{0}$$

$$= \lim_{\delta \to 0} \frac{2 \, s^2 \left[(-1/2) \, \epsilon^{-\delta s/2} + \epsilon^{-\delta s}\right]}{s} = s \tag{9–5-22}$$

9–6. A Family of Functions. The unit first-order impulse and the unit second-order impulse, as presented in the preceding article, are two members of a family of functions which can be obtained by successive differentiation or integration of other members of the family. The unit impulse denoted by $u_0(t)$ can be used as the starting point for this family. If the unit impulse is integrated, the result is the unit step function denoted by $u_{-1}(t)$. If the unit step function is integrated, the result is the unit ramp function denoted by $u_{-2}(t)$, etc.

In going the other way from the unit impulse, it can be differentiated, and the result is the unit second-order impulse denoted by $u_{+1}(t)$. If in turn this function is differentiated, the result is the unit third-order impulse denoted by $u_{+2}(t)$. This family of functions and the corresponding transforms are shown in Table 9–1.

Table 9–2 is developed to aid in visualization of higher-order impulse functions. In each row the appropriate impulse shown in column A results

TABLE 9–1

$f(t)$	$F(s)$
$u_{-n}(t)$	$1/s^n$

$u_{-2}(t)$	$1/s^2$
$u_{-1}(t)$	$1/s$
$u_0(t)$	1
$u_{+1}(t)$	s
$u_{+2}(t)$	s^2

$u_{+n}(t)$	s^n

as the limit as $\delta \to 0$ of either of the curves shown in column B or C. The curves of column C are developed in such a manner as to make differentiation a simple matter, and the derivative of this curve is placed in column B of the following row.

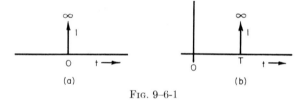

FIG. 9–6-1

In writing $u_0(t)$ it is understood that the unit impulse occurs at $t = 0$, as shown in Fig. 9–6-1a. Therefore $u_0(t - T)$ means that the impulse occurs at $t = T$. Likewise $u_{-1}(t)$ is a unit step function with the step

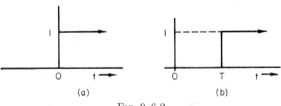

FIG. 9–6-2

occurring at $t = 0$, as shown in Fig. 9-6-2a. Therefore $u_{-1}(t - T)$ is a unit step function that occurs at $t = T$ as shown in Fig. 9-6-2b. The same type of notation applies to all the other members of this family.

TABLE 9-2

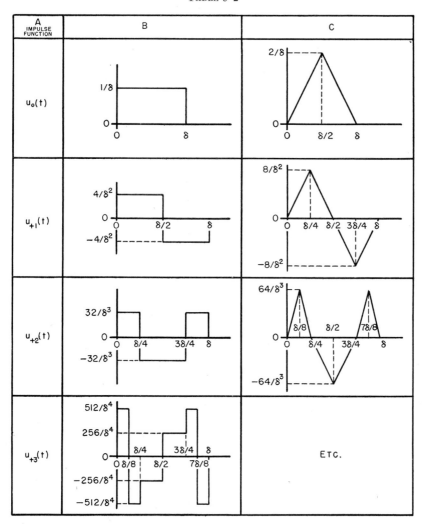

9-7. Circuit Response to Various Wave Shapes. The preceding articles illustrate the method of obtaining the Laplace transform of various wave shapes. Some of these wave shapes are now applied to circuits and the responses are determined.

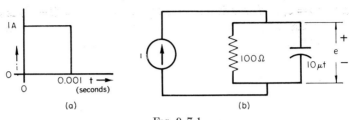

FIG. 9–7-1

EXAMPLE 9–7-1. The pulse of current i of Fig. 9–7-1a is applied to the circuit of Fig. 9–7-1b. Kirchhoff's current law can be written

$$i = i_R + i_c = \frac{e}{100} + 10 \times 10^{-6} \frac{de}{dt} \qquad (9\text{-}7\text{-}1)$$

and its transform is

$$\frac{1}{s} - \frac{1}{s}\,\epsilon^{-0.001s} = E(s)[\tfrac{1}{100} + 10 \times 10^{-6}\,s] \qquad (9\text{-}7\text{-}2)$$

where

$$E(s) = \mathcal{L}(e) \qquad (9\text{-}7\text{-}3)$$

This can be solved for $E(s)$:

$$E(s) = \frac{10^5}{s[s + 10^3]} - \frac{10^5\,e^{-0.001s}}{s[s + 10^3]} \qquad (9\text{-}7\text{-}4)$$

which, when expanded, gives

$$E(s) = 100\left[\frac{1}{s} - \frac{1}{s + 10^3}\right] - 100\left[\frac{1}{s} - \frac{1}{s + 10^3}\right]\epsilon^{-0.001s} \qquad (9\text{-}7\text{-}5)$$

The inverse transform of $E(s)$ is

$$e = 100[1 - \epsilon^{-10^3 t}] - 100[1 - \epsilon^{-10^3(t-0.001)}]u_{-1}(t - 0.001) \qquad (9\text{-}7\text{-}6)$$

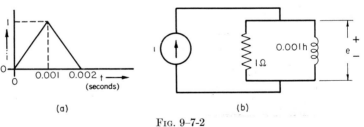

FIG. 9–7-2

EXAMPLE 9–7-2. The pulse of current i shown in Fig. 9–7-2a is applied to the circuit shown in Fig. 9–7-2b. Kirchhoff's current law can be written

$$i = i_R + i_L = \frac{e}{1} + \frac{1}{0.001}\int_0^t e\,dt \qquad (9\text{-}7\text{-}7)$$

and its transform is

$$\frac{1000}{s^2} - \frac{2000}{s^2}\epsilon^{-0.001s} + \frac{1000}{s^2}\epsilon^{-0.002s} = E(s)\left[1 + \frac{10^3}{s}\right] \qquad (9\text{-}7\text{-}8)$$

This can be solved for $E(s)$ and expanded:

$$E(s) = \left[\frac{1}{s} - \frac{1}{s+10^3}\right] - 2\left[\frac{1}{s} - \frac{1}{s+10^3}\right]\epsilon^{-0.001s} + \left[\frac{1}{s} - \frac{1}{s+10^3}\right]\epsilon^{-0.002s}$$
$$(9\text{-}7\text{-}9)$$

The inverse transform is

$$e = [1 - \epsilon^{-10^3 t}] - 2[1 - \epsilon^{-10^3(t-0.001)}]u_{-1}(t - 0.001)$$
$$+ [1 - \epsilon^{-10^3(t-0.002)}]u_{-1}(t - 0.002) \qquad (9\text{-}7\text{-}10)$$

EXAMPLE 9-7-3. Let it be supposed that the current i in Fig. 9-7-3 is

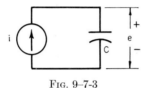

FIG. 9-7-3

one member of the family of functions listed in Table 9-1; that is,

$$i = u_n(t) = C\frac{de}{dt} \qquad (9\text{-}7\text{-}11)$$

The transform of this equation is

$$s^n = CsE(s) \qquad (9\text{-}7\text{-}12)$$

or

$$E(s) = \frac{1}{C}s^{n-1} \qquad (9\text{-}7\text{-}13)$$

The inverse transform is

$$e = \frac{1}{C}u_{n-1}(t) \qquad (9\text{-}7\text{-}14)$$

This development shows that, if the current is the nth-order member of the family of functions, the voltage is $1/C$ times the $(n-1)$th-order member. That is, if the current is a step function, the voltage is a ramp function; if the current is an impulse function, the voltage is a step function; if the current is a second-order impulse function, the voltage is a first-order impulse function; etc.

It is to be emphasized that either the current can be applied and a voltage is the result, or the voltage can be applied and a current is the result. Either way, the preceding statements are true.

FIG. 9–7-4

EXAMPLE 9–7-4. A development similar to that presented in the preceding article is performed for the circuit of Fig. 9–7-4. The circuit equation is

$$i = u_n(t) = \frac{1}{L} \int_0^t e \, dt \qquad (9\text{--}7\text{-}15)$$

and its transform is

$$s^n = \frac{1}{L} \frac{E(s)}{s} \qquad (9\text{--}7\text{-}16)$$

or

$$E(s) = Ls^{n+1} \qquad (9\text{--}7\text{-}17)$$

The inverse transform is

$$e = Lu_{n+1}(t) \qquad (9\text{--}7\text{-}18)$$

It is to be concluded that, if the current is a ramp function, the voltage is a step function; if the current is a step function, the voltage is a first-order impulse function; if the current is a first-order impulse function, the voltage is a second-order impulse function; etc. Again, either the voltage or the current can be considered as the applied function and the other as the response.

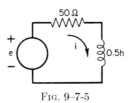

FIG. 9–7-5

EXAMPLE 9–7-5. A voltage e is applied to the circuit of Fig. 9–7-5, and the resulting circuit equation is

$$e = 50 \, i + 0.5 \frac{di}{dt} \qquad (9\text{--}7\text{-}19)$$

First, let it be assumed that the applied voltage is a unit impulse. The transformed equation is

$$1 = I(s)[50 + 0.5 \, s] \qquad (9\text{--}7\text{-}20)$$

which, when solved for $I(s)$, gives

$$I(s) = \frac{2}{s + 100} \qquad (9\text{--}7\text{-}21)$$

The inverse transform is

$$i = 2 \, \epsilon^{-100t} \qquad (9\text{--}7\text{-}22)$$

If, instead of the unit impulse, a unit step function of voltage is applied to the circuit, the response, as found in Chapter 2, is

$$i = \frac{E}{R} (1 - \epsilon^{-Rt/L}) = 0.02(1 - \epsilon^{-100t}) \qquad (9\text{-}7\text{-}23)$$

However, this answer can be obtained in another manner. The unit step function is the integral of the unit impulse function. The response to a unit step function is the integral of the response to the unit impulse function. Therefore Eq. 9-7-22 can be integrated to yield the circuit response to the unit step function of voltage:

$$i = \int_0^t 2 \, \epsilon^{-100t} \, dt = \left[-0.02 \, \epsilon^{-100t} \right]_0^t = 0.02(1 - \epsilon^{-100t}) \qquad (9\text{-}7\text{-}24)$$

The response of the circuit to a unit ramp function can be obtained by integrating Eq. 9-7-24:

$$i = \int_0^t 0.02(1 - \epsilon^{-100t}) \, dt = 0.02 \, t - 2 \times 10^{-4} + 2 \times 10^{-4} \, \epsilon^{-100t} \qquad (9\text{-}7\text{-}25)$$

Likewise the response to a unit second-order impulse can be found by differentiating Eq. 9-7-22:

$$i = 2 \, u_0(t) - 200 \, \epsilon^{-100t} \qquad (9\text{-}7\text{-}26)$$

Also, the response to a third-order impulse can be found by differentiating Eq. 9-7-26:

$$i = 2 \, u_{+1}(t) - 200 \, u_0(t) + 2 \times 10^4 \, \epsilon^{-100t} \qquad (9\text{-}7\text{-}27)$$

This result is to be checked by taking the transform of Eq. 9-7-19 when e is a third-order impulse:

$$s^2 = I(s)[0.5 \, s + 50] \qquad (9\text{-}7\text{-}28)$$

which gives for $I(s)$

$$I(s) = \frac{2 \, s^2}{s + 100} \qquad (9\text{-}7\text{-}29)$$

$I(s)$ can be expanded:

$$
\begin{array}{r}
2 \, s \;-\; 200 \\
\hline
s + 100 \overline{)\, 2 \, s^2 } \\
2 \, s^2 + 200 \, s \\
\hline
-\, 200 \, s \\
-\, 200 \, s - 2 \times 10^4 \\
\hline
+\, 2 \times 10^4
\end{array}
\qquad (9\text{-}7\text{-}30)
$$

which can be written

$$I(s) = 2 \, s - 200 + \frac{2 \times 10^4}{s + 100} \qquad (9\text{-}7\text{-}31)$$

The inverse transform is

$$i = 2 \, u_{+1}(t) - 200 \, u_0(t) + 2 \times 10^4 \, \epsilon^{-100t} \qquad (9\text{-}7\text{-}32)$$

which agrees with Eq. 9-7-27.

EXAMPLE 9–7-6. The square wave of current of Fig. 9–7-6a is applied to the circuit of Fig. 9–7-6b. The transform of $i(t)$ is

$$I(s) = \frac{I}{s} \tanh \frac{T}{4} s \qquad (9\text{-}7\text{-}33)$$

where I is defined as the maximum value of the applied square wave of current.

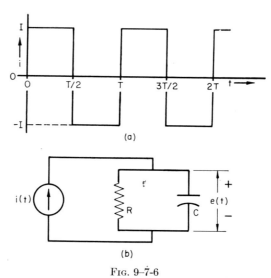

(a)

(b)

FIG. 9–7-6

Before applying the current $i(t)$ to the circuit, it is of interest to examine the inverse transform of $I(s)$, expanded as an infinite series of frequency terms. As a start in this direction, the location of the poles of $I(s)$ are examined by writing $I(s)$ in the form

$$I(s) = \frac{I}{s} \frac{\sinh (T/4)s}{\cosh (T/4)s} \qquad (9\text{-}7\text{-}34)$$

At first glance it may seem that this function has a pole at the origin $(s = 0)$; actually the function has the indeterminate form $0/0$ at this point. When the value of the function is determined at $s = 0$, it can be shown to be finite; hence, there is no pole in $I(s)$ at the origin. Therefore the poles of $I(s)$ occur when

$$\cosh \frac{T}{4} s = 0 \qquad (9\text{-}7\text{-}35)$$

or when

$$\frac{T}{4} s = \pm j \frac{\pi}{2} (2n - 1) \qquad n = 1, 2, 3, \cdots$$

or
$$s = \pm j \frac{2\pi}{T} (2n - 1) \qquad n = 1, 2, 3, \cdots \qquad (9\text{-}7\text{-}36)$$

Fig. 9–7-7 shows a part of the s-plane with the pole location indicated.

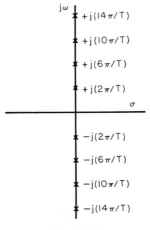

FIG. 9–7-7

The partial fraction expansion of the function can be written in the form

$$I(s) = \ldots + \frac{K_{-3}}{s + j(10\,\pi/T)} + \frac{K_{-2}}{s + j(6\,\pi/T)} + \frac{K_{-1}}{s + j(2\,\pi/T)}$$
$$+ \frac{K_{+1}}{s - j(2\,\pi/T)} + \frac{K_{+2}}{s - j(6\,\pi/T)} + \frac{K_{+3}}{s - j(10\,\pi/T)} + \cdots \quad (9\text{-}7\text{-}37)$$

where the residues can be determined by using the Heaviside expansion theorem. This is done at a few poles as illustrations:

$$K_{+1} = \frac{I \sinh \dfrac{T}{4} s}{\dfrac{d}{ds} \left[s \cosh \dfrac{T}{4} s \right]} \Bigg|_{s = +j(2\,\pi/T)} = -j \frac{2\,I}{\pi}$$

$$K_{+2} = \frac{I \sinh \dfrac{T}{4} s}{\dfrac{d}{ds} \left[s \cosh \dfrac{T}{4} s \right]} \Bigg|_{s = +j(6\,\pi/T)} = -j \frac{2}{3\,\pi} I \qquad (9\text{-}7\text{-}38)$$

$$K_{+3} = \frac{I \sinh \dfrac{T}{4} s}{\dfrac{d}{ds} \left[s \cosh \dfrac{T}{4} s \right]} \Bigg|_{s = j(10\,\pi/T)} = -j \frac{2}{5\,\pi} I$$

The residues K_{-1}, K_{-2}, and K_{-3} are the conjugates of the residues K_{+1}, K_{+2}, and K_{+3} respectively; therefore a few of the terms of $I(s)$ can be written

$$I(s) = \cdots \frac{j\frac{2}{5\pi}I}{s+j\frac{10\pi}{T}} + \frac{j\frac{2}{3\pi}I}{s+j\frac{6\pi}{T}} + \frac{j\frac{2}{\pi}I}{s+j\frac{2\pi}{T}} - \frac{j\frac{2}{\pi}I}{s-j\frac{2\pi}{T}}$$

$$- \frac{j\frac{2}{3\pi}I}{s-j\frac{6\pi}{T}} - \frac{j\frac{2}{5\pi}I}{s-j\frac{10\pi}{T}} + \cdots \qquad (9\text{-}7\text{-}39)$$

Corresponding terms of $I(s)$ can be combined in pairs:

$$\frac{j\frac{2}{\pi}I}{s+j\frac{2\pi}{T}} - \frac{j\frac{2}{\pi}I}{s-j\frac{2\pi}{T}} = \frac{\frac{8}{T}I}{s^2+\left(\frac{2\pi}{T}\right)^2}$$

which can be written

$$\frac{4I}{\pi}\left[\frac{\frac{2\pi}{T}}{s^2+\left(\frac{2\pi}{T}\right)^2}\right] \qquad (9\text{-}7\text{-}40)$$

When this is done for the other pairs of $I(s)$, it can be written

$$I(s) = \frac{4I}{\pi}\left[\frac{\frac{2\pi}{T}}{s^2+\left(\frac{2\pi}{T}\right)^2}\right] + \frac{4I}{3\pi}\left[\frac{\frac{6\pi}{T}}{s^2+\left(\frac{6\pi}{T}\right)^2}\right] + \frac{4I}{5\pi}\left[\frac{\frac{10\pi}{T}}{s^2+\left(\frac{10\pi}{T}\right)^2}\right] + \cdots$$

$$(9\text{-}7\text{-}41)$$

The inverse transform for $I(s)$ is

$$i = \frac{4I}{\pi}\sin\frac{2\pi}{T}t + \frac{4I}{3\pi}\sin\frac{6\pi}{T}t + \frac{4I}{5\pi}\sin\frac{10\pi}{T}t + \cdots \qquad (9\text{-}7\text{-}42)$$

The infinite series of Eq. 9-7-42 is known as the Fourier series development of the wave shape of Fig. 9-7-6. The current generator that supplies the square wave of current can be replaced by an infinite number of current generators connected in parallel, each supplying a sinusoidal current. This result is indicated in Fig. 9-7-8. The $u_{-1}(t)$ terms mean that each of these

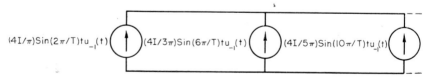

$(4I/\pi)\mathrm{Sin}(2\pi/T)tu_{-1}(t)$ $(4I/3\pi)\mathrm{Sin}(6\pi/T)tu_{-1}(t)$ $(4I/5\pi)\mathrm{Sin}(10\pi/T)tu_{-1}(t)$

FIG. 9-7-8

current components is applied to the circuit at $t=0$. By superposition each of these current terms produces a steady-state sinusoidal component of voltage plus a transient component of voltage; the total voltage is the sum of these components. Expressed as an equation:

$$e = e_{1ss} + A_1 \epsilon^{-t/RC} + e_{3ss} + A_3 \epsilon^{-t/RC} + e_{5ss} + A_5 \epsilon^{-t/RC} + \cdots \quad (9\text{-}7\text{-}43)$$

When rewritten this equation gives

$$e = e_{1ss} + e_{3ss} + e_{5ss} + \cdots + (A_1 + A_3 + A_5 + \cdots) \epsilon^{-t/RC} \quad (9\text{-}7\text{-}44)$$

or

$$e = e_{1ss} + e_{3ss} + e_{5ss} + \cdots + A \epsilon^{-t/RC} \quad (9\text{-}7\text{-}45)$$

where

$$A = A_1 + A_3 + A_5 + \cdots \quad (9\text{-}7\text{-}46)$$

Eq. 9-7-45 is now to be developed for the situation where the current of Fig. 9-7-6a is applied to the circuit of Fig. 9-7-6b. Kirchhoff's current law is

$$i = i_R + i_c = \frac{e}{R} + C \frac{de}{dt} \quad (9\text{-}7\text{-}47)$$

and the transformed equation is

$$\frac{I}{s} \tanh \frac{T}{4} s = E(s) \left[\frac{1}{R} + Cs \right] \quad (9\text{-}7\text{-}48)$$

which, when solved for $E(s)$, yields

$$E(s) = \frac{I \tanh \dfrac{T}{4} s}{sC \left[s + \dfrac{1}{RC} \right]} \quad (9\text{-}7\text{-}49)$$

To make the problem more specific, the following values are assumed for the various constants:

$$I = 1 \text{ amp} \qquad R = 100 \text{ ohms} \qquad C = 100 \ \mu\text{f} \qquad T = 0.02 \text{ sec} \quad (9\text{-}7\text{-}50)$$

With these values $E(s)$ becomes

$$E(s) = \frac{10^4}{s[s + 100]} \frac{\sinh 0.005 \ s}{\cosh 0.005 \ s} \quad (9\text{-}7\text{-}51)$$

A few of the poles of Eq. 9-7-51 are shown on the sketch of a portion of

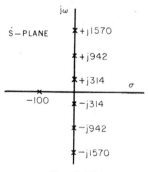

FIG. 9 7-9

the s-plane of Fig. 9–7-9. Eq. 9–7-51 can be expanded in partial fraction:

$$E(s) = \cdots + \frac{K_{-j1570}}{s+j\,1570} + \frac{K_{-j942}}{s+j\,942} + \frac{K_{-j314}}{s+j\,314} + \frac{K_{+j314}}{s-j\,314}$$

$$+ \frac{K_{+j942}}{s-j\,942} + \frac{K_{+j1570}}{s-j\,1570} + \cdots + \frac{K_{-100}}{s+100} \qquad (9\text{–}7\text{-}52)$$

The residue K_{-100} can be found by covering up the $(s+100)$ term in Eq. 9–7-51 and letting $s = -100$ in the result; thus

$$K_{-100} = \frac{10^4 \sinh 0.005\,s}{s \cosh 0.005\,s}\bigg|_{s=-100} = 46.2 \qquad (9\text{–}7\text{-}53)$$

For the other residues the denominator of Eq. 9–7-51 is differentiated:

$$\frac{d}{ds}\left[(s^2 + 100\,s)\cosh 0.005\,s\right] = (s^2 + 100\,s)(0.005)\,\sinh 0.005\,s$$

$$+ (2\,s + 100)\cosh 0.005\,s \qquad (9\text{–}7\text{-}54)$$

Since all the other poles at which the residues are to be evaluated are zeros of $\cosh 0.005\,s$, the second term of Eq. 9–7-54 drops out in calculating these residues. The method of obtaining the remaining residues is demonstrated through this example; thus,

$$K_{+j314} = \frac{2 \times 10^6}{s(s+100)}\bigg|_{s=j314} = 19.3\underline{/-162.3°}$$

$$K_{+j942} = \frac{2 \times 10^6}{s(s+100)}\bigg|_{s=j942} = 2.24\underline{/-173.9°} \qquad (9\text{–}7\text{-}55)$$

and

$$K_{+j1570} = \frac{2 \times 10^6}{s(s+100)}\bigg|_{s=j1570} = 0.81\underline{/-176.3°}$$

Eq. 9–7-52 can now be written as

$$E(s) = \cdots + \left\{ \frac{19.3\underline{/162.3°}}{s+j\,314} + \frac{19.3\underline{/-162.3°}}{s-j\,314} \right\}$$

$$+ \left\{ \frac{2.24\underline{/173.9°}}{s+j\,942} + \frac{2.24\underline{/-173.9°}}{s-j\,942} \right\}$$

$$+ \left\{ \frac{0.81\underline{/176.3°}}{s+j\,1570} + \frac{0.81\underline{/-176.3°}}{s-j\,1570} \right\} + \cdots + \frac{46.2}{s+100} \qquad (9\text{–}7\text{-}56)$$

The inverse transform of $E(s)$ is

$$e = 39.6 \sin (314\,t - 72.3°) + 4.48 \sin (942\,t - 83.9°)$$

$$+ 1.62 \sin (1570\,t - 86.3°) + \cdots + 46.2\,\epsilon^{-100t} \qquad (9\text{–}7\text{-}57)$$

which is the desired response.

PROBLEMS

9-1. Work any of the problems or examples of Chapter 8 by using the transform method.

9-2. In the circuit of Fig. 9–P-1, S has been closed until the circuit reaches

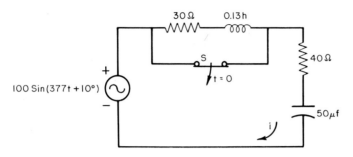

100 Sin(377t +10°)

30 Ω   0.13 h   40 Ω   50 μf   S   t = 0   i

Fɪɢ. 9–P-1

steady-state conditions. At $t = 0$, S is opened. Find the equation for i after $t = 0$.

9-3. In the circuit of Fig. 9–P-1, is there any value of δ such that S can be opened and thus yield a transient term of zero?

9-4. Similar to Prob. 9–2, except that S is open until steady-state conditions are reached and then, at $t = 0$, S is closed.

9-5. In the circuit of Fig. 9–P-2, S is open until steady-state conditions are reached. At $t = 0$, S is closed. Find the equation for i after $t = 0$.

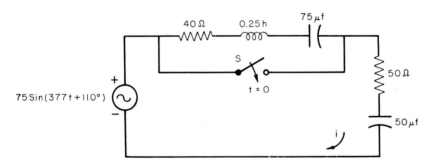

75 Sin(377t +110°)

40 Ω   0.25 h   75 μf   50 Ω   50 μf   S   t = 0   i

Fɪɢ. 9–P-2

9-6. Similar to Prob. 9–5, except add a 0.35-henry inductor in series with the 50-μf capacitor.

9-7. Similar to Prob. 9–6, except that S is closed until steady-state conditions are reached and S is opened at $t = 0$.

9-8. Same as the circuit of Fig. 9–3-1, except that S is thrown to position 2 first and then to position 1 at $t = 0$.

9-9. Same as the circuit of Fig. 9–3-2, except that S is thrown to position 2 first and then to position 1 at $t = 0$.

9–10. In the circuit of Fig. 9–P-3, S is thrown to position 1 until steady-state conditions are reached and, at $t = 0$, S is thrown to position 2. Find i after $t = 0$.

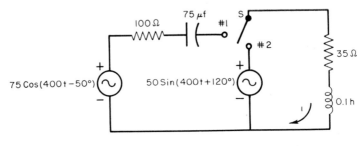

Fig. 9–P-3

9–11. Similar to Prob. 9–10 except that S is thrown to position 2 first and then to position 1.

9–12. In the circuit of Fig. 9–P-4, S is opened at $t = 0$. Find the equation for e.

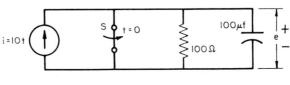

Fig. 9–P-4

9–13. In the circuit of Fig. 9–P-5, S is opened at $t = 0$. Find the equation for e.

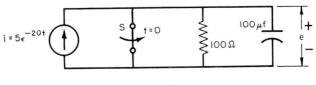

Fig. 9–P-5

9–14. In the circuit of Fig. 9–P-6, S is opened at $t = 0$. Find the equation for e.

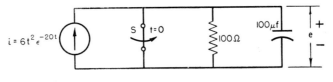

Fig. 9–P-6

9-15. Determine the transform for the wave shapes shown in Fig. 9–P-7.

$$a \quad F(\tau) = \frac{50}{2^2} - \frac{50}{2^2} e^{-0.02\tau} - \frac{1}{2} e^{-0.02\tau}$$

$$b \quad F(\tau) = \frac{50}{2^2} - \frac{50}{2^2} e^{-0.02\tau} - \frac{0.5}{2} e^{-0.02\tau} - \frac{0.5}{2} e^{-0.04\tau}$$

$$c \quad F(\tau) = \frac{1}{2} - \frac{2}{2^2} e^{-0.1\tau} + \frac{1}{2} e^{-0.4\tau}$$

$$d \quad F(\tau) = \frac{40}{2^2} - \frac{60}{2^2} e^{-0.05\tau} - \frac{1}{2} e^{-0.05\tau} + \frac{20}{2^2} e^{-0.1\tau}$$

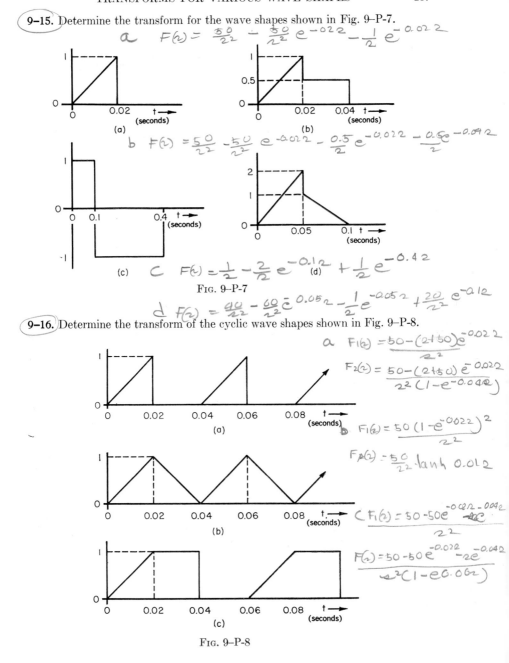

(a)

(b)

(c)

(d)

Fig. 9–P-7

9-16. Determine the transform of the cyclic wave shapes shown in Fig. 9–P-8.

$$a \quad F_1(\tau) = 50 - \frac{(2+50)e^{-0.02\tau}}{2^2}$$

$$F_2(\tau) = \frac{50 - (2+50)e^{-0.02\tau}}{2^2(1-e^{-0.04\tau})}$$

$$b \quad F_1(\tau) = \frac{50(1-e^{-0.02\tau})^2}{2^2}$$

$$F_p(\tau) = \frac{50}{2^2} \tanh 0.01\tau$$

$$c \quad F_1(\tau) = \frac{50 - 50 e^{-0.02\tau} - 0.04\tau}{2^2}$$

$$F(\tau) = \frac{50 - 50 e^{-0.02\tau} - 2e^{-0.04\tau}}{2^2(1-e^{-0.06\tau})}$$

(a)

(b)

(c)

Fig. 9–P-8

9-17. Start with the transform determined for the wave shape shown in Fig. 9-P-8b and perform the inverse transform, thus obtaining the Fourier series. Carry the solution out to three terms.

$$f(t) = \frac{1}{2} - \frac{4}{\pi^2}\left(\cos 60\pi t + \frac{1}{9}\cos 130\pi t + \frac{1}{25}\cos 250\pi t + \sim \right)$$

9-18. In the circuit of Fig. 9–P-9 the voltage e is the wave shape shown in Fig. 9–P-8b. Find the equation for the current i, carrying the solution out to three sinusoidal frequency terms.

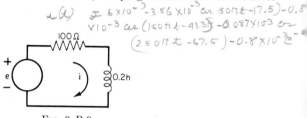

$$i(t) = 6 \times 10^{-3} - 3.86 \times 10^{-3} \cos(60\pi t - 17.5) - 0.5$$
$$\times 10^{-3} \cos(150\pi t - 43.3) - 0.087 \times 10^{-3} \cos$$
$$(250\pi t - 67.5) - 0.8 \times 10^{-3} \varepsilon^{-}$$

FIG. 9–P-9

9-19. Demonstrate that the transform of $u_{+2}(t)$ is s^2.

9-20. Extend Table 9–2 to the next higher-order impulse.

9-21. In the circuit of Fig. 9–7-1b the current is that shown in Fig. 9–P-7a. Find the equation for e.

9-22. In the circuit of Fig. 9–7-2b the current is that shown in Fig. 9–P-7d. Find the equation for e.

9-23. For the circuit shown in Fig. 9–7-1b the current i is a unit step function. Find the equation for the voltage e. Differentiate the result to obtain the response of the circuit to a unit impulse. Differentiate this result to obtain the response to a second-order impulse. Check the last two results by the transform method.

9-24. For the circuit shown in Fig. 9–7-2b the current is a unit step function. Find the equation for the voltage e. Differentiate the result to obtain the response of the circuit to a unit impulse. Differentiate this result to obtain the response to a second-order impulse. Check the last two results by the transform method.

9-21

$$e = 3000\, t - 5 + 5e^{-1000t} - [5000(t-0.02) - 5 + 5e^{-1000(t-0.02)}] u_{-1}(t-0.02)$$
$$u_{-1}(t-0.02) - [100 - 100 e^{-1000(t-0.02)}]$$

CHAPTER 10

TRANSIENTS AND STEADY-STATE RELATIONSHIPS

10–1. Thevenin's and Norton's Theorems. Up to this point Thevenin's and Norton's theorems have been used only on the resistive portions of circuits. However, these theorems can be used on portions of circuits containing L's and C's, as is demonstrated on the circuit in Fig. 10–1-1a.

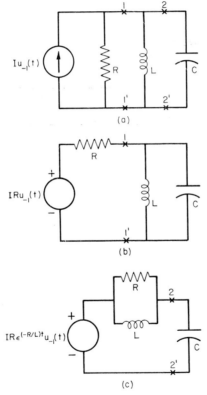

FIG. 10–1-1

If the circuit is broken at points 1-1′ and Thevenin's theorem is used on the portion of the circuit to the left, the Thevenin's theorem equivalent circuit shown in Fig. 10–1-1b is obtained. As far as the L-C portions of the circuits are concerned, the circuits of Figs. 10–1-1a and b give identical results.

The circuit of Fig. 10–1-1a can be broken at points 2-2' and Thevenin's theorem used on the portion of the circuit to the left of these points. The circuit of Fig. 10–1-1c is then obtained. The voltage $IR\epsilon^{-Rt/L}u_{-1}(t)$ is the voltage that appears at the open-circuited 2-2' terminals, and this voltage is placed in series with the circuit seen looking into the 2-2' terminals with the energy source replaced by its internal resistance. As far as the C portions of the circuits are concerned, the circuits of Figs. 10–1-1a, b, and c give identical results.

The circuit of Fig. 10–1-1a is redrawn in Fig. 10–1-2a in order to rearrange the circuit elements. If, in the result, the circuit is broken at

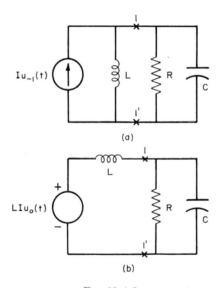

(a)

(b)

Fig. 10–1-2

points 1-1', the Thevenin's theorem equivalent is shown in Fig. 10–1-2b. The Thevenin's theorem voltage is an impulse of value LI. The current has a discontinuity of I amperes at $t = 0$, and the voltage $e = L \, (di/dt)$ is L times the impulse generated by the derivative of the current.

This example is pursued further by redrawing the circuit as shown in Fig. 10–1-3a, and first by breaking the circuit at 1-1' points. The equivalent circuit (as far as the R-L portion of the circuit is concerned) is shown in Fig. 10–1-3b. The circuit of Fig. 10–1-3a could likewise be broken at points 2-2'; the equivalent circuit (as far as the L portion of the circuit is concerned) is shown in Fig. 10–1-3c.

This example is concluded by redrawing the circuit as shown in Fig. 10–1-4a and by breaking the circuit at points 1-1'. The equivalent circuit (as far as the R portion of the circuit is concerned) is shown in Fig. 10–1-4b.

Norton's theorem can likewise be used on R-L-C portions of the circuits, but, since the details are so similar to those already presented, use of this theorem is reserved to the problems at the end of the chapter.

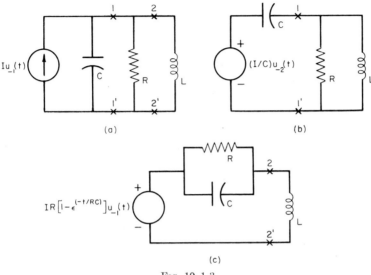

(a)   (b)

(c)

FIG. 10–1-3

The use of these circuit theorems does not make the work of obtaining numerical solutions any less tedious, but in many cases it aids in formulating the equations in the first place. For example, if the Laplace transform

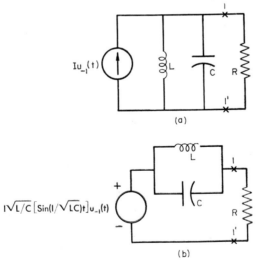

(a)

(b)

FIG. 10–1-4

method is used to obtain the current through the capacitor C in the circuits of Fig. 10–1-1, exactly the same transform is obtained from each circuit. This must be true if all the circuits are equivalent as far as C is concerned. Therefore the labor in obtaining the inverse transform is the same in each case. One use to which these theorems can be put to advantage is in handling initial conditions, as is illustrated in subsequent articles.

10–2. Operational Approach to Circuits. In Chapter 8 it is pointed out that, if the Laplace transform of a circuit equation is taken in the case where the initial stored energy is zero, the a-c circuit steady-state equations can be obtained by letting $s = j\omega$. If this procedure is reversed, it is possible to write the transformed equations by methods analogous to a-c circuit techniques by letting s replace $j\omega$. As in previous chapters, this procedure is developed briefly, no past knowledge of a-c circuit methods being assumed.

The transformed impedances of the R, L, and C elements are respectively

$$R \qquad sL \qquad \frac{1}{sC} \tag{10–2-1}$$

and the transformed admittances are respectively

$$\frac{1}{R} \qquad \frac{1}{sL} \qquad sC \tag{10–2-2}$$

This operational impedance concept for single elements is clarified by an

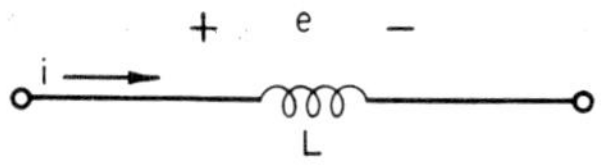

$$+ \quad e \quad -$$

FIG. 10–2-1

example for the inductor. For the circuit of Fig. 10–2-1, the equation is

$$e = L \frac{di}{dt} \tag{10–2-3}$$

and the transform, assuming no stored energy, is

$$E(s) = sLI(s) \tag{10–2-4}$$

where

$$E(s) = \mathcal{L}(e) \quad \text{and} \quad I(s) = \mathcal{L}(i) \tag{10–2-5}$$

The operational impedance, defined as

$$Z(s) = \frac{E(s)}{I(s)} \tag{10–2-6}$$

is in this case

$$Z(s) = sL \tag{10–2-7}$$

If a number of impedances are connected in series, the total impedance is the sum of the individual impedances. This can be shown to be true by

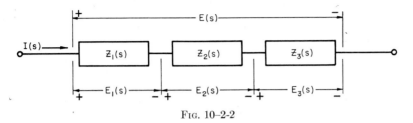

FIG. 10–2-2

referring to Fig. 10–2-2 and by writing the equation

$$E(s) = E_1(s) + E_2(s) + E_3(s) \qquad (10\text{-}2\text{-}8)$$

which can be written

$$I(s)Z(s) = I(s)Z_1(s) + I(s)Z_2(s) + I(s)Z_3(s) \qquad (10\text{-}2\text{-}9)$$

or

$$I(s)Z(s) = I(s)[Z_1(s) + Z_2(s) + Z_3(s)] \qquad (10\text{-}2\text{-}10)$$

from which is obtained the result that

$$Z(s) = Z_1(s) + Z_2(s) + Z_3(s) \qquad (10\text{-}2\text{-}11)$$

If a number of admittances are connected in parallel, the total admittance

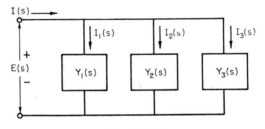

FIG. 10–2-3

is the sum of the individual admittances. This can be shown to be true by referring to Fig. 10–2-3 and by writing the equation

$$I(s) = I_1(s) + I_2(s) + I_3(s) \qquad (10\text{-}2\text{-}12)$$

which can be written

$$E(s)Y(s) = E(s)Y_1(s) + E(s)Y_2(s) + E(s)Y_3(s) \qquad (10\text{-}2\text{-}13)$$

or

$$E(s)Y(s) = E(s)[Y_1(s) + Y_2(s) + Y_3(s)] \qquad (10\text{-}2\text{-}14)$$

from which is obtained the result

$$Y(s) = Y_1(s) + Y_2(s) + Y_3(s) \qquad (10\text{-}2\text{-}15)$$

In the special case of two impedances connected in parallel the total impedance can be found:

$$\frac{1}{Z(s)} = \frac{1}{Z_1(s)} + \frac{1}{Z_2(s)} \qquad (10\text{–}2\text{–}16)$$

which can be solved:

$$Z(s) = \frac{Z_1(s)Z_2(s)}{Z_1(s) + Z_2(s)} \qquad (10\text{–}2\text{–}17)$$

By using these techniques the operational impedance of most circuits

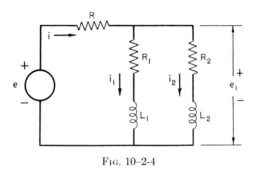

Fig. 10–2–4

can be found. The circuit of Fig. 10–2–4 is taken as an example. The impedance seen by the voltage generator is

$$Z(s) = R + \frac{(R_1 + sL_1)(R_2 + sL_2)}{R_1 + R_2 + s(L_1 + L_2)} \qquad (10\text{–}2\text{–}18)$$

which can be written

$$Z(s) = \frac{s^2 L_1 L_2 + s(R_2 L_1 + R_1 L_2 + RL_1 + RL_2) + R_1 R_2 + R_1 R + R_2 R}{s(L_1 + L_2) + R_1 + R_2}$$

$$(10\text{–}2\text{–}19)$$

If $E(s)$ is the transform of the driving voltage e, the transform of the current i is

$$I(s) = \frac{E(s)}{Z(s)} = E(s)Y(s)$$

$$= \frac{E(s)[s(L_1 + L_2) + R_1 + R_2]}{s^2 L_1 L_2 + s(R_2 L_1 + R_1 L_2 + RL_1 + RL_2) + R_1 R_2 + R_1 R + R_2 R}$$

$$(10\text{–}2\text{–}20)$$

This equation assumes that the initial stored energy is zero. With a specific e, $E(s)$ can be determined, and from the inverse transform of $I(s)$ the solution for i can be found. If the voltage e is sinusoidal and only the steady-state component of current is desired, the solution obtained by letting $s = j\omega$ is

$$I = \frac{E[(R_1 + R_2) + j\omega(L_1 + L_2)]}{R_1R_2 + R_1R + R_2R - \omega^2L_1L_2 + j\omega[R_2L_1 + R_1L_2 + RL_1 + RL_2]}$$

$$(10\text{-}2\text{-}21)$$

If e is a d-c voltage and only the steady-state component of the current is desired, the solution can be obtained by letting $s = 0$ in Eq. 10–2-20:

$$I = \frac{E[R_1 + R_2]}{R_1R_2 + R_1R + R_2R}$$

$$(10\text{-}2\text{-}22)$$

It is interesting to note that the denominator of Eq. 10–2-20 (which is the numerator of Eq. 10–2-19) is the characteristic polynomial of the circuit. If one prefers to use classical methods of solution, this fact provides an extremely rapid method of obtaining the characteristic polynomial for many circuits. This subject is taken up again after a brief digression into the subject of the characteristic polynomials.

If the equation for the transformed voltage $E_1(s)$ (the voltage across the parallel combination) is desired, it can be obtained:

$$E_1(s) = I(s)\frac{Z_1(s)Z_2(s)}{Z_1(s) + Z_2(s)}$$

$$(10\text{-}2\text{-}23)$$

where

$$Z_1(s) = R_1 + sL_1 \quad \text{and} \quad Z_2(s) = R_2 + sL_2$$

$$(10\text{-}2\text{-}24)$$

Upon substitution of $I(s)$ from Eq. 10–2-20, the equation for $E_1(s)$ becomes

$$E_1(s) = \frac{E(s)[R_1 + sL_1][R_2 + sL_2]}{s^2L_1L_2 + s(R_2L_1 + R_1L_2 + RL_1 + RL_2) + R_1R_2 + R_1R + R_2R}$$

$$(10\text{-}2\text{-}25)$$

If the equation for the transformed current $I_2(s)$ is desired, it can be obtained:

$$I_2(s) = \frac{E_1(s)}{Z_2(s)} = \frac{I(s)Z_1(s)}{Z_1(s) + Z_2(s)}$$

$$(10\text{-}2\text{-}26)$$

and upon substitution of $I(s)$ of Eq. 10–2-20 yields

$$I_2(s) = \frac{E(s)[R_1 + sL_1]}{s^2L_1L_2 + s(R_2L_1 + R_1L_2 + RL_1 + RL_2) + R_1R_2 + R_1R + R_2R}$$

$$(10\text{-}2\text{-}27)$$

Regardless of the transformed voltage or current solved for in the circuit shown in Fig. 10-2-4 (where the voltage is the driving function), the denominator is exactly the same. Since the denominator is the characteristic polynomial, this means that all the quantities i, i_1, i_2, e, etc., have the same characteristic polynomial. This conclusion is in agreement with what was stressed in Chapters 2, 3, and 4.

Assuming that one prefers classical methods of solutions, let it be supposed that the circuit has initial stored energy. As these initial conditions do not affect the characteristic polynomial, he can obtain the operational impedance of the circuit and use the numerator of the result as the characteristic polynomial. (This assumes that the circuit is driven by a voltage source.) He can write the form of the solution and proceed to evaluate the arbitrary constants in the result in the usual manner. This approach may be termed a mixture of operational and classical methods.

Let it be supposed that the circuit of Fig. 10–2-4 is driven by a current source and the equation for the voltage e is desired. On an operational basis the equation

$$E(s) = I(s)Z(s) \qquad (10\text{–}2\text{-}28)$$

can now be written. For this circuit the equation becomes

$$E(s) = \frac{I(s)[s^2 L_1 L_2 + s(R_2 L_1 + R_1 L_2 + RL_1 + RL_2) + R_1 R_2 + R_1 R + R_2 R]}{s(L_1 + L_2) + R_1 + R_2}$$

$$(10\text{–}2\text{-}29)$$

One important point to observe is that the denominator of $Z(s)$ is now the characteristic polynomial. At first thought, it may seem that this result is inconsistent with what has been said before. That is, for a given circuit, every response of voltage and current in the circuit is determined by the same characteristic polynomial. The apparent confusion is clarified if it is realized that the circuit has been changed.

The internal resistance of a voltage source is zero; therefore, for the case in which the circuit of Fig. 10–2-4 is driven by a voltage source, the resulting circuit is shown in Fig. 10–2-5a. The internal resistance of a current source is infinite; so, when the circuit of Fig. 10–2-4 is driven by a current source, the resulting circuit is that shown in Fig. 10–2-5b. By

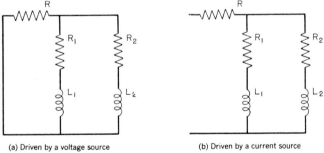

(a) Driven by a voltage source   (b) Driven by a current source

FIG. 10–2-5

inspection, it can be seen that the circuit of Fig. 10–2-5b has the characteristic polynomial

$$s(L_1 + L_2) + R_1 + R_2 \qquad (10\text{–}2\text{-}30)$$

which is quite different from the characteristic polynomial for the circuit of Fig. 10–2-5a.

In the circuit of Fig. 10–2-4 let it be supposed that the voltage e is moved into the R_1-L_1 branch, as shown in Fig. 10–2-6. The impedance as seen by

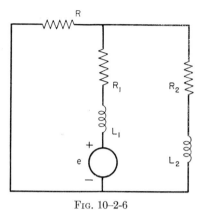

FIG. 10–2-6

the voltage source at this point is determined to be

$$Z_A(s) = R_1 + sL_1 + \frac{R(R_2 + sL_2)}{R + R_2 + sL_2} \qquad (10\text{–}2\text{-}31)$$

which can be rewritten

$$Z_A(s) = \frac{s^2 L_1 L_2 + s(R_2 L_1 + R_1 L_2 + RL_1 + RL_2) + R_1 R_2 + R_1 R + R_2 R}{R + R_2 + sL_2}$$

$$(10\text{–}2\text{-}32)$$

Because, for a voltage source which has zero internal resistance, the resulting circuit reduces to that shown in Fig. 10–2-5a, the numerator of $Z(s)$ of Eq. 10–2-19 must be the same as the numerator of $Z_A(s)$ of Eq. 10–2-32,

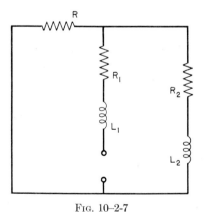

FIG. 10–2-7

since these are the characteristic polynomials for the same circuit. However, the denominator of $Z(s)$ and $Z_A(s)$ are different because the resulting circuits are different when driven by current sources. If the circuit of Fig. 10–2-6 is driven by a current source located where the voltage source is shown, the resulting circuit is that shown in Fig. 10–2-7.

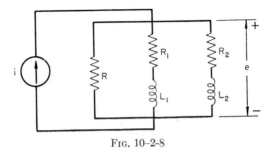

FIG. 10–2-8

Before leaving this example, let it be supposed that the circuit is driven by a current source as shown in Fig. 10–2-8. The equation

$$E(s) = I(s)Z_B(s) \qquad (10\text{--}2\text{--}33)$$

can certainly be written involving this circuit where now the denominator of $Z_B(s)$ must be the characteristic polynomial for the circuit of Fig. 10–2-5a; this can be verified from

$$\frac{1}{Z_B(s)} = \frac{1}{R} + \frac{1}{R_1 + sL_1} + \frac{1}{R_2 + sL_2} \qquad (10\text{--}2\text{--}34)$$

which can be written

$$Z_B(s) = \frac{R(R_1 + sL_1)(R_2 + sL_2)}{s^2 L_1 L_2 + s(R_2 L_1 + R_1 L_2 + RL_1 + RL_2) + R_1 R_2 + R_1 R + R_2 R}$$
$$(10\text{--}2\text{--}35)$$

10–3. Poles and Zeros of Impedances. If in the equation

$$Z(s) = \frac{E(s)}{I(s)} \qquad (10\text{--}3\text{--}1)$$

the voltage and currents are associated with the same two terminals, the impedance $Z(s)$ is known as a driving-point impedance.

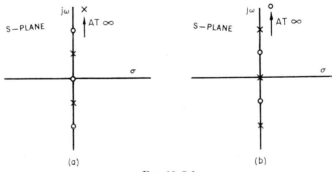

FIG. 10–3-1

The location of the poles and zeros of a driving-point impedance is characteristic of the type of network involved. For example, if the network is made up of only pure inductors and capacitors, the poles and zeros lie on the $j\omega$-axis and are simple and interlaced, as shown in Figs. 10–3-1a and Fig. 10–3-1b. The notation in Fig. 10–3-1a indicates that the network has a pole at infinity, while in Fig. 10–3-1b the network has a zero at infinity.

If the network is made up of only pure resistors and capacitors, the poles and zeros of the driving-point impedance lie on the negative real axis and are simple and interlaced. The lowest critical frequency (this refers either to a pole or a zero) is a pole, while the highest critical frequency is a zero,

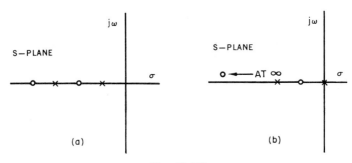

Fig. 10–3-2

as shown in Fig. 10–3-2. For an R-C driving-point admittance, the roles of the poles and zeros simply interchange.

If the network is made up of only pure resistors and inductors, the poles and zeros of the driving-point impedance lie on the negative real axis and are simple and interlaced. The lowest critical frequency is a zero and the highest critical frequency is a pole, as shown in Fig. 10–3-3. For an R-L

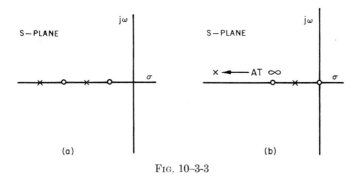

Fig. 10–3-3

driving-point admittance, the roles of the poles and zeros simply interchange.

If the network contains resistors, inductors, and capacitors, the poles and zeros of the driving-point impedance lie in the left-half plane (the $j\omega$-axis is included in the left-half plane).

If the voltage and current of Eq. 10–3-1 refer to different points in the circuit, the above statements are no longer true.

10–4. The Transient Solution to a Circuit Problem. For the circuit shown in Fig. 10–4-1, the impedance looking into points A-B can be written in

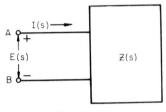

FIG. 10–4-1

the operational form as $Z(s)$. As an example, the following $Z(s)$ is assumed:

$$Z(s) = \frac{(s + Z_1)(s + Z_2)(s + Z_3)}{(s + a - j\beta)(s + a + j\beta)(s + P_3)} \qquad (10\text{--}4\text{-}1)$$

and the location of the poles and zero is indicated in Fig. 10–4-2, where the notation used is P_1 for $a - j\beta$ and P_2 for $a + j\beta$. If the circuit is driven

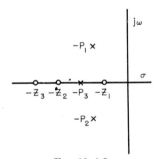

FIG. 10–4-2

from a sinusoidal voltage source, the steady-state component of the current is sinusoidal and the characteristic polynomial is that given by the numerator of $Z(s)$. Therefore the form of the solution is

$$i = i_{ss} + A_1\epsilon^{-Z_1 t} + A_2\epsilon^{-Z_2 t} + A_3\epsilon^{-Z_3 t} \qquad (10\text{--}4\text{-}2)$$

If the circuit is driven from a sinusoidal current source, the steady-state component of the voltage is sinusoidal and the characteristic polynomial is that given by the denominator of $Z(s)$. Therefore the form of the solution is

$$e = e_{ss} + \epsilon^{-at}[A_4 \cos \beta t + A_5 \sin \beta t] + A_6\epsilon^{-P_3 t} \qquad (10\text{--}4\text{-}3)$$

In Eqs. 10–4-2 and 10–4-3 the arbitrary constants are determined by the initial conditions and the driving functions and can be found by the usual procedure. As can be seen by inspecting these equations, the location of the poles and zeros has a very definite effect on the transient portion of the solution. The location of the poles and zero also has a very definite effect on the steady-state component, as discussed in the next article.

On first contact with two equations such as 10–4-2 and 10–4-3, many persons are reluctant to accept the fact that a circuit response is in accordance with one characteristic polynomial if driven from a current source, and in accordance with another characteristic polynomial if driven from a voltage source. These individuals know that the circuit ties the voltage and the current together as a pair without regard to which is the applied function and which is the response, and they feel that somehow Eqs. 10–4-2 and 10–4-3 violate this principle. To clarify this situation, let it be supposed that the sinusoidal voltage shown in Fig. 10–4-3a is applied

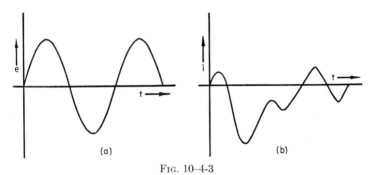

(a) (b)

Fig. 10–4-3

to the circuit of Fig. 10–4-1 and that the current shown in Fig. 10–4-3b is the response. If now the circuit is driven by a current source and the current of Fig. 10–4-3b is driven through the circuit, the voltage of Fig. 10–4-3a is the response, just as expected. However, if the circuit is driven by a current that is sinusoidal with the same magnitude in amperes as the voltage e is in volts, there is no reason to suppose that the voltage response is of exactly the same form as the current response of Fig. 10–4-3b. In fact, if it were, the circuit would have to be the dual of itself; this would reduce the circuit to a 1-ohm resistor, which is a trivial case.

10–5. Relationship between Alternating-Current Steady-State Response and Poles and Zeros. The poles and zeros of an impedance function have obvious effect on the transient response of a circuit, as is shown in the preceding example. In a somewhat similar manner, the nature of the sinusoidal steady-state response is also determined by the poles and zeros.

The a-c circuit impedance can be obtained from $Z(s)$ by replacing s by $j\omega$. If the example of $Z(s)$, as given by Eq. 10–4-1, is used, $Z(j\omega)$ is given by

$$Z(j\omega) = \frac{(j\omega + Z_1)(j\omega + Z_2)(j\omega + Z_3)}{(j\omega + a - j\beta)(j\omega + a + j\beta)(j\omega + P_3)} \quad (10\text{-}5\text{-}1)$$

The quantity $j\omega$ locates one point on the $j\omega$-axis, and each of the terms of Eq. 10-4-4 is a phasor drawn from the pole (or zero) in question to this point on the $j\omega$-axis, as shown in Fig. 10-5-1. Therefore $Z(j\omega)$ is determined

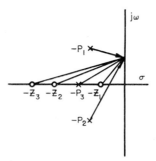

Fig. 10–5-1

by the poles and zeros of $Z(s)$ and the quantity $j\omega$. Since $\mathbf{Z}$ determines the relationship between $\mathbf{I}$ and $\mathbf{E}$, both the transient and steady-state terms are determined by the poles and zeros of $Z(s)$.

In the steady state both the applied function (voltage or current) and the response (current or voltage) are sinusoidal, so it does not matter which is considered the driving function and which the response.

If the angular frequency ω varies from zero to infinity, the variation of $Z(j\omega)$ can be visualized by observing the changes that take place in the phasors from the respective zeros and poles to the point on the $j\omega$-axis, as this point starts at the origin and moves up the $j\omega$-axis. The phasors from the zeros to this point are multiplied in the numerator of $Z(j\omega)$, and the phasors from the poles to this point are multiplied in the denominator of $Z(j\omega)$. If the driving function is a current of constant magnitude but varying frequency, the variation of voltage

$$E(j\omega) = I(j\omega)Z(j\omega)$$

is proportional to the variation of the impedance function.

If the driving function is a voltage of constant magnitude but varying frequency, the variation of current

$$I(j\omega) = \frac{E(j\omega)}{Z(j\omega)} = E(j\omega)Y(j\omega)$$

is proportional to the variation of the admittance function.

Although the poles and zeros determine the steady-state response and also the transient response in a method that can be visualized in a rather straightforward manner, this does not imply that all problems involving steady-state response and transient response are easily solved. For example, if a designer is supposed to find a pole-zero configuration such that the corresponding circuit has a certain general type of step-function response and a certain general type of steady-state response, the circuitous nature of the above relationships is such that it is a difficult problem.

10–6. Treating Initial Conditions. The operational approach to circuits discussed in Art. 10–2 assumes that no energy is stored in the circuit at $t = 0$. The initial conditions can be added in a manner identical to that discussed in Chapter 2. The following provides a brief review of these

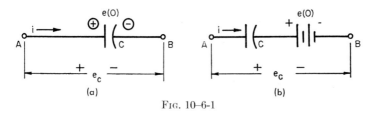

(a)   (b)

Fig. 10–6-1

methods. A capacitor with an initial charge as shown in Fig. 10–6-1a is characterized by the equation

$$e_c = \frac{1}{C} \int_0^t i \, dt + e(0) \tag{10-6-1}$$

By inspection, in so far as conditions external to terminals A-B are concerned, it is to be seen that the circuit of Fig. 10–6-1b also satisfies the same equation. Therefore a capacitor with an initial charge can be replaced by an unchanged capacitor in series with a battery whose emf is equal to the initial voltage $e(0) = q(0)C$.

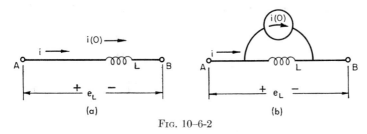

(a)   (b)

Fig. 10–6-2

An inductor with an initial current, as shown in Fig. 10–6-2a, is characterized by the equation

$$i = \frac{1}{L} \int_0^t e_L \, dt + i(0) \tag{10-6-2}$$

By inspection, in so far as conditions external to terminals A-B are concerned, it can be seen that the circuit of Fig. 10–6-2b also satisfies the same equation. Therefore an inductor with an initial current can be replaced by an inductor with no initial current in parallel with a constant current source which delivers a current equal to $i(0)$.

When the circuit equations are formulated by using Kirchhoff's voltage equations, it is convenient to change the current source of Fig. 10–6-2b to a voltage source. As far as circuit conditions after $t = 0$ are concerned, the current source of Fig. 10–6-2b can be turned on at $t = 0$, as shown in

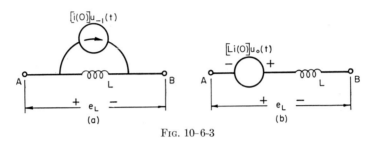

FIG. 10-6-3

Fig. 10–6-3a. It is assumed that this inductor is embedded in a circuit; and in so far as other portions of this circuit are concerned Thevenin's theorem can be used at terminals A-B. The voltage appearing at terminals A-B in the circuit of Fig. 10–6-3a is an impulse of value $Li(0)$ occurring at $t = 0$; and this Thevenin's theorem voltage $[Li(0)]u_0(t)$ can be placed in series with the inductor L, resulting in the equivalent circuit shown in Fig. 10–6-3b.

When the circuit equations are formulated by using Kirchhoff's current equations, it is convenient to change the voltage source of Fig. 10–6-1b to a current source. In so far as the circuit after $t = 0$ is concerned, the voltage source of Fig. 10–6-1b can be turned on at $t = 0$, as shown in Fig. 10–6-4a. It is assumed that this capacitor is embedded in a circuit;

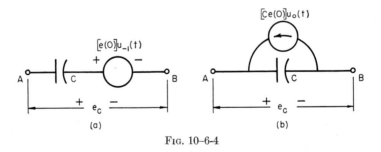

FIG. 10-6-4

and in so far as the other portions of this circuit are concerned Norton's theorem can be used on the capacitor by short-circuiting terminals A-B. The current through this short circuit is an impulse of value $Ce(0)$ occurring at $t = 0$, and this Norton's theorem current $[Ce(0)]u_0(t)$ can be placed in parallel with the capacitor C, resulting in the equivalent circuit shown in Fig. 10–6-4b.

The use of these equivalent circuits is illustrated in the next article.

10–7. Circuits with Initial Conditions. The circuit of Fig. 10–7-1a contains stored energy at $t = 0$. The circuit is to be solved for i_2 by first using the necessary Kirchhoff's voltage equations with the mesh currents i_1 and i_2 as the unknowns. Therefore the initial conditions are converted into

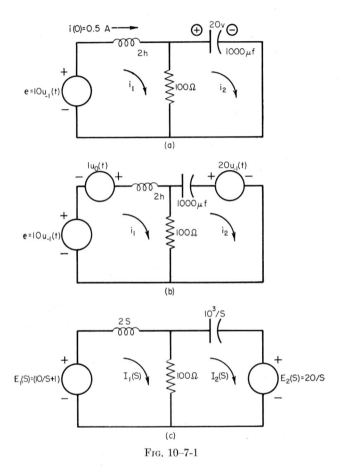

FIG. 10–7-1

voltage sources, as shown in Fig. 10–7-1b. The circuit of Fig. 10–7-1c is the transformed equivalent of that of Fig. 10–7-1b for which the following equations can be written:

$$E_1(s) = I_1(s)[2\,s] + [I_1(s) - I_2(s)][100]$$

$$- E_2(s) = [I_2(s) - I_1(s)][100] + I_2(s)\left[\frac{1000}{s}\right] \qquad (10\text{-}7\text{-}1)$$

These equations can be written

$$E_1(s) = I_1(s)[2\,s + 100] - I_2(s)[100]$$

$$- E_2(s) = - I_1(s)[100] + I_2(s)\left[100 + \frac{1000}{s}\right] \qquad (10\text{-}7\text{-}2)$$

Eqs. 10–7-2 can be written by inspection from the circuit without first writing Eqs. 10–7-1. This is done by noting that the impedance around the mesh through which $I_1(s)$ flows is $2 s + 100$, while the impedance around the mesh through which $I_2(s)$ flows is $100 + 1000/s$. The impedance common to the two branches is 100, and this term appears with a negative sign because $I_1(s)$ and $I_2(s)$ exist through it in opposite directions.

Eqs. 10–7-2 can be solved for $I_2(s)$:

$$I_2(s) = \frac{E_1(s)[0.5\ s] - E_2(s)[0.01\ s^2 + 0.5\ s]}{s^2 + 10\ s + 500} \tag{10-7-3}$$

When $E_1(s) = 10/s + 1$ and $E_2(s) = 20/s$ are substituted in Eq. 10–7-3, the result can be simplified and written

$$I_2(s) = \frac{0.3\ s - 5}{(s + 5)^2 + (21.8)^2} \tag{10-7-4}$$

for which the inverse transform is

$$i_2 = \epsilon^{-5t}[0.3 \cos 21.8\ t - 0.298 \sin 21.8\ t] \tag{10-7-5}$$

If the voltage e driving the circuit of Fig. 10–7-1a is

$$e = [10 \sin 10\ t]u_{-1}(t) \tag{10-7-6}$$

and the desired response is the steady-state component of the current i_2. This result can be obtained from Eq. 10–7-3 in the following manner. The initial current and charge of the original problem can be neglected, because they do not affect the steady-state current. Therefore $E_2(s)$ in Eq. 10–7-3 becomes zero. With the sine function chosen as reference, the voltage e is expressed in phasor notation by

$$E = 10\underline{/0°} = 10 + j\ 0 \tag{10-7-7}$$

With the additional substitution that

$$s = j\ 10 \tag{10-7-8}$$

Eq. 10–7-3 can be written

$$I_2 = \frac{10[0.5(j\ 10)]}{-100 + j\ 100 + 500} = 0.121\underline{/76°} \tag{10-7-9}$$

The steady-state component of current i_2 is

$$i_{2ss} = 0.121 \sin (10\ t + 76°) \tag{10-7-10}$$

The circuit of Fig. 10–7-1a is again solved for i_2 by using Kirchhoff's current law. The circuit is redrawn in Fig. 10–7-2a. Norton's theorem is used on the inductor by shorting node e_n to ground. The Norton's theorem current associated with the inductor is

$$\frac{1}{L} \int_0^t e\ dt + i(0) = 5t + 0.5 \tag{10-7-11}$$

The Norton's theorem current associated with the capacitor with the node e_n shorted to ground is

$$[Ce(0)]u_0(t) = 0.02\, u_0(t) \tag{10-7-12}$$

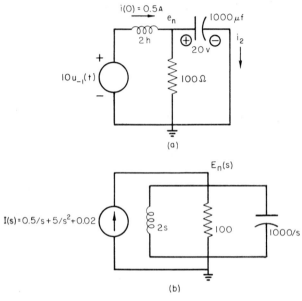

(a)

(b)

FIG. 10-7-2

The equivalent circuit, in terms of the transformed quantities, is shown in Fig. 10-7-2b. The circuit equation can be written

$$\frac{0.5}{s} + \frac{5}{s^2} + 0.02 = E_N(s)\left[\frac{1}{2\,s} + \frac{1}{100} + \frac{s}{1000}\right] \tag{10-7-13}$$

which, when solved for $E_N(s)$, yields

$$E_N(s) = \frac{20\, s^2 + 500\, s + 5000}{s[s^2 + 10\, s + 500]} \tag{10-7-14}$$

The current i_2 through the capacitor is

$$i_2 = C\frac{de_N}{dt} = 10^{-3}\frac{de_N}{dt} \tag{10-7-15}$$

and the transform is

$$I_2(s) = 10^{-3}[sE_N(s) - 20] \tag{10-7-16}$$

When $E_N(s)$ is substituted in this equation and the result simplified, $I_2(s)$ is

$$I_2(s) = \frac{0.3\, s - 5}{s^2 + 10\, s + 500} \tag{10-7-17}$$

This agrees with Eq. 10–7-4, as it should. The inverse transform yields the desired solution for i_2 as given by Eq. 10–7-5.

10–8. Inverse Networks. Two networks $Z_1(s)$ and $Z_2(s)$ are said to be inverse with respect to the resistance R if

$$Z_1(s) \cdot Z_2(s) = R^2 \tag{10–8-1}$$

Let it be assumed that $Z_1(s)$ is a resistor R_1; then $Z_2(s)$ is

$$Z_2(s) = \frac{R^2}{Z_1(s)} = \frac{R^2}{R_1} = R_2 \tag{10–8-2}$$

Thus $Z_2(s)$ is a resistor whose value is furnished by Eq. 10–8-2 if R and R_1 are given.

Let it be assumed that $Z_1(s)$ is an inductor sL_1; then $Z_2(s)$ can be determined:

$$Z_2(s) = \frac{R^2}{Z_1(s)} = \frac{R^2}{sL_1} = \frac{1}{sC_2} \tag{10–8-3}$$

where

$$C_2 = \frac{L_1}{R^2} \tag{10–8-4}$$

$Z_2(s)$ is a capacitor whose value is furnished by Eq. 10–8-4.

In a similar manner, if $Z_1(s)$ is a capacitor $1/sC_1$, $Z_2(s)$ can be determined:

$$Z_2(s) = \frac{R^2}{Z_1(s)} = R^2 s C_1 = L_2 s \tag{10–8-5}$$

where

$$L_2 = R^2 C_1 \tag{10–8-6}$$

Next let it be assumed that $Z_1(s)$ is made up of two impedances $Z_A(s)$ and $Z_B(s)$ connected in series, and that $Z_2(s)$ is made up of two impedances

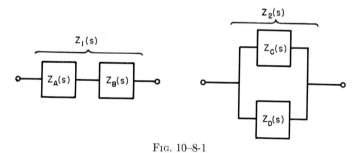

Fig. 10–8-1

$Z_C(s)$ and $Z_D(s)$ connected in parallel, as shown in Fig. 10–8-1. Also, let it be assumed that $Z_A(s)$ and $Z_C(s)$ are inverse networks with respect to some R, as

$$Z_A(s) \cdot Z_C(s) = R^2 \tag{10–8-7}$$

and that $Z_B(s)$ and $Z_D(s)$ are inverse networks with respect to the same R, as

$$Z_B(s) \cdot Z_D(s) = R^2 \tag{10–8-8}$$

The product $Z_1(s) \cdot Z_2(s)$ can be written

$$Z_1(s) \cdot Z_2(s) = [Z_A(s) + Z_B(s)] \left[\frac{Z_C(s) Z_D(s)}{Z_C(s) + Z_D(s)} \right]$$

$$= [Z_A(s) + Z_B(s)] \left[\frac{R^2/Z_A(s) \cdot R^2/Z_B(s)}{R^2/Z_A(s) + R^2/Z_B(s)} \right] = R^2 \quad (10\text{-}8\text{-}9)$$

In other words, if Eqs. 10–8-7 and 10–8-8 are satisfied, $Z_1(s)$ and $Z_2(s)$ are inverse networks.

The relationships just developed are sufficient to handle a complicated circuit. For example, it is desired to find the inverse network of the network shown in Fig. 10–8-2a.

By inspection, R_1 is in series with the rest of the network. Therefore, in the inverse network (Fig. 10–8-2b), the inverse of R_1 (which is labeled

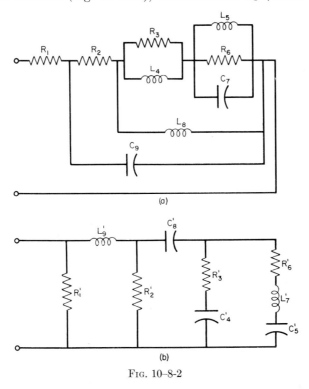

(a)

(b)

Fig. 10–8-2

R_1') is placed in parallel with the inverse of the rest of the network. Then as C_9 is in parallel with the rest of the network, in Fig. 10–8-2b the L_9' (the inverse of C_9) is placed in series with the inverse of the rest of the network. Next it is observed that R_2 is in series with the rest of the network; therefore, in Fig. 10–8-2b, R_2' (the inverse of R_2) is placed in parallel with the inverse of the rest of the network. This process is continued until the entire network shown in Fig. 10–8-2b is obtained.

If in Fig. 10–8-3 the impedances $Z_1(s)$ and $Z_2(s)$ are inverse with respect

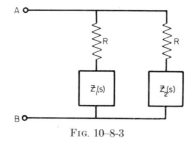

Fig. 10–8-3

to R, the impedance seen looking into terminals A-B is given by

$$Z_{AB} = \frac{[R + Z_1(s)][R + Z_2(s)]}{2R + Z_1(s) + Z_2(s)} = \frac{R^2 + RZ_1(s) + RZ_2(s) + Z_1(s)Z_2(s)}{2R + Z_1(s) + Z_2(s)}$$

$$= \frac{R[2R + Z_1(s) + Z_2(s)]}{2R + Z_1(s) + Z_2(s)} = R \qquad (10\text{–}8\text{-}10)$$

Therefore the impedance Z_{AB} is a pure resistance to any type of input signal.

The simple circuit of Fig. 10–8-4a is of interest in practice. If the time

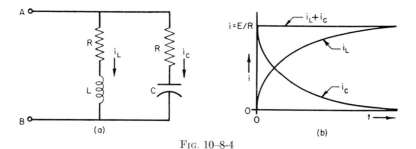

Fig. 10–8-4

constants of the R-L branch and the R-C branch are equal,

$$\frac{L}{R} = RC \qquad (10\text{–}8\text{-}11)$$

it follows that the L and C are inverse arms with respect to the R. Therefore this figure is a special case of the circuit of Fig. 10–8-3. If a constant voltage E is applied across the A-B terminals of Fig. 10–8-4, the sum of the currents i_L and i_c is a constant E/R for all values of time.

In a similar manner, the circuits of Fig. 10–8-2 are inverse. If a resistor of value R is placed in series with each of these networks and the resulting combinations are connected in parallel, the result behaves as a resistor R to any type of input signal.

Inspection of the circuit of Fig. 10–8-5 reveals that if $Z_1(s)$ and $Z_2(s)$ are inverse with respect to R, the impedance $Z'_{A'B'}$ is also equal to R. This can be seen by observing that the R-$Z_1(s)$ and R-$Z_2(s)$ paralleled branches of Fig. 10–8–5 are, respectively, the inverse of the R-$Z_2(s)$ and R-$Z_1(s)$

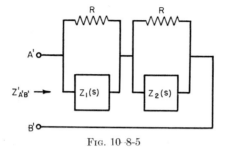

FIG. 10–8–5

series branches of Fig. 10–8–3. Therefore $Z'_{A'B'}$ and Z_{AB} are inverse with respect to R and, since Z_{AB} is equal to R, $Z'_{A'B'}$ must also be equal to R.

10–9. Reciprocal Networks. If two networks are inverse with respect to 1 ohm, they are said to be reciprocal networks, related by

$$Z_1(s) \cdot Z_2(s) = 1 \qquad (10\text{–}9\text{–}1)$$

This equation can be written

$$Z_1(s) = \frac{1}{Z_2(s)} \qquad (10\text{–}9\text{–}2)$$

or

$$Z_1(s) = Y_2(s) \qquad (10\text{–}9\text{–}3)$$

In words: When one network has an impedance that is identical in form with the admittance of another network, the two networks are reciprocal networks.

10–10. Dual Networks. If a network is given and its dual network is required, the dual network can be found in many cases by obtaining the inverse of the original network with respect to 1 ohm by the methods developed in Art. 10–8.

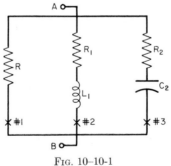

FIG. 10–10–1

The circuit of Fig. 10–10–1 is used to illustrate the procedure. First, the circuit is opened at point 1. The circuit seen looking into the resulting terminals is R in series with the $(R_1\text{-}L_1)$ and $(R_2\text{-}C_2)$ branches in parallel. The dual of this is shown in Fig. 10–10-2a. In the resulting circuit the ter-

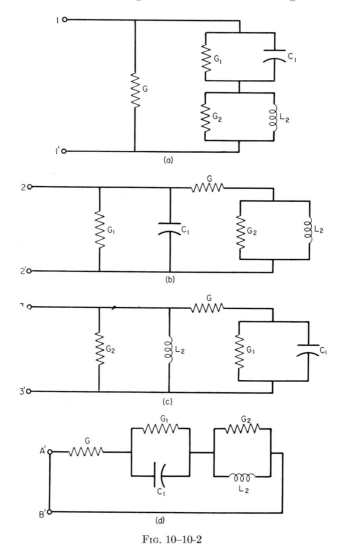

Fig. 10–10-2

minals labeled 1-1' are left open-circuited because this is the dual (inverse) of the original short-circuited terminals.

Next the circuit of Fig. 10–10-1 is opened at point 2 and the inverse of the resulting circuit with respect to 1 ohm is developed as shown in Fig. 10–10-2b. In the resulting circuit the terminals labeled 2-2' are left open-circuited. In a similar manner the original circuit is opened at point 3; the resulting dual circuit is shown in Fig. 10–10-2c.

Finally, before leaving this example, the original network is viewed from the open-circuited terminals labeled A-B. When viewed from these terminals, the resulting circuit is made up of three branches in parallel, and the dual of this is three groups of elements in series, as seen from the terminals labeled A'-B' of Fig. 10–10–2d. Since the original terminals A-B were open-circuited, the resulting terminals A'-B' must be short-circuited.

By inspection, it can be seen that the four circuits of Fig. 10–10–2 are actually the same circuit, as they should be if each is the dual of the circuit of Fig. 10–10–1.

In order to obtain the dual network by the methods outlined in this article, the original network must be such that it can be separated into groups of series and parallel elements. Under certain conditions, a network may have a dual which cannot be found by this procedure. An example of this is a network containing a bridge (or lattice) type of structure for which a more general procedure is required.*

The concept of duality requires that for each element in a network there must exist a corresponding element in the dual of the network. In addition to this, the current (or voltage) associated with the element in the original network must behave in exactly the same manner as does the voltage (or current) associated with the corresponding element in the dual network. In order for a network to have a dual, the network must be such that it can be drawn on a "flat" surface (or spherical surface, for that matter) without one branch crossing another branch. This type of network is commonly termed a "flat" network or a "mappable" network.

The term reciprocal network (or inverse network) applies to a more general category than does the term dual network. For example, the operational impedance $Z_1(s)$ of a network can be determined as a ratio of two polynomials in s. The reciprocal network can be defined as $Y_1(s)$ such that $Y_1(s) = Z_1(s)$. Then a network can be developed from this $Y_1(s)$ by procedures coming out of the field of network synthesis. The resulting network may not be such that an element in it can be identified as corresponding to an element in the original network. From this discussion it can be seen that a "nonflat" network has an operational impedance $Z_1(s)$, and hence a network (or an infinite number of networks) can be found that is its reciprocal (or inverse); however, this same network does not have a dual.

PROBLEMS

10–1. Obtain $I_c(s)$ for the circuits of Fig. 10–1–1 and the circuit of Fig. 10–1–2b and compare the results.

10–2. Obtain $I_L(s)$ for the circuits of Fig. 10–1–3.

10–3. Obtain $I_R(s)$ for the circuits of Fig. 10–1–4.

*E. A. Guillemin, *Introductory Circuit Theory*, John Wiley & Sons, Inc., New York, 1953.

10–4. Obtain the equivalent circuit by using Norton's theorem on the circuit of Fig. 10–P-1 at the following points: (a) at points 1-1′ and (b) at points 2-2′.

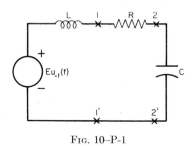

FIG. 10–P-1

Obtain $I_c(s)$ for the original circuit and for each of the circuits of (a) and (b) and compare the results.

10–5. Obtain the equivalent circuit by using Norton's theorem on the circuit of Fig. 10–P-2 at the following points: (a) at points 1-1′ and (b) at points 2-2′.

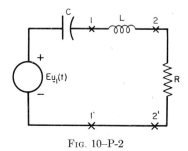

FIG. 10–P-2

Obtain $I_R(s)$ for the original circuit and for each of the circuits of (a) and (b) and compare the results.

10–6. Obtain the equivalent circuit of the circuit of Fig. 10–P-3 by using Norton's theorem at points 1-1′. Also obtain the equivalent circuit by using Thevenin's

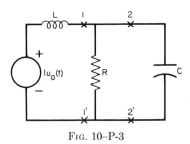

FIG. 10–P-3

theorem at points 2-2′. Obtain $I_c(s)$ for the original circuit and for each of the resulting circuits and compare.

10–7. Show that $1/sC$ is the operational impedance of a pure capacitor.

10–8. For the circuit of Fig. 10–P-4 obtain the following quantities.

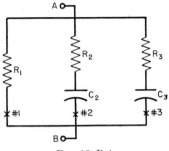

FIG. 10–P-4

(a) Open the circuit at point 1 and look in these terminals and obtain $Z_1(s)$.

(b) Open the circuit at point 2 and obtain $Z_2(s)$.

(c) Open the circuit at point 3 and obtain $Z_3(s)$.

(d) Look in terminals A-B and obtain $Z_{AB}(s)$.

(e) Examine the results of (a), (b), (c), and (d) and compare the characteristic polynomial for the original circuit obtained in each part. Identify in each part the circuit whose characteristic polynomial also appears in $Z(s)$.

10–9. For the circuit of Fig. 10–P-5 repeat Prob. 10–8.

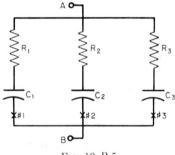

FIG. 10–P-5

10–10. For the circuit of Fig. 10–P-6 repeat Prob. 10–8.

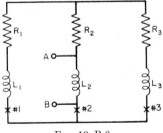

FIG. 10–P-6

10–11. For the circuit of Fig. 10–P-7 repeat Prob. 10–8.

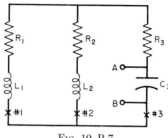

FIG. 10–P-7

10–12. The circuit of Fig. 10–P-4 is driven at point 1 by a voltage source $e = 2\,u_{-2}(t)$. Find the equation for the current in the R_1 resistor with the following circuit constants given:

$$R_1 = 100 \text{ ohms} \qquad C_2 = 100 \ \mu\text{f}$$
$$R_2 = 50 \text{ ohms} \qquad C_3 = 50 \ \mu\text{f}$$
$$R_3 = 150 \text{ ohms}$$

10–13. This problem is the same as Prob. 10–12 except that the current in R_2 is the desired solution.

10–14. Repeat Prob. 10–13 with 30 volts on C_2 with polarity (+) on top and (−) on bottom and with 50 volts on C_2 with (−) on top and (+) on bottom.

10–15. The circuit of Prob. 10–14 is driven by a voltage $e = 10 \sin 100\,t$ in place of the voltage as given in Prob. 10–12. The equation for the current in R_2 in the steady state is desired.

10–16. The circuit of Fig. 10–P-6 is driven at point 2 by a voltage source $e = 10\,u_{-1}(t)$. Find the equation for the current in the R_2 resistor with the following circuit constants:

$$R_1 = 100 \text{ ohms} \qquad L_1 = 3 \text{ henrys}$$
$$R_2 = 200 \text{ ohms} \qquad L_2 = 2 \text{ henrys}$$
$$R_3 = 300 \text{ ohms} \qquad L_3 = 1 \text{ henry}$$

10–17. This problem is the same as Prob. 10–16 except that the current in R_3 is desired.

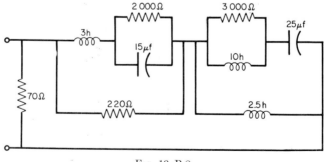

FIG. 10–P-8

10–18. The circuit of Prob. 10–16 is driven by a voltage $e = 10 \sin 100\,t$ in place of the voltage as given. The equation for the current in R_2 in the steady state is desired.

10–19. This problem is the same as Prob. 10–16 except that L_2 and L_3 both have initial currents of 1 amp in the upward direction and L_1 has an initial current of 2 amp in the downward direction.

10–20. For the circuit of Fig. 10–P-8 find the inverse network with respect to $R = 1000$ ohms.

10–21. Obtain the dual circuit to that shown in Fig. 10–P-4 by the following methods:

(a) Open the circuit at point 1.

(b) Open the circuit at point 2.

(c) Open the circuit at point 3.

(d) Look in terminals A-B.

(e) Compare the resulting networks.

10–22. Repeat Prob. 10–21 for the circuit of Fig. 10–P-5.

10–23. Repeat Prob. 10–21 for the circuit of Fig. 10–P-6.

10–24. Repeat Prob. 10–21 for the circuit of Fig. 10–P-7.

CHAPTER 11

STEADY-STATE RESPONSE TO NONSINUSOIDAL WAVE SHAPES

11-1. Introduction. If a nonsinusoidal periodic voltage is applied to a circuit, the circuit response comprises a transient component plus a steady-state component. After a sufficient length of time has elapsed, essentially only the steady-state component remains. This component is the subject to be studied in this chapter.

The following example evidences the salient features. The square wave of voltage of Fig. 11-1-1a is applied to the circuit of Fig. 11-1-1b and the

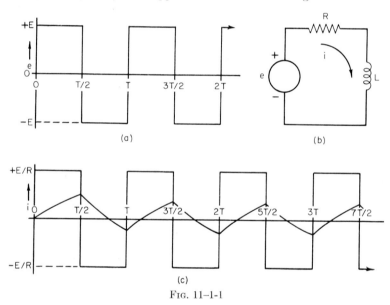

(a) (b)

(c)

Fig. 11-1-1

current response is shown in Fig. 11-1-1c. At $t = 0$ the circuit is assumed to be initially at rest; therefore $i(0)$ is zero. The current tends to the E/R value, but before it reaches this value the applied voltage reverses polarity. For convenience let it be assumed that the time constant is such that the current reaches 50 per cent of the E/R value in $T/2$ seconds.

For the half-period of time $T/2 < t < T$, the current starts at a value of $+ 0.5 \, E/R$ and tends to the steady-state value of $- E/R$. As the time constant is assumed such that the current goes through 50 per cent of its intended change in $T/2$ seconds, at $t = T$ the current therefore has a value $- 0.25 \, E/R$.

As this line of reasoning is continued, it can be seen that at the appropriate times the current has the values

$$t = \frac{3\ T}{2} \qquad i = + 0.375 \frac{E}{R} \qquad\qquad t = 2\ T \qquad i = - 0.3125 \frac{E}{R}$$

$$t = \frac{5\ T}{2} \qquad i = + 0.3438 \frac{E}{R} \qquad\qquad t = 3\ T \qquad i = - 0.3281 \frac{E}{R}; \quad \text{etc.}$$

It is to be seen that, the longer the square wave of voltage is applied to the circuit, the less is the change in the current from cycle to cycle; and, when sufficient time has elapsed, the circuit reaches steady-state conditions. Another way of stating this is to say that, after a sufficient time has elapsed for the transient component of the response to die out, only the steady-state response is left.

There are various ways of finding this steady-state response. One of the most laborious methods is to follow the response through a sufficient number of cycles until the change from cycle to cycle becomes negligibly small. Another method is to find the total response to the repeating function as presented in Chapter 9, and in the result let time become so large that the transient term disappears. If this is done, the result is an infinite series of sinusoidal terms which can also be obtained by applying the Fourier series of the driving function to the circuit term by term and by solving only for the steady-state components by a-c circuit theory. In either case, because the response is in the form of an infinite series, the results can be plotted only approximately because the infinite series must be terminated for feasible computation. Still another method of obtaining the steady-state response is to obtain a general expression for the response in the nth cycle and in the result let n go to infinity.

The method presented here is referred to as the two-point method. The basic concept is that, if a circuit is in the steady state, the response in one cycle is of the same form as the response in the next cycle. If the response is not of the same form, the circuit is not yet in the steady state. This gives the clue to the two-point method, which can best be illustrated in detail by several examples.

11–2. Square Wave Applied to Simple Circuits. EXAMPLE 11–2–1. The square wave of voltage of Fig. 11–2–1a is applied to the circuit of Fig. 11–2–1b and the steady-state current is desired. In the steady state one cycle of the current is of the same form as the next cycle; and, since in this circuit the inductor prevents the current from jumping, the current at $t = 0$ starts at some $i(0)$ value and one cycle later is at the same $i(0)$ value. The current referred to is shown in Fig. 11–2–1c. It is, of course, assumed that the voltage was applied to the circuit much earlier and that the transient response has gone to zero before the time $t = 0$.

Because of the half-cycle symmetry in this example, it is to be seen that the current at $t = 0.001$ sec is of value $- i(0)$. This symmetry forestalls

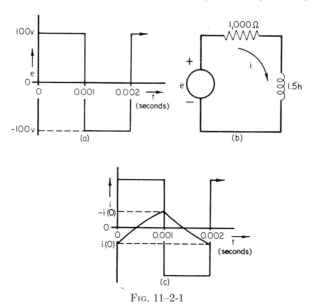

Fig. 11–2–1

the need of following the response through a whole cycle, as the half-cycle leads to the same results. The fact that the current is "fixed" at two points makes it possible to find $i(0)$, as is shown as the example proceeds.

Certain terminology is coined here to avoid confusion. The term, the response inside the cycle, is used in contrast with the term cyclic response. In this example, "the response inside the cycle" refers to the fact that for time between $0 < t < 0.001$ sec the current response is determined by a constant-voltage source of 100 volts applied to a series R-L circuit with an initial $i(0)$ current. In this interval the circuit does not know that the voltage is going to change at $t = 0.001$ sec. Therefore the current starts at some $i(0)$ value and tends to $E/R = 0.1$. At $t = 0.001$ sec the current is interrupted in its attempt to reach the $+ 0.1$ amp value and tends to $E/R = - 0.1$ in the next half-cycle. As far as the current response ("the cyclic response") to the square wave of voltage is concerned, the current is in the steady state. The usage of these terms in the following example helps to clarify the point.

The following equation is written for time inside the first half-cycle; that is, for $0 < t < 0.001$ sec

$$100 = 1000\, i + 1.5\, \frac{di}{dt} \tag{11–2–1}$$

The solution of this equation is

$$i = 0.1 + A \epsilon^{-1000t/1.5} \tag{11–2–2}$$

where A can be determined from the knowledge that $i = i(0)$ at $t = 0$, yielding

$$i = 0.1 + [i(0) - 0.1]\epsilon^{-666t} \qquad (11\text{-}2\text{-}3)$$

At the time $t = 0.001$ sec the current is equal to $-i(0)$; this gives

$$-i(0) = 0.1 + [i(0) - 0.1] \times 0.514 \qquad (11\text{-}2\text{-}4)$$

from which $i(0)$ is

$$i(0) = -0.032$$

Substituting in Eq. 11-2-3 gives

$$i = 0.1 - 0.132\,\epsilon^{-666t} \qquad (11\text{-}2\text{-}5)$$

In the interval from $0.001 < t < 0.002$ sec the current is the negative of this and thus can be written

$$i = [-0.1 + 0.132\,\epsilon^{-666(t-0.001)}]u_{-1}(t - 0.001) \qquad (11\text{-}2\text{-}6)$$

Eqs. 11-2-5 and 11-2-6 are the equations for the cyclic response of the current in steady state to the square wave of voltage. It is to be noted that these equations can be plotted as accurately as desired, and no approximations are needed as in the case of the Fourier series method of solution.

EXAMPLE 11-2-2. The square wave of voltage of Fig. 11-2-1a is applied to the circuit of Fig. 11-2-2a, and the circuit response is as in Fig. 11-2-2b. Since the current can jump from one value to another at the instant of re-

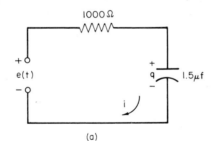

(a)

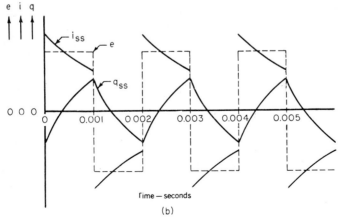

(b)

FIG. 11-2-2

versal of the voltage, the circuit is solved in terms of q. Inside the half-cycle $0 < t < 0.001$ sec the circuit equation is

$$100 = 1000 \frac{dq}{dt} + \frac{q}{1.5 \times 10^{-6}} \tag{11-2-7}$$

The solution of this equation is

$$q = 1.5 \times 10^{-4} + A\epsilon \exp\left(-\frac{t}{1000 \times 1.5 \times 10^{-6}}\right) \tag{11-2-8}$$

where A is determined from $t = 0$, $q = q(0)$:

$$q = 1.5 \times 10^{-4} + [q(0) - 1.5 \times 10^{-4}]\epsilon^{-666t} \tag{11-2-9}$$

At the time $t = 0.001$ sec, q is equal to $- q(0)$, giving the equation

$$- q(0) = 1.5 \times 10^{-4} + [q(0) - 1.5 \times 10^{-4}] \times 0.514 \tag{11-2-10}$$

From this, $q(0)$ can be found:

$$q(0) = - 0.482 \times 10^{-4} \tag{11-2-11}$$

Substituting in Eq. 11-2-9 gives

$$q = 1.5 \times 10^{-4} - 1.982 \times 10^{-4}\epsilon^{-666t} \tag{11-2-12}$$

The equation for i is the derivative of Eq. 11-2-12, or

$$i = 0.132 \, \epsilon^{-666t} \tag{11-2-13}$$

EXAMPLE 11-2-3. The square wave of current of Fig. 11-2-3a is applied

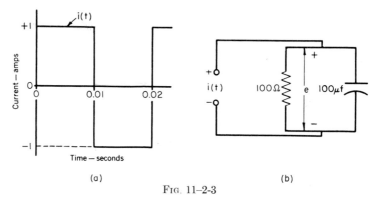

(a)   (b)

FIG. 11-2-3

to the circuit of Fig. 11-2-3b and the desired response is the voltage e. Inside the half-cycle from $0 < t < 0.01$ sec the circuit equation is

$$1 = \frac{e}{100} + 10^{-4} \frac{de}{dt} \tag{11-2-14}$$

The solution of this equation is

$$e = 100 + A\epsilon^{-t/(100 \times 10^{-4})} \tag{11-2-15}$$

where A is determined from $t = 0$, $e = e(0)$:

$$e = 100 + [e(0) - 100]\epsilon^{-100t} \tag{11-2-16}$$

At $t = 0.01$ sec, e is equal to $-e(0)$; this fact yields the equation

$$-e(0) = 100 + [e(0) - 100] \times 0.368 \qquad (11\text{-}2\text{-}17)$$

yielding for $e(0)$: $\qquad\qquad e(0) = -46.2$

Substituting in Eq. 11-2-16 gives

$$e = 100 - 146.2\,\epsilon^{-100t} \qquad (11\text{-}2\text{-}18)$$

11-3. Square Wave Applied to Circuits with Two Storage Elements.
EXAMPLE 11-3-1. The square wave of current of Fig. 11-3-1a is applied

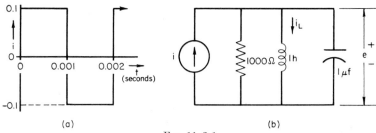

FIG. 11-3-1

to the circuit of Fig. 11-3-1b. The response inside the half-cycle from $0 < t < 0.001$ sec is given by the equation

$$0.1 = \frac{e}{1000} + \frac{1}{1}\int_0^t e\,dt + i_L(0) + 10^{-6}\frac{de}{dt} \qquad (11\text{-}3\text{-}1)$$

In this circuit there are two quantities, $i_L(0)$ and $e(0)$, to be determined; therefore two equations such as those for i_L and e must be followed through the half-cycle. As the circuit is a parallel combination of R, L, and C, the roots of the characteristic equation are

$$s_1 \text{ and } s_2 = -\frac{G}{2C} \pm \sqrt{\frac{G^2}{4C^2} - \frac{1}{LC}} = -500 \pm j\,866 \qquad (11\text{-}3\text{-}2)$$

The solutions for e and i_L are of the respective forms

$$e = \epsilon^{-500t}[B_1 \cos 866\,t + B_2 \sin 866\,t] \qquad (11\text{-}3\text{-}3)$$

$$i_L = 0.1 + \epsilon^{-500t}[B_3 \cos 866\,t + B_4 \sin 866\,t] \qquad (11\text{-}3\text{-}4)$$

The voltage and current start at $e(0)$ and $i_L(0)$ respectively. These conditions determine B_1 and B_3 but, to find B_2 and B_4, $(de/dt)(0)$ and $(di_L/dt)(0)$ need to be determined. Eq. 11-3-1 at $t = 0$ yields one of the desired quantities:

$$\frac{de}{dt}(0) = 10^5 - 10^3\,e(0) - 10^6\,i_L(0) \qquad (11\text{-}3\text{-}5)$$

and the other can be determined from

$$e = L\frac{di_L}{dt} \qquad (11\text{-}3\text{-}6)$$

which at $t = 0$ yields $\qquad \dfrac{di_L}{dt}(0) = \dfrac{e(0)}{L} = e(0) \qquad (11\text{-}3\text{-}7)$

Imposing the appropriate set of initial conditions on Eqs. 11-3-3 and 11-3-4 gives

$$e = \epsilon^{-500t}[e(0) \cos 866\,t$$
$$+ (115.5 - 0.578\,e(0) - 1.155 \times 10^3\,i_L(0))\sin 866\,t] \quad (11\text{-}3\text{-}8)$$
$$i_L = 0.1 + \epsilon^{-500t}[(i_L(0) - 0.1)\cos 866\,t$$
$$+ (1.55 \times 10^{-3}\,e(0) + 0.578\,i_L(0) - 0.0578)\sin 866\,t] \quad (11\text{-}3\text{-}9)$$

At $t = 0.001$ sec, e and i_L reach their respective values of $-e(0)$ and $-i_L(0)$. Substituting in Eqs. 11-3-8 and 11-3-9 gives

$$-53.3 = 1.126\,e(0) - 533\,i_L(0) \quad\quad (11\text{-}3\text{-}10)$$
$$-0.0342 = 5.34 \times 10^{-4}\,e(0) + 1.658\,i_L(0) \quad\quad (11\text{-}3\text{-}11)$$

The quantities $e(0)$ and $i_L(0)$, as found from these equations, are

$$e(0) = -49.5 \quad\quad i_L(0) = -4.65 \times 10^{-3} \quad\quad (11\text{-}3\text{-}12)$$

Substituting in Eqs. 11-3-8 and 11-3-9 gives

$$e = \epsilon^{-500t}[-49.5 \cos 866\,t + 149.5 \sin 866\,t] \quad\quad (11\text{-}3\text{-}13)$$
$$i_L = 0.1 + \epsilon^{-500t}[-0.1047 \cos 866\,t - 0.1178 \sin 866\,t] \quad (11\text{-}3\text{-}14)$$

EXAMPLE 11-3-2. The square-wave voltage of Fig. 11-2-1a is applied to the circuit of Fig. 11-3-2. Let it be supposed that the steady-state equa-

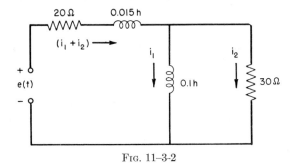

FIG. 11-3-2

tion for i_2 is desired. The response inside the half-cycle from $0 < t < 0.001$ sec is given by the equations

$$100 = 20\,i_1 + 0.115\frac{di_1}{dt} + 20\,i_2 + 0.015\frac{di_2}{dt}$$
$$100 = 20\,i_1 + 0.015\frac{di_1}{dt} + 50\,i_2 + 0.015\frac{di_2}{dt} \quad\quad (11\text{-}3\text{-}15)$$

The Laplace transform of these equations for $i_1 = i_1(0)$ and $i_2 = i_2(0)$ are

$$\frac{100}{s} = 20\,I_1 + 0.115[sI_1 - i_1(0)] + 20\,I_2 + 0.015[sI_2 - i_2(0)]$$
$$\frac{100}{s} = 20\,I_1 + 0.015[sI_1 - i_1(0)] + 50\,I_2 + 0.015[sI_2 - i_2(0)] \quad (11\text{-}3\text{-}16)$$

which can be solved as

$$I_1 = \frac{i_1(0)s^2 + [3630\ i_1(0) + 300\ i_2(0)]s + 2 \times 10^6}{s[s + 112.5][s + 3518]}$$

$$I_2 = \frac{i_2(0)s^2 - 1333\ i_1(0) + 6666}{[s + 112.5][s + 3518]} \qquad (11\text{-}3\text{-}17)$$

The inverse transforms of these equations are

$$
\begin{aligned}
i_1 &= 5 + [1.005\ i_1(0) + 0.0862\ i_2(0) - 5.22]\epsilon^{-112.5t} \\
&\quad + [-0.037\ i_1(0) - 0.088\ i_2(0) + 0.1666]\epsilon^{-3518t} \\
i_2 &= [-0.033\ i_2(0) - 0.391\ i_1(0) + 1.96]\epsilon^{-112.5t} \\
&\quad + [1.03\ i_2(0) + 0.39\ i_1(0) - 1.96]\epsilon^{-3518t}
\end{aligned}
\qquad (11\text{-}3\text{-}18)
$$

At $t = 0.001$ sec, i_1 and i_2 reach their respective values of $-i_1(0)$ and $-i_2(0)$. Substituting in Eqs. 11-3-18 gives

$$
\begin{aligned}
-0.38 &= 1.9\ i_1(0) + 0.0743\ i_2(0) \\
-1.69 &= -0.327\ i_1(0) + 1.002\ i_2(0)
\end{aligned}
\qquad (11\text{-}3\text{-}19)
$$

from which $i_1(0)$ and $i_2(0)$ are

$$i_1(0) = -0.133 \qquad i_2(0) = -1.73 \qquad (11\text{-}3\text{-}20)$$

Upon substitution, the equation for i_2 is

$$i_2 = 2.069\ \epsilon^{-112.5t} - 3.792\ \epsilon^{-3518t} \qquad (11\text{-}3\text{-}21)$$

11-4. Unsymmetrical Square Wave of Voltage Applied to R-C Circuit.
EXAMPLE 11-4-1. The voltage shown in Fig. 11-4-1a is applied to the circuit shown in Fig. 11-4-1b and the steady-state response is desired.

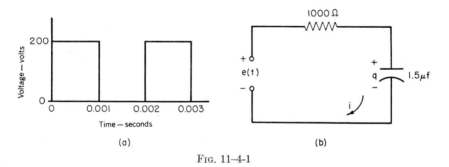

FIG. 11-4-1

By inspection it can be seen that the voltage wave of Fig. 11-4-1a can be considered to be composed of two components. The first component is the square wave of voltage of Fig. 11-2-1a plus a d-c component of 100 volts. The total response can be considered as the sum of the individual responses to the two voltage components acting alone. The charge and current components due to the square wave of voltage are denoted by q_{sw} and i_{sw} respectively. The equations for them are found in Ex. 11–2-2 for the half-period between $0 < t < 0.001$ sec:

$$q_{sw} = 1.5 \times 10^{-4} - 1.982 \times 10^{-4}\,\epsilon^{-666t} \qquad (11\text{–}4\text{-}1)$$
$$i_{sw} = 0.132\,\epsilon^{-666t} \qquad (11\text{–}4\text{-}2)$$

The charge and current components due to the d-c voltage applied until the steady state is reached are denoted by q_{dc} and i_{dc} respectively; they are

$$q_{dc} = 100 \times 1.5 \times 10^{-6} = 1.5 \times 10^{-4} \qquad (11\text{–}4\text{-}3)$$
$$i_{dc} = 0 \qquad (11\text{–}4\text{-}4)$$

The total charge and current, as given by the sum of the two components, are

$$q = 3.0 \times 10^{-4} - 1.982 \times 10^{-4}\,\epsilon^{-666t} \qquad (11\text{–}4\text{-}5)$$
$$i = 0.132\,\epsilon^{-666t} \qquad (11\text{–}4\text{-}6)$$

For the half-period between $0.001 < t < 0.002$ sec the equations for q and i are

$$q = +1.982 \times 10^{-4}\,\epsilon^{-666(t-0.001)}u_{-1}(t-0.001) \qquad (11\text{–}4\text{-}7)$$
$$i = -0.132\,\epsilon^{-666(t-0.001)}\,u_{-1}(t-0.001) \qquad (11\text{–}4\text{-}8)$$

11–5. Sawtooth Voltage Applied to R-L Circuit. EXAMPLE 11–5-1. The voltage shown in Fig. 11–5-1a is applied to the circuit of Fig. 11–5-1b and

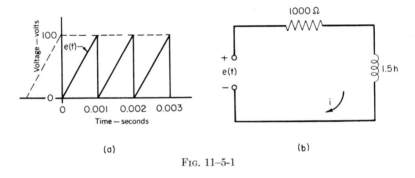

(a) (b)

FIG. 11–5-1

the steady-state current is desired. In this example the time interval of 0.001 sec is the period of the repeating applied voltage; therefore the current is followed through an entire cycle. The circuit equation inside the cycle, or from $0 < t < 0.001$ sec, is given by

$$10^5\,t = 1000\,i + 1.5\frac{di}{dt} \qquad (11\text{–}5\text{-}1)$$

It is assumed that the current starts at its $i(0)$ value, and the transformed equation solved for $\mathcal{L}(i) = I(s)$ is

$$I(s) = \frac{i(0)s + 6.66 \times 10^4}{s^2(s+666)} \qquad (11\text{–}5\text{-}2)$$

The inverse transform, by use of item 17 of the transform table in the Appendix, is

$$i = -0.15 + 100\,t + [i(0) + 0.15]\epsilon^{-666t} \qquad (11\text{-}5\text{-}3)$$

The initial current $i(0)$, as found by letting $i = i(0)$ at $t = 0.001$ sec in Eq. 11–5-3 and solving the result for $i(0)$, is

$$i(0) = 0.056 \qquad (11\text{-}5\text{-}4)$$

Substituting in Eq. 11–5-3 gives

$$i = -0.15 + 100\,t + 0.206\,\epsilon^{-666t} \qquad (11\text{-}5\text{-}5)$$

The solution is sketched in Fig. 11–5-2.

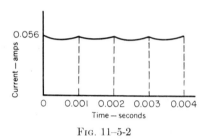

FIG. 11–5-2

11–6. Partial Sinusoidal Wave of Voltage Applied to Simple Circuits.
EXAMPLE 11–6-1. The voltage of Fig. 11–6-1a is applied to the circuit of

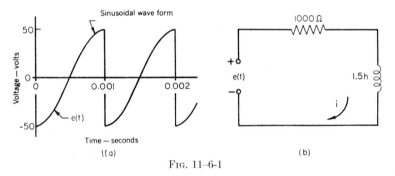

FIG. 11–6-1

Fig. 11–6-1b and the steady-state current is desired. In this example the time interval of 0.001 sec is the period of the repeating applied voltage; therefore, if the current starts at some value $i(0)$ at $t = 0$, it returns to the same value at $t = 0.001$ sec.

In this example "the response inside the cycle" is determined by the fact that at $t = 0$ the current has an $i(0)$ value when the alternating voltage is applied to the circuit. In this interval of time the circuit does not know that the voltage is going to change at $t = 0.001$ sec. Therefore in this interval the methods of solutions developed in Chapters 8 and 9 can be used.

The circuit equation for this interval of time is

$$- 50 \cos 1000 \, \pi t = 1000 \, i + 1.5 \frac{di}{dt} \qquad (11\text{-}6\text{-}1)$$

The circuit impedance at $\omega = 1000 \, \pi$ is

$$Z = 4820 \underline{/78°} \qquad (11\text{-}6\text{-}2)$$

The current, comprised of a steady-state and transient components, is

$$i = \frac{-50}{4820} \cos (1000 \, \pi t - 78°) + A \epsilon^{-1000t/1.5} \qquad (11\text{-}6\text{-}3)$$

The constant A can be found from the fact that $i = i(0)$ at $t = 0$. Evaluation of A and substitution in Eq. 11–6-3 gives

$$i = - 0.0104 \cos (1000 \, \pi t - 78°) + [i(0) + 0.00216] \epsilon^{-666t} \qquad (11\text{-}6\text{-}4)$$

The initial current $i(0)$, as found by letting $i = i(0)$ at $t = 0.001$ sec in Eq. 11–6-4 and solving for $i(0)$, is

$$i(0) = 0.00675 \qquad (11\text{-}6\text{-}5)$$

Substituting in Eq. 11–6-4 gives

$$i = - 0.0104 \cos (1000 \, \pi t - 78°) + 0.00891 \, \epsilon^{-666t} \qquad (11\text{-}6\text{-}6)$$

The solution is sketched in Fig. 11–6-2.

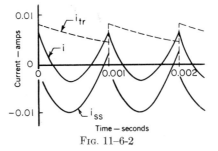

FIG. 11–6-2

It is of interest to note that, as the average value of the cyclic applied voltage is zero, the average value of the cyclic current response must also be zero.

EXAMPLE 11–6-2. The voltage of Fig. 11–6-1a is applied to the circuit of Fig. 11–6-3 and the equation for the steady-state current is desired.

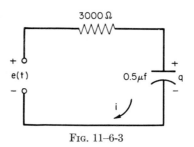

FIG. 11–6-3

Again the problem is solved in terms of q. The circuit impedance at this frequency is

$$Z = 3060\underline{/-12°} \tag{11-6-7}$$

The steady-state components of i and q are

$$i_{ss} = \frac{-50}{3060} \cos (1000\ \pi t + 12°) \tag{11-6-8}$$

$$q_{ss} = -5.2 \times 10^{-6} \sin (1000\ \pi t + 12°) \tag{11-6-9}$$

The equation for q is of the form

$$q = -5.2 \times 10^{-6} \sin (1000\ \pi t + 12°) + A\epsilon^{-666t} \tag{11-6-10}$$

At $t = 0$, $q = q(0)$, determining A, which when substituted in Eq. 11-6-10 gives

$$q = -5.2 \times 10^{-6} \sin (1000\ \pi t + 12°) + [q(0) + 1.08 \times 10^{-6}]\epsilon^{-666t} \tag{11-6-11}$$

The initial charge $q(0)$, as found by letting $q = q(0)$ at $t = 0.001$ sec in Eq. 11-6-11 and solving the result for $q(0)$, is

$$q(0) = 3.37 \times 10^{-6} \tag{11-6-12}$$

Substituting in Eq. 11-6-11 gives

$$q = -5.2 \times 10^{-6} \sin (1000\ \pi t + 12°) + 4.45 \times 10^{-6}\ \epsilon^{-666t} \tag{11-6-13}$$

The current, as obtained by differentiating the equation for q, is

$$i = -0.0164 \cos (1000\ \pi t + 12°) - 0.00296\ \epsilon^{-666t} \tag{11-6-14}$$

The solutions for q and i are sketched in Fig. 11-6-4.

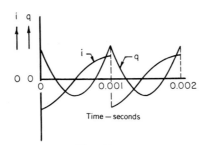

FIG. 11-6-4

11-7. Half-Wave and Full-Wave Rectifier Connected to an R Circuit.

The several articles that follow are not presented as a complete coverage of the subject of rectifiers, but to serve as examples of the determination of the steady-state solution of nonsinusoidal wave shapes.

Fig. 11-7-1 shows the circuit of a half-wave rectifier with S open or a full-wave rectifier with S closed. It is assumed in this analysis that the rectifier is perfect. That is, in the conducting direction, the rectifier is a short circuit, and in the reverse direction it is an open circuit. The voltage e

is one-half the secondary voltage as shown. The leakage inductance of the transformer is also neglected.

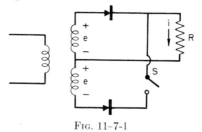

FIG. 11-7-1

When S is open, the voltage $e = E_M \sin \omega t$ is applied to the resistor R when e is positive, but is not applied when e is negative. The sketch of voltage applied to R is shown in Fig. 11-7-2. The current in the resistor

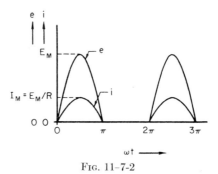

FIG. 11-7-2

is also shown in the sketch; it has the same shape as the voltage. The average value of i, as found by integrating i over one period and dividing by the length of period, is

$$i_{dc} = \frac{1}{2\pi} \int_0^\pi I_M \sin x \, dx = \frac{I_M}{\pi} = \frac{E_M}{R\pi} \tag{11-7-1}$$

With S closed the voltage applied to R is shown in Fig. 11-7-3. As soon as the voltage on one diode goes negative, the other goes positive, filling in

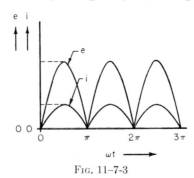

FIG. 11-7-3

what was the blank spot in the half-wave output. The average value of the current is twice that for the half-wave rectifier:

$$i_{dc} = I_M \times \frac{2}{\pi} = \frac{2}{\pi} \frac{E_M}{R} \tag{11-7-2}$$

11-8. Half-Wave and Full-Wave Rectifier Connected to an R-L Circuit. Fig. 11-8-1 is similar to Fig. 11-7-1, but an inductor has been added

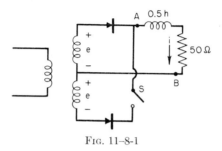

Fig. 11-8-1

in series with the R in the load. Actual circuit values are used in the following example. With S open the circuit is that of a half-wave rectifier. This connection is analyzed first. For convenience, the $t = 0$ point is taken where e goes through zero in the positive direction. For $E_M = 100$ and $\omega = 377$, the equation for e is

$$e = 100 \sin 377 \, t \tag{11-8-1}$$

Let it be assumed for the moment that, at $t = 0$, $i(0)$ is zero. This assumption is shown to be correct later. The impedance at this frequency is

$$Z = 195 \underline{/75.2°} \tag{11-8-2}$$

The current, comprised of i_{ss} and i_{tr}, can be written in the form

$$i = \tfrac{100}{195} \sin (377 \, t - 75.2°) + A \epsilon^{- 50t/0.5} \tag{11-8-3}$$

The constant A can be found from the fact that $i(0) = 0$ at $t = 0$. Evaluation of A and substitution accordingly yield the solution

$$i = 0.512 \sin (377 \, t - 75.2°) + 0.494 \, \epsilon^{-100t} \tag{11-8-4}$$

At first it may be thought that the voltage applied to points A-B for the R-L circuit is the same as that applied to R alone, as in Fig. 10-7-2; but closer inspection shows that this is not so. Sketching the solution as in Fig. 11-8-2 reveals that when the voltage e goes through zero at $t = T/2$ a current exists in the circuit. This value of i cannot cease instantaneously, because it exists through an inductor; therefore the current continues as shown by the heavy line until it reaches zero. When it reaches zero, the current cannot reverse because of the diode. When the current exists, the diode is a short circuit; therefore the voltage actually applied to the R-L circuit is that shown by the solid line labeled e. When e goes negative, the

A point remains tied to the transformer through the diode until the current reaches the value of zero.

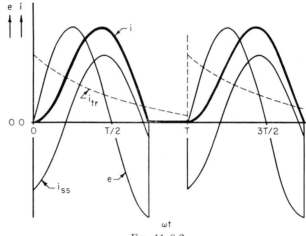

Fig. 11–8-2

With these particular circuit values i goes to zero when $t = t_1$, such that

$$0 = 0.512 \sin (377\ t_1 - 75.2°) + 0.494\ \epsilon^{-100 t_1} \qquad (11\text{–}8\text{-}5)$$

A few values obtained by trial and error show that $t_1 \doteq 0.0129$ or $\omega t_1 \doteq 270°$. After $\omega t_1 = 270°$, i equals zero until e goes positive at the beginning of the next cycle. Therefore the assumption that $i(0) = 0$ is correct. If the average value of the cyclic current is desired, the equation for i can be integrated over one period and divided by the time of the period. This average value of current is that which would be read on a d-c ammeter placed in series with the R and L. Another method of finding this average value of cyclic current is to find the average value of cyclic voltage applied to the R-L circuit and to divide this average voltage e_{dc} by R:

$$i_{dc(\text{cyclic})} = \frac{e_{dc(\text{cyclic})}}{R} = \frac{\dfrac{1}{2\ \pi} \displaystyle\int_0^{270°} 100 \sin x\ dx}{R} = \frac{15.9}{50} = 0.319 \quad (11\text{–}8\text{-}6)$$

When this value of i_{dc} is compared with the i_{dc} that exists in the 50-ohm resistor if the inductor is not present, which from Eq. 11–7-1 is

$$i_{dc} = \frac{100}{50} \times \frac{1}{\pi} = 0.636 \qquad (11\text{–}8\text{-}7)$$

it is to be seen that the inductor decreases the magnitude of i_{dc}.

If the magnitude of L is increased, the current reaches zero later in the cycle. As can be seen by inspection of the voltage curve in Fig. 11–8-2, when i reaches zero later in the cycle, the average value of cyclic voltage applied to the R-L circuit becomes smaller; therefore the average value of cyclic current (i_{dc}) becomes smaller. Thus, the larger L, the smaller is i_{dc}. Theoretically the point where i reaches zero moves over to the $t = T$ point when L becomes infinite.

If S is closed in Fig. 11–8-1, the circuit becomes that of a full-wave rectifier with an R-L load. If S is first closed at $t = 0$ on Fig. 11–8-2, the first portion of the current curve up to $t = T/2$ is the same. However, when the voltage on the plate of the upper diode of Fig. 11–8-1 goes negative, the voltage on the plate of the lower diode becomes positive and the current transfers to the second diode with an initial current $i(0)$ that is not zero. Eventually the circuit reaches the steady-state condition which is the solution to be found.

In the following it is assumed the circuit is in the steady state; this means the current starts at some $i(0)$ value and at $t = T/2$ is back to the same $i(0)$ value. Eq. 11–8-3, valid for this situation, is

$$i = 0.512 \sin (377\ t - 75.2°) + A\epsilon^{-100t} \qquad (11\text{–}8\text{-}8)$$

A has a different value, however, because $i = i(0)$ at $t = 0$, and this leads to the equation

$$i = 0.512 \sin (377\ t - 75.2°) + [i(0) + 0.494]\epsilon^{-100t} \qquad (11\text{–}8\text{-}9)$$

At the point where $\omega t = 180°$ or $t = \pi/377 = 0.00834$ sec, the current i again equals $i(0)$; when these conditions are used in Eq. 11–8-9, $i(0)$ is

$$i(0) = 1.255 \qquad (11\text{–}8\text{-}10)$$

Substituting $i(0)$ in Eq. 11–8-9 gives

$$i = 0.512 \sin (377\ t - 75.2°) + 1.75\ \epsilon^{-100t} \qquad (11\text{–}8\text{-}11)$$

The voltage applied to the circuit is that shown in Fig. 11–7-3. The average value of this cyclic voltage is

$$e_{dc(\text{cyclic})} = \frac{1}{\pi} \int_0^\pi 100 \sin x\ dx = 100\ \frac{2}{\pi} = 63.6 \qquad (11\text{–}8\text{-}12)$$

The average value of the cyclic current is

$$i_{dc(\text{cyclic})} = \frac{63.6}{50} = 1.272 \qquad (11\text{–}8\text{-}13)$$

It is to be noted that the average value of current is not affected by the value of L. No matter what the magnitude of L, the same wave shape of voltage is applied to the R-L circuit. In the steady state this produces an average value of current determined only by e_{dc} and R, as contrasted with the half-wave rectifier where i_{dc} becomes smaller as L increases.

11–9. Free-Wheeling Circuit. As just pointed out, the disadvantage of a half-wave rectifier with an R-L load is that, as the voltage e goes negative, it is still applied to the load as long as the current continues. The larger L is, the longer i flows, the smaller is e_{dc}, and, hence, the smaller is i_{dc}. The circuit of Fig. 11-9-1 is designed to overcome this disadvantage and is termed a free-wheeling circuit. A second diode is connected across the

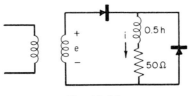

FIG. 11-9-1

load so that it does not conduct when e is positive. However, the second diode becomes a short circuit to the current when the voltage becomes negative, so that the negative voltage is no longer applied to the circuit. When the voltage is negative, the current decreases exponentially toward zero and has some value i' at the start of the next cycle. It is assumed that the circuit has been operating long enough to be in the steady state and that $t = 0$ is taken when the voltage e goes through zero in the positive direction with an initial current $i(0)$. In the interval from $t = 0$ to $t = \pi/377$ the equation for the current is

$$i = 0.512 \sin (377\,t - 75.2°) + A\epsilon^{-100t} \qquad (11\text{-}9\text{-}1)$$

A can be determined from $i = i(0)$ at $t = 0$, yielding the equation

$$i = 0.512 \sin (377\,t - 75.2°) + [i(0) + 0.494]\epsilon^{-100t} \qquad (11\text{-}9\text{-}2)$$

When $t = \pi/377 = 0.00834$ sec, the voltage applied across the R-L circuit is zero. The current at this time, as found from Eq. 11-9-2, is

$$i_{(\omega t = \pi)} = 0.709 + 0.435\,i(0) \qquad (11\text{-}9\text{-}3)$$

For convenience the $t = 0$ point is shifted to the old value of $t = 0.00834$ sec. Since the circuit is an R-L circuit with zero volts applied to it, the equation for i in the interval from $0 < t < 0.00834$ sec is of the form

$$i = A\epsilon^{-100t} \qquad (11\text{-}9\text{-}4)$$

Determining the constant A by using the current of Eq. 11-9-3 at $t = 0$ leads to the equation $\quad i = [0.709 + 0.435\,i(0)]\epsilon^{-100t} \qquad (11\text{-}9\text{-}5)$

When $t = 0.00834$ sec, the current again equals $i(0)$, because this is the beginning of the next cycle. Substituting these conditions yields

$$i(0) = 0.38 \qquad (11\text{-}9\text{-}6)$$

Substituting in Eq. 11-9-2 gives

$$i = 0.512 \sin (377\,t - 75.2°) + 0.874\,\epsilon^{-100t} \qquad (11\text{-}9\text{-}7)$$

and Eq. 11-9-5 becomes $\quad i = 0.874\,\epsilon^{-100t} \qquad (11\text{-}9\text{-}8)$

The respective $t = 0$ points and the intervals for the last two equations are as given in the preceding work.

This solution is sketched in Fig. 11–9-2. The voltage applied to the R-L circuit is a sine loop for half the cycle and zero volts for the other half.

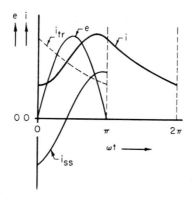

FIG. 11–9-2

The average value of the cyclic voltage is

$$e_{dc(\text{cyclic})} = \frac{100}{\pi} = 31.8 \qquad (11\text{–}9\text{-}9)$$

and the average value of the cyclic current is

$$i_{dc(\text{cyclic})} = \frac{e_{dc(\text{cyclic})}}{R} = \frac{31.8}{50} = 0.636 \qquad (11\text{–}9\text{-}10)$$

This value of i_{dc} is independent of L, because no matter what the magnitude of L the same e_{dc} is applied to the circuit. This value of i_{dc} is one-half that for the full-wave rectifier.

11–10. Thyratron Rectifier with R-L Load. The rectifier of Fig. 11–10-1 is similar to the full-wave rectifier of Fig. 11–8-1, but the diodes are replaced by thyratrons, which are gas-filled triodes. The thyratron is considered an open circuit until the grid voltage becomes more positive than some critical voltage. As long as the tube conducts, a voltage drop occurs across the tube; in this example this drop is assumed to be a constant value of 10 volts. The only effect the phase-shifting network and the critical voltage of the thyratrons have on this example is to determine the point in the voltage cycle where the tube begins to conduct. This point is assumed to be 20 degrees after the voltage goes through zero in the positive direction. If $t = 0$ is taken as the time the upper tube begins to conduct, the voltage e can be written

$$e = 100 \sin (377\, t + 20°) \qquad (11\text{–}10\text{-}1)$$

The voltage applied to the circuit at points A-B is this voltage minus the 10-volt drop across the tube; therefore the voltage equation is

$$100 \sin (377\, t + 20°) - 10 = 0.5 \frac{di}{dt} + 50\, i \qquad (11\text{--}10\text{--}2)$$

The applied voltage can be considered as comprised of two components, the first a d-c voltage and the second a sinusoidal voltage. The component of

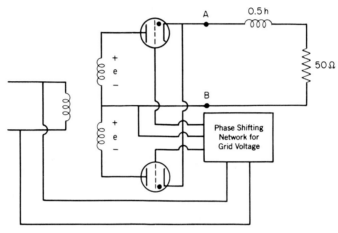

Fig. 11–10-1

current due to the d-c voltage can be written

$$i' = -\tfrac{10}{50} + A_1 \epsilon^{-Rt/L} \qquad (11\text{--}10\text{--}3)$$

The component of current due to the sinusoidal voltage can be written

$$i'' = 0.512 \sin (377\, t + 20° - 75.2°) + A_2 \epsilon^{-Rt/L} \qquad (11\text{--}10\text{--}4)$$

The total current is the sum of these two components:

$$i = -0.2 + 0.512 \sin (377\, t - 55.2°) + A \epsilon^{-100t} \qquad (11\text{--}10\text{--}5)$$

where

$$A = A_1 + A_2 \qquad (11\text{--}10\text{--}6)$$

Evaluating the constant A from $i = i(0)$ at $t = 0$, Eq. 11–10-5 becomes

$$i = -0.2 + 0.512 \sin (377\, t + 55.2°) + [0.618 + i(0)]\epsilon^{-100t} \qquad (11\text{--}10\text{--}7)$$

When $t = 0.00833$ sec, the bottom tube begins to conduct and the current has again reached $i(0)$. Imposing these conditions on Eq. 11–10-7 gives $i(0)$ as

$$i(0) = 0.843 \qquad (11\text{--}10\text{--}8)$$

Substituting in Eq. 11–10-7 gives

$$i = -0.2 + 0.512 \sin (377\, t - 55.2°) + 1.461\, \epsilon^{-100t} \qquad (11\text{--}10\text{--}9)$$

Sketches of e_{ac}, e_{dc}, and e applied to the points A-B are shown in Fig. 11–10-2 together with those for $i_{ss(ac)}$, $i_{ss(dc)}$, i_{tr}, and the total current i.

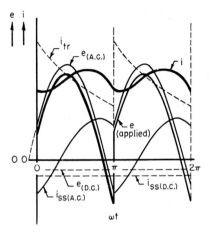

Fig. 11–10-2

To find the average value of the cyclic current $i_{dc(\text{cyclic})}$ the value of $e_{dc(\text{cyclic})}$ is found first:

$$e_{dc(\text{cyclic})} = \frac{1}{\pi} \int_0^\pi 100 \sin{(x + 20°)}\, dx - 10 = 49.7 \qquad (11\text{–}10\text{–}10)$$

This value of voltage is the average voltage applied to the R-L circuit in the steady state; correspondingly, the current that would be read on a d-c ammeter in series with the R-L load is

$$i_{dc(\text{cyclic})} = \frac{49.7}{50} = 0.995 \qquad (11\text{–}10\text{–}11)$$

A certain amount of care must be exercised in problems of this type. For one thing, the voltage on the plate must be more positive than the 10-volt drop of the tube for the assumed angle of δ. The value of $\delta = 20°$ in this example satisfies this need. For another thing, if sufficiently large values of δ are assumed and all the above steps are performed, it may be possible to obtain a negative value of $i(0)$; of course, this is physically impossible. For these values of δ the actual circuit situation is that the $i(0)$ is zero and the total current reaches zero before the end of the cycle. The situation is somewhat analogous to the half-wave rectifier circuit of Art. 11–8.

11–11. Thyratron Rectifier with Battery. The circuit for this example is that of Fig. 11–10-1 with the R-L load which is to the right of points A-B replaced by the circuit shown in Fig. 11–11-1. The 25 volts may be a battery that is being charged or the back emf of a d-c motor. Let it be assumed that the upper tube starts conduction 45 degrees after e is zero

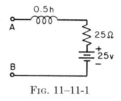

FIG. 11–11-1

going positive. The circuit equation is

$$100 \sin (377\ t + 45°) - 10 = 0.5 \frac{di}{dt} + 25\ i + 25 \qquad (11\text{–}11\text{-}1)$$

which can be rewritten

$$100 \sin (377\ t + 45°) - 35 = 0.5 \frac{di}{dt} + 25\ i \qquad (11\text{–}11\text{-}2)$$

The solution is of the form

$$i = i_{ss(dc)} + i_{ss(ac)} + i_{tr} \qquad (11\text{–}11\text{-}3)$$

The circuit impedance is

$$Z = 190/82.4° \qquad (11\text{–}11\text{-}4)$$

and $i_{ss(ac)}$ is

$$i_{ss(ac)} = \tfrac{100}{190} \sin (377\ t + 45° - 82.4°) \qquad (11\text{–}11\text{-}5)$$

The total current is

$$i = -1.4 + 0.526 \sin (377\ t - 37.4°) + A\epsilon^{-50t} \qquad (11\text{–}11\text{-}6)$$

The constant A can be evaluated from the conditions $i = i(0)$ at $t = 0$. With A evaluated, Eq. 11–11-6 becomes

$$i = -1.4 + 0.526 \sin (377\ t - 37.4°) + [1.719 + i(0)]\epsilon^{-50t} \qquad (11\text{–}11\text{-}7)$$

When $t = 0.00833$ sec, i again is equal to $i(0)$ and, with these conditions imposed on Eq. 11–11-7, $i(0)$ is

$$i(0) = 0.154 \qquad (11\text{–}11\text{-}8)$$

Substitution yields the equation for i:

$$i = -1.4 + 0.526 \sin (377\ t - 37.4°) + 1.873\ \epsilon^{-50t} \qquad (11\text{–}11\text{-}9)$$

To find $i_{dc(cyclic)}$ first the value of $e_{dc(cyclic)}$ is found:

$$e_{dc(cyclic)} = \frac{1}{\pi} \int_0^{\pi} 100 \sin (x + 45°)\ dx - 35 = 45 - 35 = 10 \quad (11\text{–}11\text{-}10)$$

As this is the average value of voltage applied across the R-L portion of the circuit, the current that would be read on a d-c ammeter in series with the R-L load is

$$i_{dc(cyclic)} = \tfrac{10}{25} = 0.4 \qquad (11\text{–}11\text{-}11)$$

The precautions mentioned in Art. 11–10 must be observed here, with the added one that the plate voltage at $t = 0$ must be larger than the drop in the tube voltage plus the value of the battery voltage.

PROBLEMS

11–1. If the voltage wave of Fig. 11–2-1a is applied to the circuit of Fig 11–P-1,

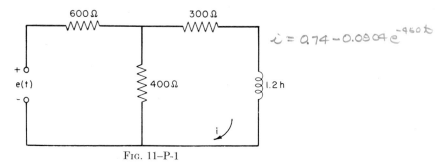

$$i = 0.74 - 0.0904\,e^{-960\,t}$$

FIG. 11–P-1

find the equation for the current i after steady state has been reached and sketch the solution.

11–2. If the voltage wave of Fig. 11–2-1a is applied to the circuit of Fig. 11–P-2,

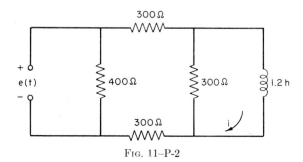

FIG. 11–P-2

find the equation for the current i after steady state has been reached and sketch the solution.

11–3. If the voltage wave of Fig. 11–4-1a is applied to the circuit of Fig. 11–P-3,

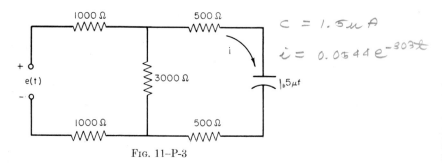

$$c = 1.5\mu A$$

$$i = 0.0544\,e^{-303\,t}$$

FIG. 11–P-3

find the equation for the current after steady state has been reached and sketch the solution.

11–4. If the voltage wave of Fig. 11–4-1a is applied to the circuit of Fig. 11–P-4,

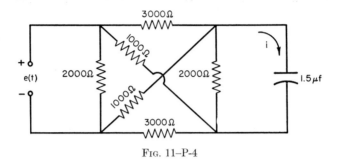

FIG. 11–P-4

find the equation for the current after steady state has been reached and sketch the solution.

11–5. If the square wave of current of Fig. 11–3-1a is applied to the circuit of

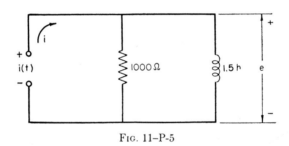

FIG. 11–P-5

Fig. 11–P-5, find the equation for the voltage after steady state has been reached and sketch the solution.

11–6. If the square wave of current of Fig. 11–3-1a is applied to the circuit of

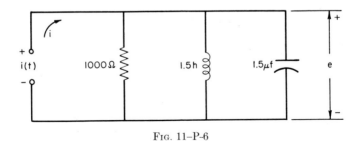

FIG. 11–P-6

Fig. 11–P-6, find the equation for the voltage e after steady state has been reached and sketch the solution.

11–7. If the unsymmetrical square wave of current of Fig. 11–P-7 is applied to the circuit of Fig. 11–2-3b, find the equation for e after steady state has been reached and sketch the solution.

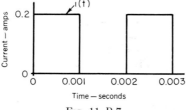

FIG 11–P-7

11–8. If the unsymmetrical square wave of current of Fig. 11–P-7 is applied to the circuit of Fig. 11–P-6, find the equation for e after steady state has been reached and sketch the solution.

11–9. If the voltage of Fig. 11–5-1a is applied to the circuit of Fig. 11–2-2a, find the equation for q and i and sketch.

11–10. If the voltage of Fig. 11–5-1a is applied to the circuit of Fig. 11–3-2 find i_2 in the steady state.

11–11. If the sawtooth wave of current of Fig. 11–P-8 is applied to the circuit of Fig. 11–2-3b, find e in steady state and sketch the solution.

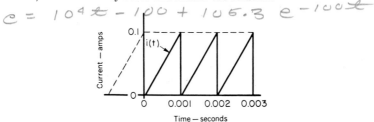

$$e = 10^4 t - 100 + 105.3\, e^{-100t}$$

FIG. 11–P-8

11–12. If the current of Fig. 11–P-8 is applied to the circuit of Fig. 11–P-5, find e in steady state and sketch the solution.

11–13. If the current of Fig. 11–P-8 is applied to the circuit of Fig. 11–3-1b, find e in steady state and sketch the solution.

11–14. If the current of Fig. 11–P-9 is applied to the circuit of Fig. 11–2-3b and

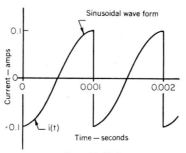

FIG. 11–P-9

left long enough for steady state to be reached, find the equation for e in steady state and sketch.

11–15. If the current of Fig. 11–P-9 is applied to the circuit of Fig. 11–P-5, find e in steady state and sketch.

11–16. If the current of Fig. 11–P-9 is applied to the circuit of Fig. 11–3-1b, find e in steady state and sketch.

11–17. Check Eq. 11–8-6 by finding the average value of i of Eq. 11–8-4.

11–18. In the circuit of Fig. 11–8-1 with S open, change L to 3 henrys and find the equation for i and find $i_{dc(cyclic)}$.

11–19. Check Eq. 11–8-13 by finding the average value of i of Eq. 11–8-11.

11–20. In the circuit of Fig. 11–8-1 with S closed, change L to 3 henrys and find the equation for i. Find the average value of this i and check with Eq. 11–8-13.

11–21. In the circuit of Fig. 11–9-1 change L to 3 henrys and find the equation for i. Find the average value for this i and check with Eq. 11–9-10.

11–22. In the circuit of Fig. 11–10-1 the only change made from the example of Art. 11–10 is that the tube starts conducting, so that the equation for e is

$$e = 100 \sin (377\,t + 40°)$$

Find the equation for i and find $i_{dc(cyclic)}$.

11–23. In the circuit of Fig. 11–11-1 the only change made from the example of Art. 11–11 is that the tube starts conducting, so that the equation for e is

$$e = 100 \sin (377\,t + 35°)$$

Find the equation for i and find $i_{dc(cyclic)}$.

CHAPTER 12

MECHANICAL AND ELECTROMECHANICAL SYSTEMS

12–1. Introduction. Although the content of the preceding chapters is concerned entirely with electric circuits, the mathematical tools developed can be used for solutions of other physical systems for which linear differential equations with constant coefficients can be written. For example, mechanical systems that are translatory in nature can be solved as easily as electric systems. Other examples are rotational mechanical systems, electromechanical systems, hydraulic systems, and acoustical systems.

Not only can the same mathematical tools be used, but also it is often helpful to correlate a mechanical system (for example) with an electric system the solution of which is already known. By this device the solution to the mechanical problem can be written through the use of its electrical analogue. By use of this concept of analogues, all theorems and techniques familiar to electrical engineers can be used on mechanical problems. As an example, the steady-state response of a mechanical system to a sinusoidal input can be found by using procedures analogous to those developed for a-c circuits.

12–2. Translatory Mechanical Systems with One Mass. The mechanical system to be studied first is that shown in Fig. 12–2-1. This system has a

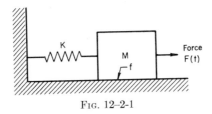

Fig. 12–2-1

single degree of freedom. The mass M is resting upon a surface, f is the coefficient of friction between the mass and the surface upon which it rests. Friction in systems of this sort often approximates viscous friction; such is assumed to be the case in the following examples. The mass is connected to a fixed support by a spring. The mass of the spring is assumed to be so small compared with M that it can be neglected. The spring has a deflection coefficient which is assumed constant. An external force $F(t)$ is applied to the right.

The system equation for this problem can be written through the application of Newton's second law of motion; thus the product of mass and acceleration is equal to the summation of all external forces acting on the mass.

One method of setting up these equations is to focus attention on the mass M itself and to see what external forces are acting on M that produce significant results. To explain what is meant by significant results, Fig. 12–2–1 is referred to in the following discussion.

The mass M has one degree of freedom, which is horizontal; only the forces which influence motion in this direction need be considered. Here the force of gravity is downward, the force with which the table pushes on the mass is upward. These forces are equal and opposite and do not influence the motion in the horizontal direction; accordingly these forces do not produce significant results in the problem at hand and can be ignored.

The forces applied to M are considered one at a time, and the superposition of these separate forces is then considered. Attention is first given to the spring. The length of the spring at rest is termed x_R. If the mass is located x_R units away from the support (as in Fig. 12–2–2a), the spring

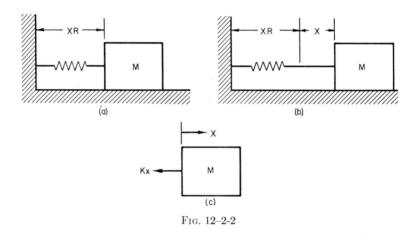

Fig. 12–2–2

exerts no force on M. It is convenient to take this location of the mass as the reference position from which x is measured. If x is chosen as positive to the right (an arbitrary choice), and the mass is moved x units in the positive direction as shown in Fig. 12–2–2b, the spring acts on M with a force Kx in the direction shown in Fig. 12–2–2c. It is to be noted that the arrow labeled Kx is the reference direction for which this force is written. By this is meant that, if the mass is moved in the negative x direction, Kx is negative with respect to the direction of the reference arrow, so that the actual force is to the right. These results can be summarized as follows. The reference direction for the force Kx is in the direction opposite to that chosen for positive x. If the positive direction for x had been chosen to the left, the arrow for Kx would be to the right.

Next the force acting on M due to viscous friction is considered. This force is

$$\text{Force} = f\frac{dx}{dt} = f \times (\text{velocity}) \qquad (12\text{--}2\text{--}1)$$

Since the positive direction for x is to the right, positive velocity dx/dt is also to the right. Therefore viscous friction acts on M with a force $f(dx/dt)$ in a direction to oppose positive velocity as in Fig. 12–2–3. Again

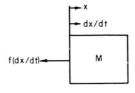

FIG. 12-2-3

it is to be noted that the arrow labeled $f(dx/dt)$ is the reference direction for which this force is written. If the mass is moving to the left, the velocity is in the negative direction and $f(dx/dt)$ is negative with respect to the direction of the reference arrow, so that the actual force is to the right.

The force $F(t)$ is applied externally to the mass and the equation for the force and the direction for the reference arrow as shown in Fig. 12–2–1 completely specify the manner in which this force acts on M.

For a specific example, let it be assumed that $F(t)$ is a constant force equal to F. All the significant forces acting on M are shown in Fig. 12–2–4.

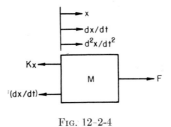

FIG. 12-2-4

The positive direction for x is taken to the right as an arbitrary choice; thus positive dx/dt and positive d^2x/dt^2 are also to the right. The forces Kx and $f(dx/dt)$ are in a direction opposite to the direction chosen for positive x. Newton's second law of motion can now be written:

$$F - Kx - f\frac{dx}{dt} = M\frac{d^2x}{dt^2} \qquad (12\text{--}2\text{--}2)$$

This equation can be rewritten

$$F = M \frac{d^2x}{dt^2} + f \frac{dx}{dt} + Kx \qquad (12\text{-}2\text{-}3)$$

It is to be noted that this is the same type of equation that was found in electric circuits with two storage elements. To be specific, Kirchhoff's voltage equation for the electric circuit of Fig. 12–2–5 is given by Eq. 12–2–4.

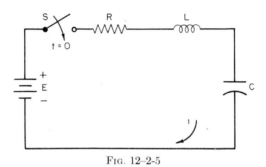

FIG. 12–2–5

This equation is rewritten as Eq. 12–2–5 in order to put it in a form that can be compared with Eq. 12–2–3 of the mechanical system.

$$E = L \frac{di}{dt} + Ri + \frac{1}{C} \int i \, dt \qquad (12\text{-}2\text{-}4)$$

$$E = L \frac{d^2q}{dt^2} + R \frac{dq}{dt} + \frac{q}{C} \qquad (12\text{-}2\text{-}5)$$

The electric circuit of Fig. 12–2–5 is said to be the analogue of the mechanical system of Fig. 12–2–4 in that the system equations for the two systems have the same form.

The circuit of Fig. 12–2–5 is not the only possible analogue for the mechanical system, as can be shown from the fact that the equation for the

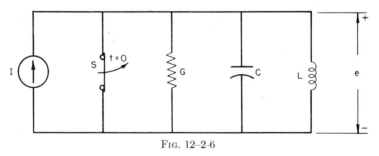

FIG. 12–2–6

dual of the circuit of Fig. 12–2–5 also has the same form. The dual circuit is shown in Fig. 12–2–6, and its equation in Eq. 12–2–6.

$$I = C \frac{de}{dt} + Ge + \frac{1}{L} \int e \, dt \qquad (12\text{-}2\text{-}6)$$

Table 12–1 shows the corresponding quantities that appear in the same location in their respective equations and are, therefore, said to be analogues of each other.

TABLE 12–1

Mechanical System	Series Electric System with Voltage Source	Parallel Electric System with Current Source
F	E	I
x	$q = \int i\, dt$	$\int e\, dt$
$\dfrac{dx}{dt}$	$\dfrac{dq}{dt} = i$	e
$\dfrac{d^2x}{dt^2}$	$\dfrac{d^2q}{dt^2} = \dfrac{di}{dt}$	$\dfrac{de}{dt}$
M	L	C
f	R	G
K	$\dfrac{1}{C}$	$\dfrac{1}{L}$

The corresponding systems of Table 12–1 behave in the same manner if they are excited similarly. For example, if the circuit of Fig. 12–2–5 is initially at rest and S is closed at $t = 0$, two initial conditions (enough to determine the solution) and the solution, assuming the oscillatory case, are

$$q(0) = 0 \qquad i(0) = 0$$

$$i = \frac{E}{\beta L}\, \epsilon^{-at} \sin \beta t \qquad\qquad (12\text{–}2\text{–}7)$$

where $\qquad\qquad a = \dfrac{R}{2L} \qquad \beta = \sqrt{\dfrac{1}{LC} - \dfrac{R^2}{4L^2}}$

If the mechanical system has analogous initial conditions, it will behave in an analogous manner. Let it be assumed that the mechanical system is initially at rest at $x = 0$ and that the force F is applied at $t = 0$. Examination of the system shows that the initial conditions are analogous to those of Eq. 12–2–7 and are zero. The differential equation and the initial condition for the mechanical system are analogous to those for the electric system, so the corresponding solutions are also analogous. By referring to Table 12–1 and the solution for the electric system, Eq. 12–2–7, the solution for the mechanical system, as written by inspection, is as given in the following equation:

$$\frac{dx(t)}{dt} = \frac{F}{\beta M} \epsilon^{-at} \sin \beta t \qquad (12\text{-}2\text{-}8)$$

where
$$a = \frac{f}{2\,M} \qquad \beta = \sqrt{\frac{K}{M} - \frac{f^2}{4\,M^2}}$$

12-3. Translatory Mechanical Systems with Two Masses. The second mechanical system to be studied is that of Fig. 12–3-1. The two masses M_1

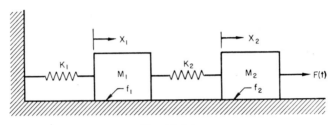

Fig. 12–3-1

and M_2 are resting upon a surface, and it is assumed that each mass has only a single degree of freedom. Again the mass of each spring is neglected and it is assumed that the friction is viscous friction. Let it also be assumed that the force $F(t)$ is of constant magnitude applied to the right to a system that is at rest at $t = 0$. The distances x_1 and x_2 are taken as positive to the right with zero values referred to their rest positions.

First, attention is focused on mass M_1, and each component of force is considered as if it were acting separately as in Fig. 12–3-2. By use of the

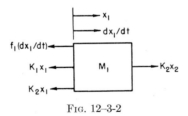

Fig. 12–3-2

superposition principle, the final motion is determined by these forces acting at the same time. If M_2 is moved in the positive x_2 direction, the resulting force on M_1 is $K_2 x_2$ acting to the right. If M_1 is moved in the positive x_1 direction, the force due to spring K_1 is $K_1 x_1$ acting to the left, and the force due to spring K_2 is $K_2 x_1$ acting to the left. The positive direction for x_1 is chosen to the right; therefore dx_1/dt is positive to the right and $f_1(dx_1/dt)$ is positive to the left.

Since positive acceleration is to the right, the system equation is

$$K_2 x_2 - K_1 x_1 - K_2 x_1 - f_1 \frac{dx_1}{dt} = M_1 \frac{d^2 x_1}{dt^2} \qquad (12\text{-}3\text{-}1)$$

The same technique can be used to establish the directions of the forces

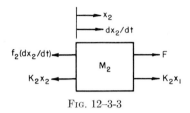

FIG. 12-3-3

acting on M_2 with the result shown in Fig. 12-3-3. The second equation for the system is

$$F + K_2 x_1 - K_2 x_2 - f_2 \frac{dx_2}{dt} = M_2 \frac{d^2 x_2}{dt^2} \qquad (12\text{-}3\text{-}2)$$

Eqs. 12-3-1 and 12-3-2 can be rewritten

$$K_2 (x_1 - x_2) + K_1 x_1 + f_1 \frac{dx_1}{dt} + M_1 \frac{d^2 x_1}{dt_2} = 0$$

$$K_2 (x_2 - x_1) + f_2 \frac{dx_2}{dt} + M_2 \frac{d^2 x_2}{dt^2} = F \qquad (12\text{-}3\text{-}3)$$

An electric circuit which is the analogue of the mechanical system of Fig. 12-3-1 can be found by referring to Table 12-1 and identifying the analogous quantities. If this procedure is followed, the resulting equations are

$$\frac{1}{C_2} (q_1 - q_2) + \frac{1}{C_1} q_1 + R_1 i_1 + L_1 \frac{di_1}{dt} = 0$$

$$\frac{1}{C_2} (q_2 - q_1) + R_2 i_2 + L_2 \frac{di_2}{dt} = E \qquad (12\text{-}3\text{-}4)$$

From these equations the circuit of Fig. 12-3-4 can be recognized.

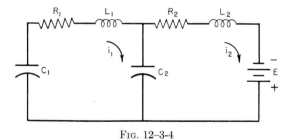

FIG. 12-3-4

The circuit of Fig. 12-3-4 is not the only circuit that is the analogue of the mechanical system of Fig. 12-3-1. Another analogue can be obtained by using the items in column 3 of Table 12-1 as the analogues of the items in column 1. This procedure leads to the circuit of Fig. 12–3-5. This resulting circuit is the dual of the circuit of Fig. 12–3-4.

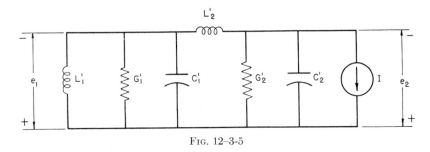

FIG. 12–3-5

12–4. Rotational Mechanical Systems with One Moment of Inertia. A rotational mechanical system is indicated by Fig. 12–4-1a. The moment

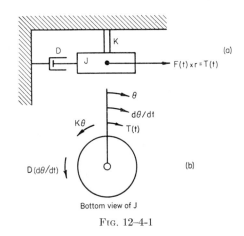

FIG. 12–4-1

of inertia of the system is J. The rotational viscous friction is indicated by the dashpot and its coefficient is labeled D. The moment of inertia of the spring is assumed to be so small compared with J that it can be neglected. The spring has a rotational coefficient K which is assumed constant. An external force $F(t)$ is applied at a radius r, and the resulting torque is $T(t)$.

The system equation for this problem can be obtained in much the same manner as that for the translatory system. First, attention is focused on the moment of inertia as indicated in Fig. 12–4-1b, which shows the J as viewed from the bottom. The angle of rotation θ is taken arbitrarily in the clockwise direction from the position of rest. Since positive θ is in the clockwise direction, positive $d\theta/dt$ and $d^2\theta/dt^2 = \alpha$ are also in the clockwise direction. If J is moved through a positive θ, $K\theta$, the component of torque due to the spring, is in the negative direction. If J is given a positive angular velocity, $D(d\theta/dt)$, the component of torque due to viscous friction, is in the negative direction. The torques producing positive angular acceleration are those acting in the clockwise direction, and assuming that $T(t)$ is a constant T, the following equation can be written:

$$T - K\theta - D\frac{d\theta}{dt} = J\frac{d^2\theta}{dt^2} \tag{12-4-1}$$

This equation can be rewritten

$$T = J\frac{d^2\theta}{dt^2} + D\frac{d\theta}{dt} + K\theta \tag{12-4-2}$$

A table similar to Table 12–1 can be developed to show the analogous quantities between mechanical rotational, mechanical translatory, and

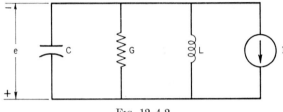

FIG. 12–4-2

electric systems. Eq. 12–4-3 is one electrical analogue of Eq. 12–4-2 and leads to the circuit of Fig. 12–4-2.

$$I = C\frac{de}{dt} + Ge + \frac{1}{L}\int e\,dt \tag{12-4-3}$$

The dual of the circuit of Fig. 12–4-2 is also an analogue of the mechanical system of Fig. 12–4-1a and is shown in Fig. 12–4-3.

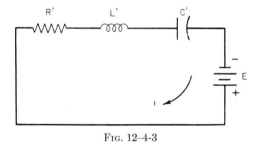

FIG. 12–4-3

12–5. Rotational Mechanical Systems with More than One Moment of Inertia. The system equation for the mechanical system of Fig. 12–5-1a is obtained by separately focusing attention on each moment of inertia as indicated in Figs. 12–5-1b through d. For example, the procedure for setting up the equations for J_2 is explained in detail. The positive assumed direction for the θ's are in the clockwise direction when the J's are viewed from the bottom. If θ_1 is turned in the positive direction, the torque $K_2\theta_1$ acting on J_2 is in the positive direction. If θ_2 is turned in the positive

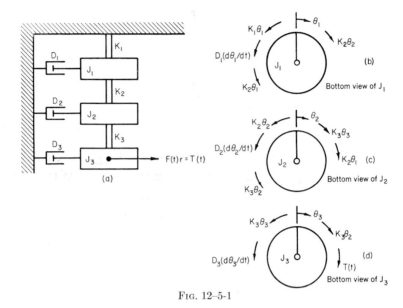

FIG. 12–5–1

direction, the two components of torque $K_2\theta_2$ and $K_3\theta_2$ acting on J_2 are in the negative direction. If J_2 is given a positive angular velocity $d\theta_2/dt$, the torque $D_2(d\theta_2/dt)$ acts in the direction opposite the positive velocity. Finally, if θ_3 is turned in the positive direction, the torque $K_3\theta_3$ acting on J_2 is in the positive direction. The system equation involving J_2 is

$$J_2 \frac{d^2\theta_2}{dt^2} + D_2 \frac{d\theta_2}{dt} + K_3(\theta_2 - \theta_3) + K_2(\theta_2 - \theta_1) = 0 \qquad (12\text{–}5\text{–}1)$$

The system equations involving J_1 and J_3 can be written in a similar manner. It is again assumed that $T(t)$ is a constant equal to T; thus

$$J_1 \frac{d^2\theta_1}{dt^2} + D_1 \frac{d\theta_1}{dt} + K_1\theta_1 + K_2(\theta_1 - \theta_2) = 0 \qquad (12\text{–}5\text{–}2)$$

$$J_3 \frac{d^2\theta_3}{dt^2} + D_3 \frac{d\theta_3}{dt} + K_3(\theta_3 - \theta_2) = T \qquad (12\text{–}5\text{–}3)$$

One set of analogous circuit equations is

$$L_2 \frac{di_2}{dt} + R_2 i_2 + \frac{1}{C_3} \int (i_2 - i_3)\, dt + \frac{1}{C_2} \int (i_2 - i_1)\, dt = 0 \qquad (12\text{–}5\text{–}4)$$

$$L_1 \frac{di_1}{dt} + R_1 i_1 + \frac{1}{C_1} \int i_1\, dt + \frac{1}{C_2} \int (i_1 - i_2)\, dt = 0 \qquad (12\text{–}5\text{–}5)$$

$$L_3 \frac{di_3}{dt} + R_3 i_3 + \frac{1}{C_3} \int (i_3 - i_2)\, dt = E \qquad (12\text{–}5\text{–}6)$$

The circuit of Fig. 12–5–2 can be obtained by inspection from these equations.

The dual of the circuit of Fig. 12–5–2, also an analogue of the mechanical system of Fig. 12–5–1a, is shown in Fig. 12–5–3.

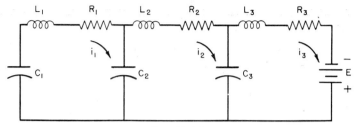

Fig. 12-5-2

12-6. Electromechanical Systems. EXAMPLE 12-6-1. If the system to be analyzed is a combined electric and mechanical system, the same pro-

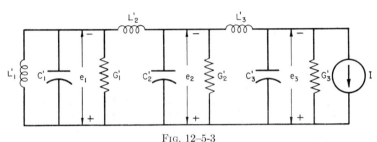

Fig. 12-5-3

cedures can be used, as illustrated by the system of Fig. 12-6-1. Here the

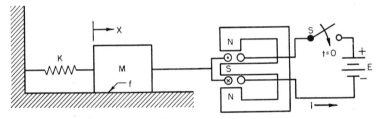

Fig. 12-6-1

battery E is connected through the switch S to a movable coil that is suspended in a radial magnetic field. The coil is fastened to a mass M that is connected to a rigid support by a spring. The example is assumed to have the following constants, in the proper units:

Magnetic flux density, $B = 1.5$
Number of turns of coil, $N = 5$
Radius of coil, $r = 0.04$
Resistance of electric circuit, $R = 2$
Inductance of electric circuit, $L = 0.05$
Voltage of battery, $E = 10$
Mass, $M = 0.5$
Friction coefficient, $f = 2.5$
Spring deflection coefficient, $K = 8$

When current exists in the coil in the direction shown by the dot and cross, the force $F(t)$ is acting to the right, where $F(t)$ is given by

$$F(t) = Bli \qquad (12\text{-}6\text{-}1)$$

Fig. 12-6-2 shows the forces acting on the mass M. The forces acting

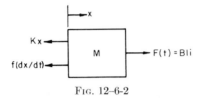

FIG. 12-6-2

to the right produce positive acceleration; therefore the following equation can be written:

$$M \frac{d^2x}{dt^2} = Bli - Kx - f \frac{dx}{dt} \qquad (12\text{-}6\text{-}2)$$

The electric circuit is an E-R-L series circuit with the addition that a voltage is induced in the coil because it is moving in a magnetic field. As this induced voltage is of such a polarity as to oppose change in the current, the voltage equation is

$$E = Ri + L \frac{di}{dt} + Bl \frac{dx}{dt} \qquad (12\text{-}6\text{-}3)$$

Substituting the numerical values in Eqs. 12-6-2 and 12-6-3 gives

$$1.89\, i = 0.5 \frac{d^2x}{dt^2} + 2.5 \frac{dx}{dt} + 8\, x$$

$$10 = 2\, i + 0.05 \frac{di}{dt} + 1.89 \frac{dx}{dt} \qquad (12\text{-}6\text{-}4)$$

It is assumed that the system is at rest when the switch S is closed at $t = 0$; therefore the initial conditions are

$$x(0) = 0 \qquad \frac{dx}{dt}(0) = 0 \qquad i(0) = 0 \qquad (12\text{-}6\text{-}5)$$

Taking the Laplace transform of Eqs. 12-6-4 yields

$$1.89\, \mathcal{L}(i) = 0.5\, s^2 \mathcal{L}(x) + 2.5\, s \mathcal{L}(x) + 8\, \mathcal{L}(x)$$

and

$$\frac{10}{s} = 2\, \mathcal{L}(i) + 0.5\, s \mathcal{L}(i) + 1.89\, s \mathcal{L}(x) \qquad (12\text{-}6\text{-}6)$$

Solution by determinants for $\mathcal{L}(x)$ gives

$$\mathcal{L}(x) = \frac{\begin{vmatrix} -1.89 & 0 \\ 2 + 0.05\, s & \dfrac{10}{s} \end{vmatrix}}{\begin{vmatrix} -1.89 & 0.5\, s^2 + 2.5\, s + 8 \\ 2 + 0.05\, s & 1.89\, s \end{vmatrix}} \qquad (12\text{-}6\text{-}7)$$

which, after expansion, yields

$$\mathcal{L}(x) = \frac{756}{s[s^3 + 45\,s^2 + 359\,s + 640]} \qquad (12\text{–}6\text{–}8)$$

Factoring the denominator gives

$$\mathcal{L}(x) = \frac{756}{s[(s+2.55)(s+7.1)(s+35.35)]} \qquad (12\text{–}6\text{–}9)$$

The inverse transform of Eq. 12–6-9 is

$$x(t) = 1.18 - 1.984\ \epsilon^{-2.55t} + 0.828\ \epsilon^{-7.1t} - 0.023\ \epsilon^{-35.35t} \qquad (12\text{–}6\text{–}10)$$

EXAMPLE 12–6-2. As a second example, the system of Fig. 12–6-1 is again considered, but this time the battery and S are replaced by a short

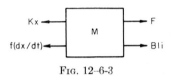

FIG. 12–6-3

circuit. At $t = 0$ a constant force F of 10 units acting in the positive x direction is applied to the mass. The forces acting on the mass M are shown in Fig. 12–6-3. The system equations are

$$F + Bli - Kx - f\frac{dx}{dt} = M\frac{d^2x}{dt^2}$$

$$0 = Ri + L\frac{di}{dt} + Bl\frac{dx}{dt} \qquad (12\text{–}6\text{–}11)$$

Inserting numerical values gives

$$10 + 1.89\,i = 0.5\frac{d^2x}{dt^2} + 2.5\frac{dx}{dt} + 8\,x$$

$$0 = 2\,i + 0.05\frac{di}{dt} + 1.89\frac{dx}{dt} \qquad (12\text{–}6\text{–}12)$$

It is assumed that the system is at rest when the force is applied; therefore the initial conditions are

$$x(0) = 0 \qquad \frac{dx}{dt}(0) = 0 \qquad i(0) = 0 \qquad (12\text{–}6\text{–}13)$$

The Laplace transforms of Eqs. 12–6-12 are

$$\frac{10}{s} + 1.89\ \mathcal{L}(i) = 0.5\ s^2\mathcal{L}(x) + 2.5\ s\mathcal{L}(x) + 8\ \mathcal{L}(x)$$

$$0 = 2\ \mathcal{L}(i) + 0.05\ s\mathcal{L}(i) + 1.89\ s\mathcal{L}(x) \qquad (12\text{–}6\text{–}14)$$

Solving for $\mathcal{L}(i)$ gives

$$\mathcal{L}(i) = \frac{\begin{vmatrix} \dfrac{10}{s} & 0.5\,s^2 + 2.5\,s + 8 \\[2mm] 0 & 1.89\,s \end{vmatrix}}{\begin{vmatrix} -1.89 & 0.5\,s^2 + 2.5\,s + 8 \\[2mm] 2 + 0.05\,s & 1.89\,s \end{vmatrix}} \qquad (12\text{–}6\text{–}15)$$

and simplification yields

$$\mathcal{L}(i) = -\frac{756}{s^3 + 45\,s^2 + 359\,s + 640} \qquad (12\text{-}6\text{-}16)$$

The inverse transform of Eq. 12–6-16 is

$$i(t) = -5.06\,\epsilon^{-2.55t} + 5.88\,\epsilon^{-7.1t} - 0.812\,\epsilon^{-35.35t} \qquad (12\text{-}6\text{-}17)$$

It is to be noted that Eq. 12–6-17 is the negative of the derivative of Eq. 12–6-10. This result could have been anticipated by virtue of the reciprocity theorem. The voltage E at location A produces a displacement x at location B. In an all electric system, the reciprocity theorem would move the voltage from location A to B. In this system the quantity analogous to voltage at location B is a force, and the resulting quantity at A which is analogous to displacement is q. The desired result is current and, since $i = dq/dt$, differentiation of Eq. 12–6-10 gives Eq. 12–6-17. The negative sign is a result of the direction chosen for the force.

Just as it is possible to obtain an electrical analogue of a mechanical system, it is also possible to obtain an electrical analogue of an electromechanical system. This is done for the system of Fig. 12–6-1 with the

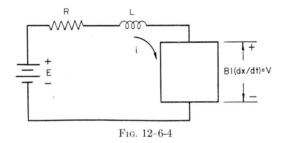

Fig. 12-6-4

help of Fig. 12–6-4. The effect of the mechanical system on the electric circuit is a voltage

$$v = Bl\frac{dx}{dt} \qquad (12\text{-}6\text{-}18)$$

This can be solved for dx/dt:

$$\frac{dx}{dt} = \frac{v}{Bl} \qquad (12\text{-}6\text{-}19)$$

Solution of Eq. 12–6-2 for the current i gives

$$i = \frac{M}{Bl}\frac{d^2x}{dt^2} + \frac{f}{Bl}\frac{dx}{dt} + \frac{K}{Bl}x \qquad (12\text{-}6\text{-}20)$$

Eq. 12–6-20 suggests that the current i comprises three components. Combining dx/dt of Eq. 12–6-19 (and its derivative and integral) with Eq. 12–6-20 gives

$$i = \frac{M}{(Bl)^2}\frac{dv}{dt} + \frac{fv}{(Bl)^2} + \frac{K}{(Bl)^2}\int v\,dt \qquad (12\text{-}6\text{-}21)$$

Use of the following analogous quantities leads to Eq. 12–6-23 and the circuit of Fig. 12–6-5:

$$C' = \frac{M}{(Bl)^2} \qquad R' = \frac{(Bl)^2}{f} \qquad L' = \frac{(Bl)^2}{K} \tag{12–6-22}$$

$$i = C' \frac{dv}{dt} + \frac{v}{R'} + \frac{1}{L'} \int v \, dt \tag{12–6-23}$$

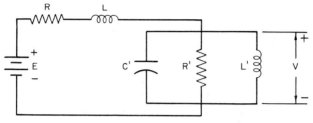

FIG. 12–6-5

12–7. Electric Machines. The conventional study of electric machines is concerned with their steady-state behavior. However, the transient behavior in many cases is just as important as the steady-state response. Since electric machines contain magnetic material such as silicon steel, the behavior of the machine becomes nonlinear if the machine is driven so that the magnetic material saturates. Analysis of nonlinear systems is beyond the scope of this book; however, if the machine is operated below saturation, the characteristics are substantially linear and a calculated result is a good approximation to an actual response of the machine.

EXAMPLE 12–7-1. Fig. 12–7-1 indicates a separately excited d-c motor

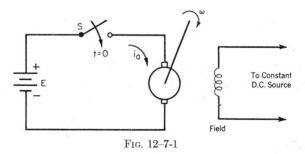

FIG. 12–7-1

energized by a voltage E placed across the armature at $t = 0$. The parameters of the motor are as follows:

R_{am} = resistance of the armature
L_{am} = inductance of the armature
K_{vm} = back emf constant
K_{tm} = torque constant
J_m = moment of inertia
D_m = viscous friction constant

It is assumed that the system is at rest at $t = 0$ when the voltage E is applied, and that the equation for the angular velocity $\omega(t)$ is desired. The electrical equation can be written

$$E = R_{am}i_a + L_{am}\frac{di_a}{dt} + K_{vm}\omega \qquad (12\text{-}7\text{-}1)$$

In this equation the term $K_{vm}\omega$ is a voltage due to the back emf of the motor.

The current i_a produces a torque which leads to the equation

$$K_{tm}i_a = J_m\frac{d\omega}{dt} + D_m\omega \qquad (12\text{-}7\text{-}2)$$

Since it is assumed that the system starts at rest, the $t = 0$ conditions are

$$i_a(0) = 0 \qquad \omega(0) = 0 \qquad (12\text{-}7\text{-}3)$$

Transformation of Eqs. 12-7-1 and 12-7-2 gives

$$\frac{E}{s} = [R_{am} + sL_{am}]\mathcal{L}(i_a) + K_{vm}\mathcal{L}(\omega)$$
$$0 = -K_{tm}\mathcal{L}(i_a) + [sJ_m + D_m]\mathcal{L}(\omega) \qquad (12\text{-}7\text{-}4)$$

Solution for $\mathcal{L}(\omega)$ yields

$$\mathcal{L}(\omega) = \frac{\begin{vmatrix} R_{am} + sL_{am} & \dfrac{E}{s} \\ -K_{tm} & 0 \end{vmatrix}}{\begin{vmatrix} R_{am} + sL_{am} & K_{vm} \\ -K_{tm} & sJ_m + D_m \end{vmatrix}} \qquad (12\text{-}7\text{-}5)$$

Expanding the determinants and simplifying give

$$\mathcal{L}(\omega) = \frac{EK_{tm}}{J_mL_{am}}\left[\frac{1}{s\left\{s^2 + \dfrac{(J_mR_{am} + D_mL_{am})s}{J_mL_{am}} + \dfrac{D_mR_{am} + K_{tm}K_{vm}}{J_mL_{am}}\right\}}\right] \qquad (12\text{-}7\text{-}6)$$

A problem at the end of the chapter gives numerical values for the parameters, and this problem can be worked to complete the example.

EXAMPLE 12-7-2. Fig. 12-7-2 indicates a separately excited motor with

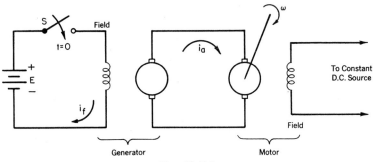

Fig. 12-7-2

armature current supplied by a generator, which in turn is energized by a voltage E placed on its field winding by closing the switch S at $t = 0$.

In addition to the parameters already defined for the motor in the preceding example, the following parameters occur for the generator:

R_{ag} = resistance of the armature
L_{ag} = inductance of the armature
R_{fg} = resistance of the field
L_{fg} = inductance of the field
K_{vg} = generator voltage constant

It is assumed again that the system is at rest at $t = 0$. When the voltage E is applied to the field of the generator, the following set of equations and initial conditions describes the system.

$$E = R_{fg}i_f + L_{fg}\frac{di_f}{dt} \tag{12-7-7}$$

$$K_{vg}i_f = (R_{ag} + R_{am})i_a + (L_{ag} + L_{am})\frac{di_a}{dt} + K_{vm}\omega \tag{12-7-8}$$

$$K_{tm}i_a = J_m\frac{d\omega}{dt} + D_m\omega \tag{12-7-9}$$

$$i_a(0) = i_f(0) = \omega(0) = 0 \tag{12-7-10}$$

Transformation of Eqs. 12–7-7 through 12–7-10 and solution of the resulting equations for $\mathcal{L}(\omega)$ give

$$\mathcal{L}(\omega) = \frac{\dfrac{EK_{vg}K_{tm}}{L_{fg}J_m[L_{am} + L_{ag}]}}{s\left(s + \dfrac{R_{fg}}{L_{fg}}\right)\left\{s^2 + \dfrac{[J_m(R_{am} + R_{gm}) + D_m(L_{am} + L_{ag})]s}{J_m[L_{am} + L_{ag}]} + \dfrac{D_m(R_{am} + R_{ag}) + K_{tm}K_{vm}}{J_m[L_{am} + L_{ag}]}\right\}} \tag{12-7-11}$$

A problem at the end of this chapter gives numerical values for the parameters. This problem can be worked to complete the example.

12–8. Sinusoidal Steady-State Response. The sinusoidal steady-state response of mechanical and electromechanical systems can be found in much the same manner as has been used for the electric systems. The following examples illustrate the method.

EXAMPLE 12–8-1. The mechanical system of Fig. 12–8-1 has the force

$$F(t) = 4 \sin 10\, t \tag{12-8-1}$$

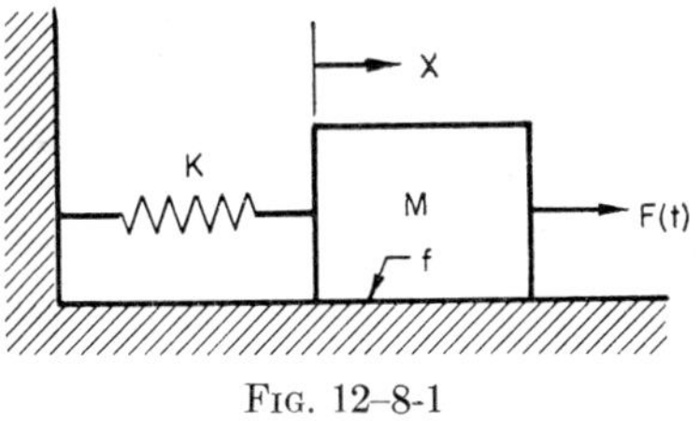

FIG. 12–8-1

applied to the mass M. The following constants characterize the system:

$$M = 0.248 \qquad f = 2 \qquad K = 6 \tag{12-8-2}$$

The system equation is

$$F(t) = 0.248\frac{d^2x}{dt^2} + 2\frac{dx}{dt} + 6\,x \tag{12-8-3}$$

Transforming Eq. 12-8-3 under the assumption that all the initial conditions are zero gives

$$\mathcal{L}(F) = [0.248\,s^2 + 2\,s + 6]\mathcal{L}(x) \tag{12-8-4}$$

The ratio of output to input transforms is

$$\frac{\mathcal{L}(x)}{\mathcal{L}(F)} = \frac{1}{0.248\,s^2 + 2\,s + 6} \tag{12-8-5}$$

Substitution of $s = j\omega$ in Eq. 12-8-5 gives

$$\frac{x(j\omega)}{F(j\omega)} = \frac{1}{6 - 0.248\,\omega^2 + j\,2\,\omega} \tag{12-8-6}$$

For $\omega = 10$ in this example,

$$\frac{x(j\,10)}{F(j\,10)} = \frac{1}{6 - 24.8 + j\,20} = 0.0367\underline{/-132.9°} \tag{12-8-7}$$

Eq. 12-8-7 evidences that the ratio of the magnitude of $x(j\omega)$ to $F(j\omega)$ is 0.0367 and that $x(j\omega)$ lags $F(j\omega)$ by 132.9 degrees. Correspondingly, the equation for $x(t)$ in the steady state is

$$x(t)_{ss} = 4 \times 0.0367 \sin{(10\,t - 132.9°)} = 0.1468 \sin{(10\,t - 132.9°)} \tag{12-8-8}$$

EXAMPLE 12-8-2. The mechanical system of Fig. 12-8-2 has the sinus-

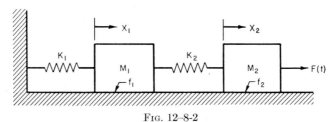

FIG. 12-8-2

oidal force $F(t) = 4 \sin 10\,t$ acting to the right as shown.

The parameters of the system are

$$\begin{array}{lll} M_1 = 0.248 & f_1 = 2 & K_1 = 6 \\ M_2 = 0.124 & f_2 = 1.33 & K_2 = 4 \end{array} \tag{12-8-9}$$

The system equations are

$$F(t) = 0.124\frac{d^2x_2}{dt^2} + 1.33\frac{dx_2}{dt} + 4(x_2 - x_1)$$

$$0 = 4(x_1 - x_2) + 0.248\frac{d^2x_1}{dt^2} + 2\frac{dx_1}{dt} + 6\,x_1 \tag{12-8-10}$$

Transforming these equations under the assumption that all initial conditions are zero gives

$$\mathcal{L}(F) = -4\,\mathcal{L}(x_1) + (0.124\,s^2 + 1.33\,s + 4)\mathcal{L}(x_2)$$
$$0 = (0.248\,s^2 + 2\,s + 10)\mathcal{L}(x_1) - 4\,\mathcal{L}(x_2) \qquad (12\text{-}8\text{-}11)$$

Solving Eqs. 12–8-11 for

$$\frac{\mathcal{L}(x_1)}{\mathcal{L}(F)} = \frac{4}{0.0307\,s^4 + 0.577\,s^3 + 4.89\,s^2 + 21.3\,s + 24} \qquad (12\text{-}8\text{-}12)$$

and substituting $s = j\,10$ in the result give

$$\frac{x_1(j\omega)}{F(j\omega)} = \frac{4}{307 - 489 + 24 + j(213 - 577)} = 0.0101\underline{/113.5^\circ} \quad (12\text{-}8\text{-}13)$$

The equation for the desired $x_1(t)$ in the steady state is

$$x_1(t)_{ss} = 4 \times 0.0101 \sin(10\,t + 113.5^\circ) = 0.0404 \sin(10\,t + 113.5^\circ) \quad (12\text{-}8\text{-}14)$$

EXAMPLE 12–8-3. As a last example of this type, consider the electromechanical system of Fig. 12-6-1, where for this example the battery E and switch S are replaced by a sinusoidal source of voltage

$$e = 50 \sin 10\,t \qquad (12\text{-}8\text{-}15)$$

It is desired to find the equation for $x(t)$ in the steady state. The following equation can be written when it is realized that the $10/s$ in Eq. 12–6-7 is actually $\mathcal{L}(e)$:

$$\mathcal{L}(x) = \frac{\begin{vmatrix} -1.89 & 0 \\ 2 + 0.05\,s & \mathcal{L}(e) \end{vmatrix}}{\begin{vmatrix} -1.89 & 0.5\,s^2 + 2.5\,s + 8 \\ 2 + 0.05\,s & 1.89\,s \end{vmatrix}} \qquad (12\text{-}8\text{-}16)$$

Eq. 12–8-16 can be solved for the ratio of $\mathcal{L}(x)$ to the $\mathcal{L}(e)$:

$$\frac{\mathcal{L}(x)}{\mathcal{L}(e)} = \frac{1.89}{0.025\,s^3 + 1.125\,s^2 + 8.97\,s + 16} \qquad (12\text{-}8\text{-}17)$$

When $s = j\,10$ is substituted in Eq. 12–8-17, the result is

$$\frac{x(j\omega)}{E(j\omega)} = \frac{1.89}{16 - 112.5 + j(89.7 - 25)} = 0.0163\underline{/-146.3^\circ} \quad (12\text{-}8\text{-}18)$$

Correspondingly, the desired result of $x(t)$ in the steady state is

$$x(t) = 50 \times 0.0163 \sin(10\,t - 146.3^\circ) = 0.815 \sin(10\,t - 146.3^\circ) \quad (12\text{-}8\text{-}19)$$

PROBLEMS

12–1. For the mechanical system of Fig. 12-2-1 the following parameters are given:

$F(t) = F = 12$ lb
Weight of mass $= 8$ lb
$K = 6$ lb/ft
$f = 1.2$ lb/ft/sec

The mass is at rest when the force is applied at $t = 0$. Find the equation for $x(t)$ after $t = 0$.

12-2. For the mechanical system of Fig. 12–2-1 the following parameters are given:

$F(t) = 0$
Weight of mass $= 10$ lb
$K = 12$ lb/ft
$f = 3.5$ lb/ft/sec

The mass is moving with a velocity $dx/dt = -5$ ft/sec and is positioned at $x = 2$ ft at time $t = 0$. Find the equation for $x(t)$ after $t = 0$.

12-3. For the mechanical system of Fig. 12–P-1 the following parameters are given:

Weight of mass $M_1 = 100$ lb
Weight of mass $M_2 = 50$ lb
$K = 30$ lb/ft
$f = 10$ lb/ft/sec

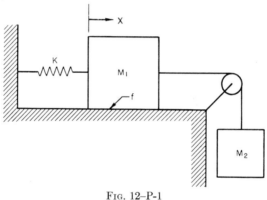

FIG. 12–P-1

Before $t = 0$ the mass M_2 is so supported that it exerts no force upon M_1 and the system is at rest. At $t = 0$, M_2 is released. Find the equation for $x(t)$ after $t = 0$.

12-4. The mechanical system of Fig. 12–P-2 is at rest when, at $t = 0$, the A end of the spring is given a constant velocity of H units to the right. Write the equa-

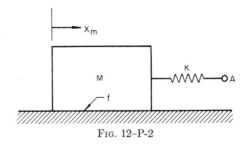

FIG. 12–P-2

tions for this system and determine two electric circuits that are the analogues of this system.

12–5. Verify that the circuit of Fig. 12–3-5 is also the analogue of the mechanical system of Fig. 12–3-1 by starting with Eq. 12–3-3 and by using the quantities in column 3 of Table 12–1 as the quantities analogous to those of the mechanical system.

12–6. Verify that the circuit of Fig. 12–5-3 is also the analogue of the mechanical system.

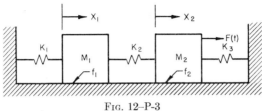

FIG. 12–P-3

12–7. The mechanical system of Fig. 12–P-3 is at rest when a constant force $F(t) = F$ is applied to the system at $t = 0$. Write the equations for the system and determine two electric circuits that are the analogues of this system.

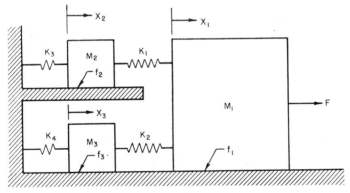

FIG. 12–P-4

12–8. The mechanical system of Fig. 12–P-4 is at rest when a constant force F is applied to the system at $t = 0$. Write the equations for the system and determine two electric circuits that are the analogues of this system.

12–9. Repeat Prob. 12–8, but apply the force F to M_2 instead of M_1.

12–10. The mechanical system of Fig. 12–P-5 is at rest when a constant force F is applied to the system at $t = 0$. Write the equations for the system, and determine two electric circuits that are analogues of this system.

12–11. Repeat Prob. 12–10, but apply the force F to M_2 instead of M_1.

12–12. Given the system and the values of M, K, and f of Prob. 12–1. A force, in pounds, $F(t) = \sin 3t$ is applied to the system and left long enough for steady-state conditions to be reached. Find the equation for $x(t)$ in the steady state.

12–13. Consider the system of Ex. 12–8-2, except that the force $F(t)$ is applied to M_1 instead of M_2. Find the equation for $x_2(t)$ in the steady state.

12–14. Consider the system of Ex. 12–6-1 with the following changes. The constant-voltage source E and the switch are replaced by a short circuit. A force

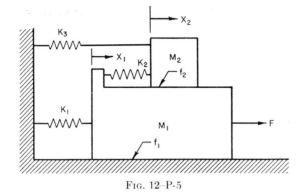

Fig. 12–P-5

$F(t) = 10 \cos 5\,t$ is applied to the mass and left long enough for the system to reach the steady state. Find the equation for i in the steady state.

12–15. Consider the d-c motor of Ex. 12–7-1 with the following parameters:

$$E = 50 \text{ volts}$$
$$R_{am} = 28 \text{ ohms}$$
$$L_{am} = 0.7 \text{ henry}$$
$$K_{vm} = 1.8 \text{ volts/rev/sec}$$
$$K_{tm} = 50 \text{ in.-oz/amp}$$
$$J_m = 0.2 \text{ lb.-in.}^2$$
$$D_m = 500 \times 10^{-6} \text{ lb-ft/rad/sec}$$

Find the equation for $\omega(t)$ after $t = 0$.

12–16. Consider the d-c motor of Prob. 12–15 except that a sinusoidal voltage $e = 50 \sin 30\,t$ is applied to the motor and left long enough for the system to reach steady-state conditions. Find the equation for $\omega(t)$ in the steady state.

12–17. Consider the motor-generator system of Ex. 12–7-2. The parameters of the motor are those given in Prob. 12–15. The generator has the following parameters:

$$R_{ag} = 38 \text{ ohms}$$
$$L_{ag} = 0.5 \text{ henry}$$
$$R_{fg} = 1200 \text{ ohms}$$
$$L_{fg} = 14 \text{ henrys}$$
$$K_{vg} = 1300 \text{ volts/amp}$$

The voltage E applied to the field of the generator is 50 volts. Find the equation for $\omega(t)$ after $t = 0$.

12–18. Consider the motor-generator system of Prob. 12–17 except that a sinusoidal voltage $e = 50 \sin 30\,t$ is applied to the generator and left long enough for the system to reach steady-state conditions. Find the equation for $\omega(t)$ in the steady state.

CHAPTER 13

REGULATORS AND SERVOMECHANISMS

Regulators and servomechanisms are devices which have been developed for the purpose of performing a given task as quickly and reliably as possible with a minimum of a human operator's time. As industrial operations have become more complicated and as the requirements for the performance of certain equipment have become more demanding, more and more automatic control systems have been developed.

The only aspect of the theory of control systems to be presented in this book involves determination of the transient response of such systems, as this is in keeping with the subject of this book. However, before presenting the transient analysis portion of this chapter, it is desirable to review the general nature of the performance of control systems through simple examples.

13–1. Open-Loop and Closed-Loop Control Systems. Control systems are generally divided into two categories: open-loop and closed-loop systems. In an open-loop system the input is applied to the system and the output behaves in accordance with the characteristics of the system. An example of this is a house heated by a gas furnace with the input valve controlling the flow of gas at a certain setting. The output, which is the temperature of the house, takes on the value determined by the outside temperature and wind velocity, gas pressure, thermal characteristics of the house, etc.

In contrast, a closed-loop system for heating the same house is a system where the temperature of the house itself is used to determine the amount of gas supplied to the furnace. This is usually done by use of a thermostat of some type set at a desired value. If the house temperature is below the setting of the thermostat, the furnace operates until the temperature is brought to the desired value, as set on the thermostat. The cycle is closed in the sense that the temperature of the house acts through the thermostat to operate the furnace which heats the house and produces the desired temperature.

Some of the advantages of closed-cycle systems over open-cycle systems can be deduced from this simple example. A man trying to control the temperature of his house by use of an open-cycle system may look up the weather forecast in the paper each morning and decide at what value to set the input valve to the furnace. If, as sometimes happens, the weather forecast happens to be incorrect and the temperature is much colder than expected, the temperature of the house falls far below the desired value. Contrast this performance with that of a closed-cycle system operating under the same conditions. The thermostat is set at a certain value, and while the outside temperature is mild the furnace operates very little. If the outside temperature falls, then, instead of the house temperature falling, the thermostat simply turns on the furnace for longer periods of time.

13–2. Block Diagram. The basic operation of open-loop and closed-loop systems can be shown by the block diagrams of Fig. 13–2-1.

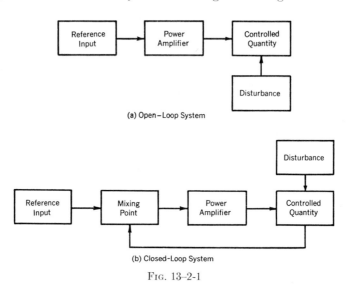

(a) Open–Loop System

(b) Closed-Loop System

Fig. 13–2-1

The input of the open-loop system feeds into a power amplifier stage, which in turn drives the controlled quantity. A disturbance is an undesired signal which can also affect the controlled quantity. An example of a disturbance is that just given in the above example of an open-loop system, in which the outside temperature fell by an unexpected amount, causing the house temperature to fall below the desired value.

The input of the closed-loop system feeds into a mixing point along with a signal returned from the controlled quantity which is the output of the entire system. The signal from this mixing point is the difference between the input and output signals and is termed the actuating signal, because it is this signal that is the input to (or actuates) the power amplifier stage which in turn drives the controlled quantity. A disturbance can also affect the controlled quantity. However, because of the nature of the closed loop, as the controlled quantity is affected by the disturbance the output signal changes; this change in turn changes the actuating signal, which makes a correction (or at least a partial correction) in the controlled quantity and thus overcomes a large part of the effect of the disturbance.

In the simple system of Fig. 13–2-1b the actuating signal could also be termed an error signal. By this is meant that ideally it is desired to have the controlled quantity exactly follow the commands of the reference input. If the output does not take on this desired value, it is in error by an amount equal to the difference between the desired value and the actual value. In this system this error is equal to the actuating signal. In a more general system than that shown in Fig. 13–2-1, there may be an element in the feedback path. (This is the path from the controlled quantity back to the mixing point.) With an element in the feedback path, the error and the actuating signal are not the same.

At first glance it may seem as though the designer of a servomechanism is in an impossible situation; he desires the error to be zero, but the closed-loop system cannot follow a time-varying input unless there is an error. The answer to this is that nothing in the world is exact and things can only be done within certain tolerances. If the error of operation of a closed-loop system can be kept within specified tolerances, the operation of the system is satisfactory.

13–3. Examples of Servomechanisms. EXAMPLE 13–3-1. The system of Fig. 13–3-1 shows rather crudely how the position of the mass M can be

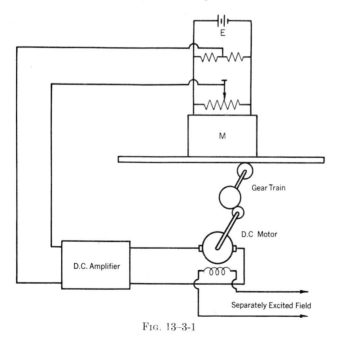

FIG. 13–3-1

controlled. A voltage E is placed across a center-tapped resistor and across a potentiometer that is mounted on the mass M. If the pointer of the potentiometer is at the midpoint, the voltage between the pointer and the center tap of the resistor is zero; hence the voltage into the direct-coupled amplifier is zero, so the voltage applied to the motor is zero and the mass remains stationary. Now let it be supposed that the pointer of the potentiometer is moved to the right. This causes a voltage to be developed at the input to the amplifier, which in turn places a voltage on the motor of such a polarity as to cause the motor to move the mass to the right. If the pointer is moved to the left, a voltage of opposite polarity is applied to the motor; this moves the mass to the left.

By this device the location of the mass M can be controlled by the movement of the pointer on the potentiometer. It is to be emphasized that the only energy required by the control device is that necessary to move the pointer on a potentiometer, whereas the energy required to move the mass is supplied by the amplifier and motor. By such a device the movement of a finger can control the location of an extremely large mass.

The system of Fig. 13–3–1 can be used to locate the cutting tool on a lathe. The material can be fed at a constant velocity and the cutting tool located in accordance with the input to the control system, and thus the material is cut in accordance with a preset pattern. Actually, the same input can be applied to any number of lathes which are carrying out duplicate operations.

EXAMPLE 13–3-2. The system of Fig. 13–3-2 is a somewhat more elaborate system that can be used to locate the angular position of a moment

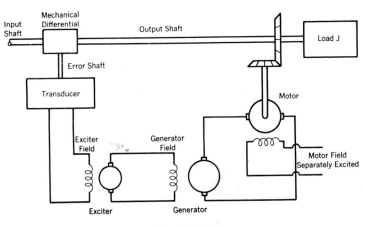

FIG. 13–3-2

of inertia J. The position of the input shaft is the reference position which it is desired to have the load J follow within a certain tolerance. The mechanical differential has three shafts. For the present these shafts are referred to as the input shaft, output shaft, and error shaft. The differential is a device whereby the error shaft takes an angular position which is the difference between the position of the input and output shafts, as described by the equation

$$\text{Angle}_{\text{error shaft}} = \text{angle}_{\text{input shaft}} - \text{angle}_{\text{output shaft}} \qquad (13\text{-}3\text{-}1)$$

The error shaft actuates a transducer which produces a voltage proportional to the angular displacement of the error shaft. The voltage from the transducer is applied to the field of an exciter. The output of the exciter is applied to the field of the generator. The output of the generator is applied to the motor, which in turn drives the output shaft and the load.

In order to study the method of operation of the system, it is assumed that the system is at rest. That is, the input and output shafts are stationary and are in alignment. If this is so, the error shaft is at its zero position and the voltages produced by the transducer, exciter, and generator are zero and therefore the motor is at rest.

Let it be supposed that from this rest position the input shaft is turned through an angle θ_1 in the clockwise direction at $t = 0$. The moment of inertia J keeps the output stationary at $t = 0$; that is, the error shaft turns through the same angle θ_1 and a voltage is produced at the output of the transducer, which applies a voltage to the field of the exciter. Then the exciter applies a voltage to the generator, which applies a voltage to the motor, which causes the load to turn until the output shaft is again in alignment with the input shaft.

As in the preceding example, the energy necessary to drive the load is supplied by the power devices and the energy supplied to the input is only that amount of energy necessary to turn the input shaft.

13-4. Types of Input Signals. Because of the wide variety of inputs that a servomechanism may be expected to follow, it is impossible to analyze a system under actual input conditions. However, the actual input can usually be interpreted so that test inputs can be applied to the system; and, if the system response is satisfactory to the test input, the system response to the actual input is also satisfactory. Typical test inputs are a unit step function, a unit ramp function, and sinusoidal functions.

13-5. Simple Servomechanism. Fig. 13-5-1 shows the block diagram of a servomechanism to be analyzed with various test inputs. One purpose

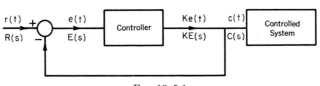

FIG. 13-5-1

of this block diagram is to indicate that all systems that fit it can be analyzed in the same manner. That is, this diagram could be a hydraulic system, a pneumatic system, a system involving a chemical reaction, a translatory mechanical system, as in Ex. 13–3-1 or a rotational mechanical system, as in Ex. 13–3-2, etc. The following discussions refer to the system of Ex. 13–3-2 because frequently it is helpful to think in specific terms.

On the block diagram of Fig. 13–5-1, $r(t)$, $e(t)$, and $c(t)$ refer to the time functions of the reference input, the actuating signal, and the controlled variable respectively, and $R(s)$, $E(s)$, and $C(s)$ are their Laplace transforms. The arrows on the diagram represent the direction of signal flow and the $(+)$ and $(-)$ on the mixing point indicate that the $r(t)$ comes through $(+)$ while the $c(t)$ comes through $(-)$, as demonstrated by the equation

$$e(t) = r(t) - c(t) \qquad (13\text{--}5\text{-}1)$$

The controller of the block diagram represents the transducer, the exciter, the generator, and the motor of the rotational system of Fig. 13–3-2. For the present the output of the controller is assumed to be a torque, which is proportional to the actuating signal, where K is the constant of proportionality. To investigate the significance of this assumption, let it be assumed that the output shaft is blocked and that the shaft entering the transducer is turned through an angle. The voltage output of the transducer produces a current in the field of the exciter, which produces a current in the field of the generator, which produces a current in the armature of the motor, which produces a torque. If the inductance of the fields and armatures of the exciter, generator, and motor can be neglected and if each piece of machinery is operating on the linear portion of its characteristics, the torque supplied by the motor to the output shaft is proportional to the actuating signal. For this proportionality to be true with the output shaft rotating, an additional assumption is implied: that the back emf of the motor is zero.

The block denoted as the controlled system represents the moment of inertia J of all the moving parts and the friction D, which is assumed to be viscous.

It may seem that many assumptions are involved in replacing the system by this particular block diagram. As many of these assumptions as possible are eliminated or minimized as the analysis is developed.

13–6. Response to a Ramp Input Function. For the system of Fig. 13–5-1 it is assumed that the system is at rest and at $t = 0$, and a ramp function is applied to the input:

$$r(t) = \omega_1 t \qquad (13\text{--}6\text{-}1)$$

The system equations are

$$Ke = J\frac{d^2c}{dt^2} + D\frac{dc}{dt}$$

and $\qquad (13\text{--}6\text{-}2)$

$$e(t) = r(t) - c(t)$$

Eqs. 13-6-2 can be solved in terms of either $c(t)$ or $e(t)$. Sometimes it is convenient to solve these equations in terms of the actuating signal; thus

$$Ke = J\left[\frac{d^2r}{dt^2} - \frac{d^2e}{dt^2}\right] + D\left[\frac{dr}{dt} - \frac{de}{dt}\right] \tag{13-6-3}$$

This equation can be rewritten

$$J\frac{d^2e}{dt^2} + D\frac{de}{dt} + Ke = J\frac{d^2r}{dt^2} + D\frac{dr}{dt} \tag{13-6-4}$$

Eq. 13-6-4 applies to any input signal. Rewriting this equation for the ramp input of Eq. 13-6-1 gives

$$J\frac{d^2e}{dt^2} + D\frac{de}{dt} + Ke = D\omega_1 \tag{13-6-5}$$

The associated two initial conditions are

$$r(0) = 0 \qquad c(0) = 0 \qquad e(0) = r(0) - c(0) = 0$$
$$\frac{dr}{dt}(0) = \omega_1 \qquad \frac{dc}{dt}(0) = 0 \qquad \frac{de}{dt}(0) = \frac{dr}{dt}(0) - \frac{dc}{dt}(0) = \omega_1 \tag{13-6-6}$$

The Laplace transform of Eq. 13-6-5 is

$$J[s^2E(s) - s(0) - \omega_1] + D[sE(s) - 0] + KE(s) = \frac{D\omega_1}{s} \tag{13-6-7}$$

and solution for $E(s)$ gives

$$E(s) = \frac{\omega_1(s + D/J)}{s[s^2 + (D/J)s + K/J]} \tag{13-6-8}$$

An examination of Eq. 13-6-8 indicates that the system response may be nonoscillatory, critically damped, or oscillatory, depending on the relationship among D, J, and K. These three cases will be taken up in the order mentioned.

Nonoscillatory Case. For convenience let

$$a = \frac{D}{2J} \quad \text{and} \quad b = \sqrt{\frac{D^2}{4J^2} - \frac{K}{J}} \tag{13-6-9}$$

With this notation, Eq. 13-6-8 can be written

$$E(s) = \frac{\omega_1(s + D/J)}{s[(s + a)^2 - b^2]} \tag{13-6-10}$$

The inverse transform is put into a convenient form by using the identity

$$\mathcal{L}^{-1}\left[\frac{s + \alpha}{s[(s + a)^2 - b^2]}\right] = \frac{\alpha}{a^2 - b^2}$$
$$+ \epsilon^{-at}\left[\frac{\alpha}{b^2 - a^2}\cosh bt + \frac{b^2 - a^2 + a\alpha}{b(b^2 - a^2)}\sinh bt\right] \tag{13-6-11}$$

Then

$$e(t) = \omega_1\frac{D}{K} + \epsilon^{-at}\left[-\frac{\omega_1 D}{K}\cosh bt + \frac{\omega_1(1 - D^2/2JK)}{b}\sinh bt\right] \tag{13-6-12}$$

The condition that the system is nonoscillatory means that b^2 of Eq. 13–6-9 is positive; this means that

$$\frac{D^2}{4\,J^2} > \frac{K}{J}$$

or   (13–6-13)

$$D > 2\sqrt{KJ}$$

Critically Damped Case. If K and J are considered fixed and D variable, then, as D is decreased, it eventually takes on a value such that b of Eq. 13–6-9 is zero. This condition corresponds to the critically damped case, and the relationship among the coefficients is given by

$$D_c = 2\sqrt{KJ} \tag{13–6-14}$$

The response of the critically damped system can be found by substituting $b = 0$ in Eq. 13–6-12. This yields an indeterminant term:

$$\lim_{b \to 0} \frac{\sinh bt}{b} = \frac{0}{0} \tag{13–6-15}$$

which can be evaluated by using l'Hospital's rule as

$$\lim_{b \to 0} \frac{\sinh bt}{b} = \lim_{b \to 0} \frac{t \cosh bt}{1} = t \tag{13–6-16}$$

The response of the critically damped system is

$$e(t) = \frac{\omega_1 D_c}{K} - \epsilon^{-D_c t/2\,J}\left[\frac{\omega_1 D_c}{K} + \omega_1 t\right] \tag{13–6-17}$$

Oscillatory Case. If D is decreased below the value for the critically damped case, the response of the system becomes oscillatory. As the term b of Eq. 13–6-9 becomes imaginary, it is convenient to define a real parameter β as

$$\beta = \sqrt{\frac{K}{J} - \frac{D^2}{4\,J^2}} \tag{13–6-18}$$

whence b can be written

$$b = j\beta \tag{13–6-19}$$

In this case the relationship among the coefficients is given by

$$D < 2\sqrt{KJ} \tag{13–6-20}$$

When $b = j\beta$ is substituted in Eq. 13–6-12, the equation for the response of the oscillatory system is found to be

$$e(t) = \frac{\omega_1 D}{K} + \epsilon^{-at}\left[-\frac{\omega_1 D}{K}\cos \beta t + \frac{\omega_1(1 - D^2/2\,JK)}{\beta}\sin \beta t\right] \tag{13–6-21}$$

If D is decreased to the limiting value of zero, the response is still of the oscillatory type and the particular results are of interest. When D is zero, a and β are

$$a = 0 \qquad \beta = \sqrt{\frac{K}{J}} \tag{13–6-22}$$

and Eq. 13-6-21 becomes

$$e(t) = \omega_1 \sqrt{\frac{J}{K}} \sin \sqrt{\frac{K}{J}} t \qquad (13\text{-}6\text{-}23)$$

This equation indicates that the system oscillates indefinitely at an angular velocity which is commonly referred to as the natural undamped radian frequency of oscillation and is denoted by

$$\omega_n = \sqrt{\frac{K}{J}} \qquad (13\text{-}6\text{-}24)$$

With this notation Eq. 13-6-23 can be written

$$e(t) = \frac{\omega_1}{\omega_n} \sin \omega_n t \qquad (13\text{-}6\text{-}25)$$

The response of this system is a pure sinusoidal function with magnitude proportional to ω_1 and inversely proportional to ω_n. The period of oscillation is given by

$$T = \frac{1}{f_n} = \frac{2\pi}{\omega_n} \qquad (13\text{-}6\text{-}26)$$

When the equations for the input and actuating signals are known, the equation for the output with $D = 0$ is

$$c(t) = r(t) - e(t) = \omega_1 t - \frac{\omega_1}{\omega_n} \sin \omega_n t \qquad (13\text{-}6\text{-}27)$$

The input $r(t)$, output $c(t)$, and actuating signal $e(t)$, are shown in Fig. 13-6-1.

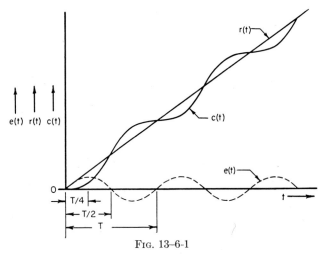

FIG. 13-6-1

The response of the system as shown by Fig. 13-6-1 is examined briefly. At $t = 0$ the actuating signal is zero; therefore no torque results from the controller; the output is stationary; and the derivative of $c(t)$ is zero.

After $t = 0$, $e(t)$ has a value, and the torque delivered by the controller has a value which causes the output to accelerate. At $t = T/4$ the output rotates at the same angular velocity as the input; the torque $Ke(t)$ is maximum because $e(t)$ is maximum; and the angular velocity of the output continues to increase, becoming greater than that of the input. At $t = T/2$, the angular velocity of the output is twice that of the input. Since $e(t)$ is zero, the torque acting on the output is zero; and $c(t)$ becomes greater than $r(t)$, thus producing a negative $e(t)$. At $t = 3\,T/4$ the output has the same angular velocity as the input, but $e(t)$ is a negative maximum. At $t = T$ the ouput is at rest, and the system is ready to repeat the same cycle in the next period T.

13–7. Universal Curves for the System Equations.

Examination of the equations developed in Art. 13–6 shows that the response of the system is determined by the ratio of the actual damping present to the value of the critical damping. Therefore it is convenient to define a factor that expresses this ratio:

$$\zeta = \frac{D}{D_c} \tag{13–7-1}$$

The coefficients of the system equation can be written in terms of this damping ratio ζ and ω_n, as demonstrated by the following examples:

$$a = \frac{D}{2\,J} = \frac{2\,\zeta\sqrt{KJ}}{2\,J} = \zeta\sqrt{\frac{K}{J}} = \zeta\omega_n \tag{13–7-2}$$

$$\beta = \sqrt{\frac{K}{J} - \left(\frac{D}{2\,J}\right)^2} = \sqrt{\omega_n{}^2 - \zeta^2\omega_n{}^2} = \omega_n\sqrt{1 - \zeta^2} \tag{13–7-3}$$

$$\frac{D}{K} = \frac{2\,\zeta\sqrt{KJ}}{K} = 2\,\zeta\sqrt{\frac{J}{K}} = \frac{2\,\zeta}{\omega_n} \tag{13–7-4}$$

For the oscillatory case, in terms of the parameters ζ and ω_n, Eq. 13–6-21 is

$$e(t) = \frac{\omega_1}{\omega_n}\left\{2\,\zeta + \epsilon^{-\zeta\omega_n t}\left[-2\,\zeta\cos\sqrt{1 - \zeta^2}\omega_n t + \frac{1 - 2\,\zeta^2}{\sqrt{1 - \zeta^2}}\sin\sqrt{1 - \zeta^2}\omega_n t\right]\right\} \tag{13–7-5}$$

This equation is not yet in a universal form, as the response depends upon ω_1 and ω_n. However, multiplying the equation by ω_n and dividing it by ω_1 permits plots to be made of a set of universal curves as a function of $\omega_n t$ with ζ as the parameter, from the corresponding equations:

Oscillatory case: $\zeta < 1$

$$e(t)\frac{\omega_n}{\omega_1} = 2\,\zeta$$
$$+ \epsilon^{-\zeta\omega_n t}\left[-2\,\zeta\cos\sqrt{1 - \zeta^2}\omega_n t + \frac{1 - 2\,\zeta^2}{\sqrt{1 - \zeta^2}}\sin\sqrt{1 - \zeta^2}\omega_n t\right] \tag{13–7-6}$$

Critically damped case: $\zeta = 1$

$$e(t)\,\frac{\omega_n}{\omega_1} = 2 + \epsilon^{-\omega_n t}[-2 - \omega_n t] \qquad (13\text{-}7\text{-}7)$$

Nonoscillatory case: $\zeta > 1$

$$e(t)\,\frac{\omega_n}{\omega_1} = 2\,\zeta$$

$$+\,\epsilon^{-\zeta\omega_n t}\left[-2\,\zeta \cosh \sqrt{\zeta^2 - 1}\;\omega_n t + \frac{1 - 2\,\zeta^2}{\sqrt{\zeta^2 - 1}}\,\sinh \sqrt{\zeta^2 - 1}\;\omega_n t\right] \quad (13\text{-}7\text{-}8)$$

Fig. 13-7-1 shows the curves for a few values of ζ.

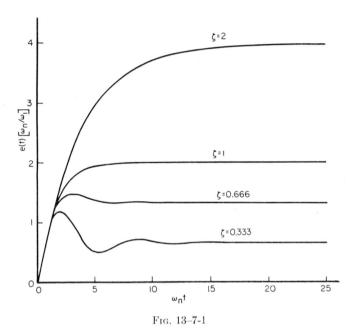

FIG. 13–7-1

Fig. 13-7-2 shows the corresponding set of curves for $c(t)$. It is to be noted that no practical advantage results in a system with a ζ larger than unity. The response for the critically damped case ($\zeta = 1$) moves into its steady-state value without oscillations. So does the curve for $\zeta > 1$, the only difference being that the steady-state actuating signal is greater and the resulting system has no compensating advantages. An examination of the $\zeta = 0.666$ curve shows that, although the response is oscillatory, the magnitudes of oscillation can be tolerated in many instances in practice, and this system has the advantage of a smaller steady-state actuating signal. For these reasons one well-used rule of thumb is to the effect that, for a system of this type, a value of ζ of about 0.5 to 0.6 is desirable.

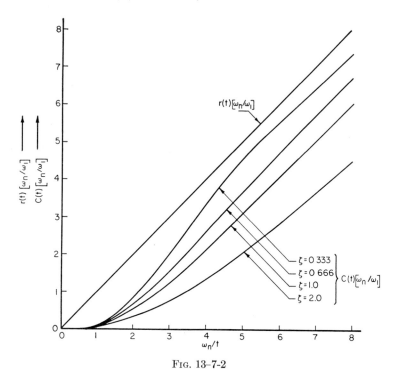

Fig. 13–7-2

13–8. Response to a Step Input Function. For the system of Fig. 13–5-1 (redrawn as Fig. 13–8-1 for convenience) it is assumed that the system is

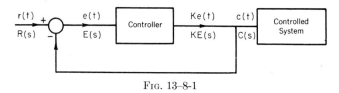

Fig. 13–8-1

at rest and at $t = 0$ a step function is applied to the input as given by the equation

$$r(t) = \theta_1 \tag{13–8-1}$$

Although the response of this system can be found by setting up the basic equation and solving as in Art. 13–7 for the ramp input function, another method is used for variety.

A unit step function is the derivative of a unit ramp function. Since the system is linear, the response of the system to a unit step function is the derivative of the response to a unit ramp function. However, in the example just considered the ramp function is not a unit function; therefore Eq. 13-7-5 must be divided by ω_1 to obtain a unit ramp function response, and the derivative of this result then multiplied by θ_1 to obtain the desired response. Doing these steps and differentiating Eq. 13-7-5 yield

$$e(t) = \frac{\theta_1}{\omega_n} \epsilon^{-\zeta\omega_n t} \left[\left(2\,\zeta\sqrt{1-\zeta^2}\,\omega_n - \frac{1-2\,\zeta^2}{\sqrt{1-\zeta^2}}\,\zeta\omega_n \right)(\sin \sqrt{1-\zeta^2}\omega_n t) \right.$$
$$\left. + \left(\frac{1-2\,\zeta^2}{\sqrt{1-\zeta^2}}\sqrt{1-\zeta^2}\,\omega_n + 2\,\zeta^2\omega_n \right) \cos \sqrt{1-\zeta^2}\omega_n t \right] \qquad (13\text{--}8\text{--}2)$$

This equation can be simplified and written in universal form:

$$\frac{e(t)}{\theta_1} = \epsilon^{-\zeta\omega_n t} \left[\cos \sqrt{1-\zeta^2}\omega_n t + \frac{\zeta}{\sqrt{1-\zeta^2}} \sin \sqrt{1-\zeta^2}\omega_n t \right] \qquad (13\text{--}8\text{--}3)$$

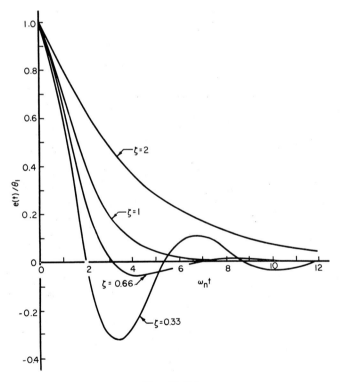

FIG. 13-8-2

Fig. 13-8-2 shows the response curves of the actuating signal $e(t)/\theta_1$, and Fig. 13-8-3 shows the output $c(t)/\theta_1$ for several values of ζ.

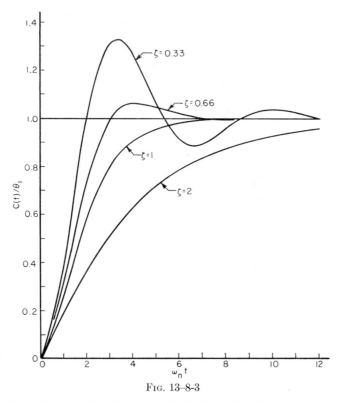

FIG. 13–8-3

13–9. Specifications in Terms of Unit Step Function Response. Often in practice the performance specifications for a system are stated in terms

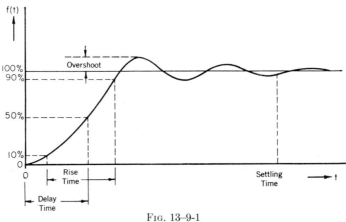

FIG. 13–9-1

of the system response to a unit step function. The quantities most often used are: percent overshoot, rise time, settling time and delay time. These quantities are indicated on Fig. 13–9-1.

The percent overshoot is the percentage of the final value by which the output exceeds the input. The rise time is the time required for the system to go from 10 percent to 90 percent of the final value. Settling time is a measure of the time required for the system to settle to within 5 percent of the final value and not to exceed this percentage later in the response. Delay time is the time required for the system to reach 50 percent of its final value. Sometimes different percentage values are used in defining these terms (as for rise time and settling time), but the essential interpretation of the definitions remains the same.

13–10. Response to Sinusoidal Input Functions. The system of Fig. 13–8-1 is described by Eqs. 13–6-2, repeated here for convenience:

$$Ke = J \frac{d^2c}{dt^2} + D \frac{dc}{dt} \tag{13-10-1}$$
$$e(t) = r(t) - c(t)$$

If a sinusoidal input is applied to this system, the steady-state response can be found in much the same way as in earlier chapters. Let it be supposed that the ratio of the output to the input is desired as a complex quantity. The variable $e(t)$ can be eliminated from Eqs. 13–10-1:

$$Kr = J \frac{d^2c}{dt^2} + D \frac{dc}{dt} + Kc \tag{13-10-2}$$

The Laplace transform of Eq. 13–10-2 for zero initial conditions is

$$KR(s) = [Js^2 + Ds + K]C(s) \tag{13-10-3}$$

The ratio of output to input (or transfer function) is

$$\frac{C(s)}{R(s)} = \frac{K}{Js^2 + Ds + K} \tag{13-10-4}$$

When $s = j\omega$ is substituted in Eq. 13–10-4,

$$\frac{C(j\omega)}{R(j\omega)} = \frac{K}{K - \omega^2 J + j\omega D} \tag{13-10-5}$$

Eq. 13–10-5 can be put into universal form in much the same manner as used above for the transient responses. Eq. 13–10-5 is divided by K, giving

$$\frac{C(j\omega)}{R(j\omega)} = \frac{1}{1 - \omega^2 J/K + j\omega D/K} \tag{13-10-6}$$

which can be written

$$\frac{C(j\omega)}{R(j\omega)} = \frac{1}{1 - (\omega/\omega_n)^2 + j \, 2 \, \zeta(\omega/\omega_n)} \tag{13-10-7}$$

If the ratio of ω to the ω_n is denoted by

$$\frac{\omega}{\omega_n} = \gamma \tag{13-10-8}$$

the equation can be written

$$\frac{C(j\gamma)}{R(j\gamma)} = \frac{1}{1 - \gamma^2 + j\,2\,\zeta\gamma} = M\underline{/\alpha} \qquad (13\text{-}10\text{-}9)$$

where M is the magnitude and α is the angle of $C(j\gamma)/R(j\gamma)$.

Fig. 13-10-1 shows a few response curves plotted for M, the magnitude of $C(j\gamma)/R(j\gamma)$. When ζ is below 0.707, the M curve attains a maximum

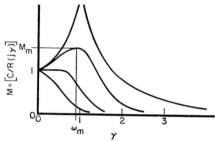

Reading curves from left to right, $\zeta = 5.0$, $\zeta = 0.66$, $\zeta = 0.33$, and $\zeta = 0$.

Fig. 13-10-1

and then decreases. The maximum value of M is denoted by M_m; the frequency at which this M_m occurs is termed the resonant frequency ω_m. These are indicated for $\zeta = 0.33$.

If the magnitude M of Eq. 13-10-9 is differentiated with respect to γ and the result set equal to zero, the following equation can be obtained:

$$\omega_m = \omega_n\sqrt{1 - 2\,\zeta^2} \qquad (13\text{-}10\text{-}10)$$

and when this is substituted in the magnitude equation M_m is found as

$$M_m = \frac{1}{2\,\zeta\sqrt{1 - \zeta^2}} \qquad (13\text{-}10\text{-}11)$$

13-11. Comparison of Transient and Frequency Response. As is explained in subsequent articles, the transient response method has not proved satisfactory when used alone in the design of systems that are more complicated than the second-order systems analyzed thus far. Therefore the frequency response method has been developed in order to circumvent some of these difficulties. This has brought up the problem of comparing results obtained in the time domain (transient response) with those obtained in the frequency domain.

For the present second-order system this comparison can be made easily. For example, the overshoot to a unit step function input for a system with $\zeta = 0.33$ is shown in Fig. 13-8-3 to be approximately 30 percent. The frequency response curves of Fig. 13-10-1 shows that this same system has an M_m of approximately 1.6; this means that the magnitude of the sinusoidal output is 60 percent greater than the magnitude of the sinusoidal input. A similar comparison for $\zeta = 0.66$ shows a 6 percent overshoot and an M_m of 1.04.

An often-used rule of thumb is that, if M_m is approximately 1.3, the transient response is satisfactory. By satisfactory is meant an overshoot of 30 percent or less. In this specific example an M_m of 1.3 corresponds roughly to a 25 percent overshoot. This rule of thumb has been verified in a large number of cases, but there is always a feeling of doubt when such a rule is applied to a new situation.

Another comment can be made after a comparison of the curves of Figs. 13-8-2 and 13-10-1. If in a system of this type it is desired to determine its parameters, frequency response curves similar to those of Fig. 13-10-1 can be obtained by applying a sinusoidal input function of variable frequency and plotting the M curve versus frequency. From the experimental value of M_m and Eq. 13-10-11, the value of ζ can be determined. From this value of ζ the experimentally determined value of ω_m and, with Eq. 13-10-10, ω_n can be found. Then from ω_n and ζ the value of β, or the natural radian frequency of oscillation, can be found through

$$\beta = \omega_n \sqrt{1 - \zeta^2} \qquad (13\text{-}11\text{-}1)$$

13-12. Examples. EXAMPLE 13-12-1. The servomechanism of Fig. 13-8-1 has a moment of inertia J of 0.25 slug-ft^2, its input member is to be driven at a constant angular velocity of 30 rpm, and the steady-state error is not to exceed $\pi/20$ radian. It is desired to design the system with $\zeta = 0.5$. Determine the constants K and D and the power loss in horsepower due to viscous friction after the system has reached the steady state.

Solution.

$$\omega_1 = \tfrac{30}{60} \times 2\,\pi = \pi$$

The equation for the steady-state actuating signal

$$e(t)_{ss} = \frac{\pi}{20} = 2\,\zeta\,\frac{\omega_1}{\omega_n}$$

can be solved for ω_n:

$$\omega_n = \frac{2\,\zeta\omega_1}{e(t)_{ss}} = 20$$

The defining equation for ω_n, $\omega_n = \sqrt{K/J}$, can be solved for K, yielding $K = \omega_n{}^2 J = 100$. The coefficient of friction is $D = 2\,\zeta\sqrt{KJ} = 5$. The torque and horsepower in the steady state are

$$T = Ke(t)_{ss} = D\omega_1 = 5\,\pi$$

$$\mathrm{Hp} = \frac{2\,\pi TN}{550} = \frac{2\,\pi(5\,\pi)(0.5)}{550} = 0.09$$

EXAMPLE 13-12-2. The servomechanism of Fig. 13-8-1 has the following constants, all in the proper units: $\zeta = 0.07$, $K = 2.5$, $J = 0.0013$. It is excited by the input function until steady-state conditions are reached: $r(t) = 1.5 \sin(25\,t + 70°) - 0.5 \cos(50\,t - 30°)$. Find the equation for the output.

Solution. The factor ω_n is

$$\omega_n = \sqrt{\frac{K}{J}} = 43.8$$

and the following table is set up:

ω	γ	$\dfrac{1}{1 - \gamma^2 + j\,2\,\zeta\gamma}$
25	0.57	$\dfrac{1}{0.675 + j\,0.0798} = 1.47\underline{/-6.75°}$
50	1.14	$\dfrac{1}{-3.0 + j\,0.1595} = 2.94\underline{/-152°}$

Solution for the output response yields

$$c(t) = 1.5 \times 1.47 \sin(25\,t + 70° - 6.75°) - 0.5 \times 2.94 \cos(50\,t - 30° - 152°)$$

or

$$c(t) = 2.2 \sin(25\,t + 63.25°) - 1.47 \cos(50\,t - 182°)$$

EXAMPLE 13–12–3. A sinusoidal input of varying frequency is applied to the servomechanism of Fig. 13–8–1, and it is found that M_m is 1.6 and ω_m is 14 cps. Tests are made on the controller, and it is found that the constant K is 12.5 ft-lb/radian. Find ω_n, J, and D.

From Eq. 13–10–11

$$\zeta = 0.33$$

and from Eq. 13–10–10

$$\omega_n = 100$$

Thus

$$J = \frac{K}{\omega_n{}^2} = 0.00125$$

and

$$D = 2\,\zeta\sqrt{KJ} = 0.0825$$

13–13. Back EMF of Motor. In work to this point the back emf of the motor has been neglected. The following development shows how this factor can be handled.

The block diagram of Fig. 13–8–1 is shown in Fig. 13–13–1 in a more de-

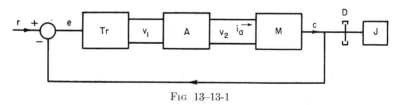

FIG 13–13–1

tailed form. The block labeled T_r represents the transducer with output voltage v_1:

$$v_1 = T_r e \qquad (13\text{–}13\text{–}1)$$

The block labeled A represents the amplifier stage (or stages) of the system with output voltage v_2:

$$v_2 = Av_1 = AT_re \qquad (13\text{-}13\text{-}2)$$

The block labeled M represents the motor, and i_a is the armature current in this motor. The motor has a back emf constant K_{vm} and a torque constant K_{tm}. The armature resistance is R_a, and the inductance of the armature is to be neglected.

The equation characterizing the electric circuit of the motor armature is

$$v_2 = R_a i_a + K_{vm} \frac{dc}{dt} \qquad (13\text{-}13\text{-}3)$$

The torque of the motor, proportional to armature current, is

$$\text{Torque} = K_{tm} i_a \qquad (13\text{-}13\text{-}4)$$

Eliminating i_a between Eqs. 13–13-3 and 13–13-4 and substituting Eq. 13–13-2 for v_2 give

$$\text{Torque} = \frac{K_{tm}}{R_a} AT_re - \frac{K_{tm}}{R_a} K_{vm} \frac{dc}{dt} \qquad (13\text{-}13\text{-}5)$$

The torque of the motor is opposed by the torques of the rotational mechanical system; thus

$$\frac{K_{tm}}{R_a} AT_re - \frac{K_{tm}K_{vm}}{R_a} \frac{dc}{dt} = J \frac{d^2c}{dt^2} + D \frac{dc}{dt} \qquad (13\text{-}13\text{-}6)$$

Let

$$\frac{K_{tm}AT_r}{R_a} = K$$

and

$$\frac{K_{tm}K_{vm}}{R_a} = D' \qquad (13\text{-}13\text{-}7)$$

Then Eq. 13–13-6 can be written

$$Ke = J \frac{d^2c}{dt^2} + (D + D') \frac{dc}{dt} \qquad (13\text{-}13\text{-}8)$$

Comparing Eq. 13–13-8 with the system equation 13–6-2, which neglects the back emf of the motor,

$$Ke = J \frac{d^2c}{dt^2} + D \frac{dc}{dt} \qquad (13\text{-}13\text{-}9)$$

reveals that the effect of the back emf is to give an apparent increase in the coefficient of viscous friction. In other words, if analysis of a system is to encompass the back emf, this system can be replaced by a fictitious system in which D is increased appropriately to $(D + D')$, and the resulting system can then be analyzed in a similar manner. By this technique all the equations and curves already developed can be applied directly to the new situation.

Also the increase in D to $(D + D')$ makes less severe another of the original assumptions; namely, that the friction present is viscous friction. This assumption is the basis for stating that D is a constant. In the usual situation the term D' is many times larger than D, and the sum $(D + D')$ can be assumed to be constant with a much smaller percentage of error than for D alone.

Before leaving this subject, it is to be emphasized that $(D + D')$ should replace D every time it appears in the original equations. Therefore the steady-state component of the actuating signal for a system which has a ramp function $\omega_1 t$ applied to the input is given by

$$e(t)_{ss} = \left(\frac{D + D'}{K}\right)\omega_1 \qquad (13\text{--}13\text{--}10)$$

13–14. Simulation of Viscous Friction. Ex. 13-12-1 is perhaps typical of a certain type of design problem for a simple servomechanism. That is, the known factors are the input angular velocity, the moment of inertia of the rotational system, and the magnitude of the permissible error. In this simple system the error is the actuating signal. The general nature of the desired response is known, and from it ζ can be determined. In this example the value of $\zeta = 0.5$ was picked as giving satisfactory performance. With these requirements the coefficients K and D can be determined. Adjustment of the term K in terms of design causes no trouble because this involves the gain of the system and can probably be adjusted by turning the knob of a potentiometer. However, adjustment of D requires more consideration.

In all likelihood, use of $\zeta = 0.5$ requires an increase in D to a value above that present in the form of friction and the back emf. One method of increasing D is to add a device such as a dashpot that would actually add viscous friction to the system. This procedure has two important disadvantages: an increase in viscous friction represents an unnecessary loss of energy in the added friction; an increase in viscous friction increases the steady-state error to a ramp function input.

The development showing that the back emf of the motor produces an apparent increase in viscous friction suggests the interesting possibility of increasing D purposely by making use of a voltage obtained from a tachometer situated on the output shaft. A block diagram of such a system is shown in Fig. 13–14-1.

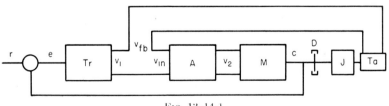

Fig. 13–14-1

The voltage out of the transducer is

$$v_1 = T_r e \qquad\qquad (13\text{--}14\text{--}1)$$

and the voltage out of the tachometer is

$$v_{fb} = T_{ao}\frac{dc}{dt} \qquad\qquad (13\text{--}14\text{--}2)$$

The symbol T_{ao} indicates that the tachometer is located on the output shaft. The voltage v_{fb} is fed back in such polarity as to combine with v_1:

$$v_{in} = v_1 - v_{fb} = T_r e - T_{ao}\frac{dc}{dt} \qquad\qquad (13\text{--}14\text{--}3)$$

The voltage out of the amplifier is

$$v_2 = A v_{in} = A T_r e - A T_{ao}\frac{dc}{dt} \qquad\qquad (13\text{--}14\text{--}4)$$

It is assumed that the back emf of the motor has already been evaluated and that D has been increased by an appropriate amount. Therefore the torque out of the motor is proportional to the voltage applied to the motor armature and M is the constant of proportionality. The torque is given by

$$\text{Torque} = M v_2 = M A T_r e - M A T_{ao}\frac{dc}{dt} \qquad\qquad (13\text{--}14\text{--}5)$$

This torque is opposed by the torques of the rotational mechanical system; thus

$$M A T_r e - M A T_{ao}\frac{dc}{dt} = J\frac{d^2c}{dt^2} + D\frac{dc}{dt} \qquad\qquad (13\text{--}14\text{--}6)$$

Let

$$M A T_r = K$$

and

$$M A T_{ao} = D'' \qquad\qquad (13\text{--}14\text{--}7)$$

Then Eq. 13–14-6 can be written

$$K e = J\frac{d^2c}{dt^2} + (D + D'')\frac{dc}{dt} \qquad\qquad (13\text{--}14\text{--}8)$$

Eq. 13–14-8 indicates that the desired result has been achieved in that the total D can be increased (or decreased for that matter) by a desired amount without incurring the energy loss associated with a dashpot type of device.

13–15. Tachometer on Error Shaft. It is to be pointed out that the second disadvantage mentioned before still exists for the system analyzed in the preceding article in that increase of D by this procedure also increases the steady-state error to a ramp function input. A review of the reasons for this is instructive.

When the system equation

$$K e = J\frac{d^2c}{dt^2} + (D + D'')\frac{dc}{dt} \qquad\qquad (13\text{--}15\text{--}1)$$

is combined with the equations

$$r(t) = \omega_1 t \quad \text{and} \quad e(t) = r(t) - c(t)$$

the result is

$$J \frac{d^2 e}{dt^2} + (D + D'') \frac{de}{dt} + Ke = (D + D'')\omega_1 \qquad (13\text{-}15\text{-}2)$$

The coefficient D'' appearing on the left side of this equation is desirable because it offers control of the stability of the system. However, the appearance of the coefficient D'' on the right side of this equation is not desirable because it increases the steady-state error.

The system shown in the block diagram of Fig. 13–15–1 moves the

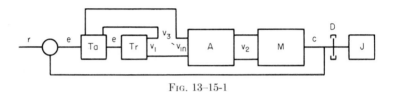

FIG. 13–15–1

tachometer from the output shaft to the error shaft to overcome this disadvantage.

The output voltages from the transducer and tachometer are, respectively,

$$v_1 = T_r e$$
$$v_3 = T_{ae} \frac{de}{dt} \qquad (13\text{-}15\text{-}3)$$

The symbol T_{ae} indicates that the tachometer is located on the error shaft. These two voltages are combined in such a polarity as to give

$$v_{in} = v_1 + v_3 = T_r e + T_{ae} \frac{de}{dt} \qquad (13\text{-}15\text{-}4)$$

The output voltage of the amplifier is

$$v_2 = A v_{in} = A T_r e + A T_{ae} \frac{de}{dt} \qquad (13\text{-}15\text{-}5)$$

It is again assumed the D includes the back emf of the motor; therefore the torque of the motor and that of the mechanical system are given by

$$M A T_r e + M A T_{ae} \frac{de}{dt} = J \frac{d^2 c}{dt^2} + D \frac{dc}{dt} \qquad (13\text{-}15\text{-}6)$$

Let

$$M A T_r = K$$

and

$$M A T_{ae} = K_1 \qquad (13\text{-}15\text{-}7)$$

Then Eq. 13–15–6 can be written

$$Ke + K_1 \frac{de}{dt} = J \frac{d^2 c}{dt^2} + D \frac{dc}{dt} \qquad (13\text{-}15\text{-}8)$$

When Eq. 13–15-8 is combined with the equations

$$r(t) = \omega_1 t \qquad e = r - c \qquad (13\text{–}15\text{-}9)$$

the result is

$$J\frac{d^2 e}{dt^2} + (D + K_1)\frac{de}{dt} + Ke = \omega_1 D \qquad (13\text{–}15\text{-}10)$$

The conclusion that can be drawn from Eq. 13–15-10 is that the term K_1 appears on the left side of the equation and therefore offers a means of control of the stability but does not appear on the right side, thus producing an unnecessary increase in the steady-state error. This can be seen by observing that the steady-state error of Eq. 13–15-10 is

$$e(t)_{ss} = \frac{\omega_1 D}{K} \qquad (13\text{–}15\text{-}11)$$

Fig. 13–15-2 shows this system in block diagram form.

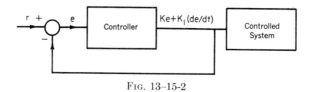

FIG. 13–15-2

When a ramp function $\omega_1 t$ is applied to the input of this system, initially at rest, the Laplace transform of the actuating signal is

$$E(s) = \frac{\omega_1\left[s + \dfrac{D}{J}\right]}{s\left[s^2 + \left(\dfrac{K_1 + D}{J}\right)s + \dfrac{K}{J}\right]} \qquad (13\text{–}15\text{-}12)$$

The inverse transform of Eq. 13–15-12 can be taken in the usual manner and the response curves plotted for specific values of the coefficients, although universal curves similar to those obtained before are not possible in such simple form because of the added K_1 term. In this case the sum of K_1 and D determines whether the system is critically damped (or underdamped, etc.); critical damping corresponds to

$$(K_1 + D)_c = 2\sqrt{KJ} \qquad (13\text{–}15\text{-}13)$$

Therefore, for the critically damped case, instead of having one universal curve as before, a whole family of curves exists depending on how much of the sum of $(K_1 + D)_c$ comes from K_1 (or from D). This, of course, is also true for all other possible values of ζ.

13–16. Integration of Actuating Signal. The addition of the $K_1(de/dt)$ torque component to the output of the controller means that the effective damping can be increased without a corresponding increase in steady-state error with a ramp function input. However, this addition does not decrease the steady-state error due to the viscous friction inherently present in all rotational systems and to the back emf of the motor. If another torque component proportional to the integral of the error is added to the output of the controller, the steady-state error is then brought to zero for the ramp function input. Such a system is shown in block form in Fig. 13–16-1.

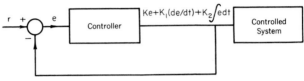

Fig. 13–16-1

Before this system is analyzed mathematically, an intuitive approach is considered to investigate its operation. It is stated that the integral term brings the steady-state error to zero. To show that this is true, the contrary is assumed. If a steady-state error exists, the integral of this error goes off to infinity as time goes to infinity. However, only a finite torque is needed to overcome the viscous friction of the rotational system; hence assumption that a steady-state exists is incorrect.

The equations for the quiescent system with a ramp function input are

$$Ke + K_1\frac{de}{dt} + K_2\int_0^t e\,dt = J\frac{d^2c}{dt^2} + D\frac{dc}{dt} \tag{13-16-1}$$

$$e = r - c \quad \text{and} \quad r = \omega_1 t$$

and the Laplace transform of the actuating (error) signal is

$$E(s) = \frac{\omega_1\left[s + \dfrac{D}{J}\right]}{\left[s^3 + \left(\dfrac{D + K_1}{J}\right)s^2 + \dfrac{K}{J}s + \dfrac{K_2}{J}\right]} \tag{13-16-2}$$

To proceed with this analysis the following values for the coefficients, all in proper units, are assumed:

$$J = 0.0025 \qquad K = 1.425 \qquad D = 0.01$$
$$K_1 = 0.03 \qquad K_2 = 7.63 \qquad r(t) = 2\,\pi t \tag{13-16-3}$$

When these values are substituted in Eq. 13–16-2, the result is

$$E(s) = \frac{2\,\pi[s + 4]}{[s^3 + 16\,s^2 + 569\,s + 3054]} \tag{13-16-4}$$

When the denominator is factored, Eq. 13–16-4 becomes

$$E(s) = \frac{2\,\pi[s + 4]}{[s + 6][(s + 5)^2 + (22)^2]} \tag{13-16-5}$$

and the inverse transform is

$$e(t) = -0.026\,\epsilon^{-6t} + 0.286\,\epsilon^{-5t}\sin(22\,t + 5.2) \tag{13-16-6}$$

The possibility of obtaining universal curves that are useful in this case is remote. For a given value of D and K_1 a whole family of curves results as K_2 is varied, etc. The more complicated the system, the smaller is the possibility of analyzing the system by use of universal curves.

The preceding example indicates the prime limitation to the transient approach for design of servomechanisms. The following discussion expands this point.

Let it be supposed that the designer knows approximately the type of response required of a servomechanism when a ramp function is applied. Of the coefficients given by Eqs. 13–16-3, J and D are fixed by the existing equipment, but K, K_1, and K_2 are variables at the designer's disposal. First, let it be supposed the designer picks the values of K, K_1, and K_2 given in the example, in the hope of obtaining the desired response of the system. When he compares the actual response of Eq. 13–16-6 with the desired response, he discovers that the pole at $s = -6$ should be moved farther to the left in the s-plane to $s = -20$, and that the real part of the complex poles at $s = -5 \pm j\,22$ should be moved to approximately $s = -10 \pm j\,22$. The designer now faces the problem: What values of K, K_1, and K_2 should be chosen to obtain the new pole location as closely as possible? Because of the devious manner in which polynomials are factored, no direct relationship exists between the coefficients K, K_1, and K_2 and the pole location. About the best the designer can do is a trial and error procedure.

When Routh's criterion is used with the denominator of Eq. 13–16-2, certain general relationships among the coefficients can be seen. The denominator is

$$s^3 + \left(\frac{D + K_1}{J}\right) s^2 + \frac{K}{J} s + \frac{K_2}{J} \qquad (13\text{–}16\text{-}7)$$

and the corresponding Routh schedule is

$$
\begin{array}{ll}
1 & \dfrac{K}{J} \\[2ex]
\dfrac{D + K_1}{J} & \dfrac{K_2}{J} \\[2ex]
\dfrac{(D + K_1)K - K_2 J}{(D + K_1)J} & \\[2ex]
\dfrac{K_2}{J} &
\end{array}
\qquad (13\text{–}16\text{-}8)
$$

The only possible change of sign in the first column is for the third term to be negative. If the third term is negative, this negative sign in the first column indicates an unstable system. This system is unstable if

$$K_2 > \frac{(D + K_1)K}{J} \qquad (13\text{–}16\text{-}9)$$

The K_1 term is added to make the system more stable by increasing the apparent dampening. The K_2 is added to bring the steady-state error with a ramp function input to zero. However, Eq. 13-16-9 indicates that adding K_2 has the effect of decreasing the stability and even, possibly, of producing an unstable system.

Routh's test only indicates absolute stability; it does not give a general idea as to how to proceed to increase stability. Thus, for the example just discussed, relative to choosing K, K_1, and K_2 for a specific pole location, Routh's test is not of much help.

13-17. Summary. If it is desired to determine the theoretical response of a servomechanism to some input, the method for finding the transient response is straightforward. However, if the response found by this analysis is not the desired response and some of the system coefficients must be changed to improve the system, the transient procedure is not very satisfactory in complicated systems because of the devious relationship that exists between the system coefficients and the pole locations and, hence, the system response.

For these reasons other design methods have been developed. The procedure that has received extensive attention is to design in terms of the frequency response of the open-loop system, that is, the system with the feedback path opened. Through graphical techniques this procedure allows the designer to see the effects of the change in various system coefficients and to determine the frequency response of the closed-loop system (feedback path closed).

The procedure of designing in terms of frequency response brings up the problem of correlating the frequency response and the transient response of the system. That is, if a system is designed by frequency response methods, does it have a satisfactory transient response? The rule of thumb that M_m approximates 1.3 has been used as a criterion. However, many systems exist that have an M_m of 1.3 and that have entirely different transient responses. Therefore the designer who has designed on a frequency basis must still perform a transient analysis of the system to be certain the transient response is satisfactory. This means that the transient analysis of a servomechanism is still a vital part of the over-all problem.

PROBLEMS

13-1. The servomechanism of Fig. 13-5-1 has a torque output from the controller of K times the actuating signal. The moment of inertia of the moving parts is 0.1 slug-ft^2, and its input member is to be driven at the constant angular velocity of 90 rpm. The steady-state error is not to exceed $\pi/10$ radian. It is desired to design the system with $\zeta = 0.7$. Determine the constants K and D and the power loss in horsepower due to viscous friction after the system has reached the steady state. Obtain the expressions for $e(t)$ and $c(t)$ and plot rough sketches of both functions.

13–2. The servomechanism of Fig. 13–5-1 has a torque output from the controller of K times the actuating signal. The moment of inertia of the moving parts is 10×10^{-4} slug-ft^2, and its input member is to be driven at the constant angular velocity of 360 rpm. It is desired to design the system to have a damping factor of $\zeta = 0.333$. The maximum error that may occur during the transient period is to be not greater than $\pi/10$ radian. Determine the constants K and D and the power loss in horsepower due to viscous friction after the system has reached the steady state. Obtain the expressions for $e(t)$ and $c(t)$ and plot rough sketches of both functions.

13–3. The servomechanism of Fig. 13–5-1 has a torque output from the controller of K times the actuating signal. The moment of inertia of the moving parts is 0.1 slug-ft^2, and its input member is to be driven at the constant angular velocity of 360 rpm. Assume that $\zeta = 0$. The maximum transient error that can occur is not to be greater than $\pi/10$ radian. Determine the maximum horsepower necessary to drive this load.

13–4. The servomechanism of Fig. 13–5-1 has a torque output from the controller of K times the actuating signal. The system has the following constants:

$$J = 10 \times 10^{-6} \text{ slug-ft}^2$$
$$D = 2.0 \times 10^{-4} \text{ ft-lb/radian/sec}$$
$$K = 3.5 \times 10^{-3} \text{ ft-lb/radian}$$

The system is initially at rest when at $t = 0$ the input is suddenly turned through $\pi/3$ radian in the positive direction. Find the equations for $e(t)$ and $c(t)$ and find the angular velocity of the output shaft at $t = 0.05$ sec.

13–5. The servomechanism of Prob. 13–4 is driven at the constant angular velocity of 360 rpm until steady-state conditions are reached. At $t = 0$ the input is stopped. Find the equations for $e(t)$ and $c(t)$.

13–6. The servomechanism of Prob. 13–4 is driven at a constant angular velocity of 240 rpm until steady-state conditions are reached. At $t = 0$ the input angular velocity is changed to 120 rpm. Find the equations for $e(t)$ and $c(t)$.

13–7. The servomechanism of Prob. 13–4 is at rest when at $t = 0$ a constant disturbance torque T_1 is instantly applied to the load in such a direction to tend to make $c(t)$ positive at $t = 0$. Find the equations for $e(t)$ and $c(t)$.

13–8. The servomechanism of Fig. 13–5-1 has a torque output from the controller of K times the actuating signal. The system has the following constants:

$$J = 0.5 \text{ slug-ft}^2$$
$$D = 100 \text{ ft-lb/radian/sec}$$
$$K = 20{,}000 \text{ ft-lb/radian}$$

The system is driven at the constant angular velocity of 240 rpm, and the system has been operating long enough for it to reach steady-state conditions. At $t = 0$, D is changed from 100 to 200 ft-lb/radian/sec. Find the equations for $e(t)$ and $c(t)$.

13–9. The servomechanism of Prob. 13–8 (with $D = 100$) is driven at the constant angular velocity of 180 rpm, and the system has been operating long enough for it to reach steady-state conditions. At $t = 0$ the gain on an amplifier is increased by a factor of 2; that is, K becomes 40,000 ft-lb/radian. Find the equations for $e(t)$ and $c(t)$.

13–10. The servomechanism of Prob. 13–4 has the following function applied to its input until steady-state conditions are reached:

$$r(t) = 1.8 \cos (10\,t - 30°) - 1.2 \sin (30\,t + 15°)$$

Find the equations for $e(t)$ and $c(t)$.

13–11. The servomechanism of Prob. 13–4 has the following function applied to its input until steady-state conditions are reached:

$$r(t) = 5 \sin (15\,t + 45°)$$

The input member is stopped at $t = 0$. Find the equations for $e(t)$ and $c(t)$ after $t = 0$.

13–12. A sinusoidal input of varying frequency is applied to the servo system of Fig. 13–5-1 (torque output from the controller is proportional to the actuating signal), and it is found that the maximum amplitude of the output is 1.8 times the amplitude of the input and occurs at a frequency of 9 cps. Tests made on the controller show that the constant K equals 15 ft-lb/radian. Find ω_n, J, and D.

13–13. The servomechanism of Prob. 13–4 has the function shown in Fig. 13–P-1 applied to its input and left long enough for steady-state conditions to be reached.

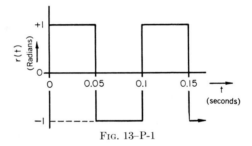

Fɪɢ. 13–P-1

Use Fourier series terminated after 3 terms and find equations for $e(t)$ and $c(t)$. Plot $c(t)$ for one-half cycle on the same sheet of paper with $r(t)$.

13–14. The servomechanism of Fig. 13–13-1 is such that the friction of the moving parts can be neglected, but the back emf of the motor is of such a magnitude that its effect must be considered. A test made on the controller with the output shaft blocked and with an actuating signal of 1 radian gives an output torque of 3.5 ft-lb. With the feedback path open, an actuating signal of 1 radian is applied to the controller and left until steady-state conditions are reached, and the output angular velocity is found to be 40 rps. The moment of inertia J for the entire system is 150×10^{-6} slug-ft². The feedback path is connected and with the system at rest, the input is suddenly turned through an angle of $\pi/10$ radian. Find the equations for $e(t)$ and $c(t)$.

13–15. The servomechanism of Fig. 13–14-1 has a moment of inertia J of 0.01 slug-ft² and a coefficient D due to the inherent viscous friction of 0.2 ft-lb/radian/sec. It is desired to drive this system at 600 rpm with a steady-state error of $\pi/10$ radian and to have a ratio of maximum transient error to steady-state error of 1.3. The tachometer on the output shaft is used to increase the apparent viscous friction. The characteristic of the transducer is 1 volt/degree. The tachometer produces a voltage

$$E_{fb} = T_{ao} \frac{dc}{dt}$$

Determine the constant T_{ao} necessary to satisfy the above conditions. Find the power loss in horsepower due to viscous friction after the system has reached steady-state conditions. How does this compare with the power that would be lost if all damping were viscous friction?

13–16. The servomechanism of Fig. 13–15-1 has a moment of inertia J of 0.025 slug-ft^2, and the coefficient for the inherent viscous friction in the moving parts is $D = 0.3$ ft-lb/radian/sec. It is desired that the steady-state error of this system shall equal $\pi/100$ radian when the input member rotates at the constant angular velocity of 300 rpm. The characteristic of the transducer is 1 volt/degree. It is desired to have the system critically damped by adjusting the voltage

$$T_{ae} \frac{de}{dt}$$

Find the constant T_{ae} necessary to do this.

13–17. The servomechanism of Fig. 13–15-2 has the following constants:

$J = 15 \times 10^{-6}$ slug-ft^2 $\qquad\qquad$ $K_1 = 0.99 \times 10^{-4}$ ft-lb/radian/sec

$D = 1.1 \times 10^{-4}$ ft-lb/radian/sec $\qquad$ $K = 4.0 \times 10^{-3}$ ft-lb/radian

The system is driven at a constant angular velocity of 200 rpm long enough for the system to reach steady-state conditions. At $t = 0$ the input is stopped. Find the equations for $e(t)$ and $c(t)$.

13–18. The servomechanism of Prob. 13–17 has the following function applied to its input and left long enough for the system to reach steady-state conditions:

$$r(t) = 1.4 \sin (10\,t + 30°) - 2.0 \cos (30\,t - 50°)$$

Find the equations for $e(t)$ and $c(t)$.

13–19. The servomechanism of Fig. 13–16-1 has the following constants, all in the proper units:

$J = 0.001$ $\qquad$ $K = 2.1$

$K_1 = 0.016$ $\qquad$ $K_2 = 16$

$D = 0.0065$

The system is at rest when at $t = 0$ the input member is rotated at a constant angular velocity of 180 rpm. Find the equations for $e(t)$ and $c(t)$.

13–20. The servomechanism of Prob. 13–19 has the following function applied to its input and left long enough for the system to reach steady-state conditions:

$$r(t) = 1.8 \cos (10\,t - 70°) - 2.2 \sin (20\,t + 50°)$$

Find the equations for $e(t)$ and $c(t)$.

13–21. The servomechanism of Prob. 13–19 has its input member turned at a constant angular velocity of 180 rpm until steady-state conditions are reached. At $t = 0$ the input is stopped. Find the equations for $e(t)$ and $c(t)$.

13–22. A servomechanism is described by the differential equation

$$0.0001 \frac{d^3 e}{dt^3} + 0.002 \frac{d^2 e}{dt^2} + 0.05 \frac{de}{dt} + 0.2\,e + 0.5 \int e\,dt = 0.001 \frac{d^2 c}{dt^2} + 0.002 \frac{dc}{dt}$$

The following function is applied to the input and is maintained long enough for the system to reach steady state:

$$r(t) = 2.5 \sin (10\,t + 20°) - 2.0 \sin (20\,t - 30°)$$

Find the equations for $e(t)$ and $c(t)$.

CHAPTER 14

FOURIER SERIES

14-1. Introduction. The use of Fourier series dates back to the classical work of Fourier on the theory of heat in the early part of the nineteenth century. One form of the series is

$$\frac{a_0}{2} + \sum_{n=1}^{\infty} (a_n \cos n\omega t + b_n \sin n\omega t) \qquad (14\text{-}1\text{-}1)$$

where the a's and b's are constants, the constant $\omega = 2\pi f = 2\pi/T$, f is the fundamental frequency of the series, and T is the fundamental period of the series. The summation is taken over all positive integral values of n, and t is the time variable. The first term $(a_0/2)$ represents the average value of the series and may correspond to the amount of direct current or direct voltage present. Each of the other terms in the series has a period T, and the series then represents a repeated function of time t with a period of T seconds. By taking different sets of a's and b's it is possible to represent almost all repeated time functions with period T by such a series.

One of the main problems of the Fourier series is to determine the a's and b's for a given time function $f(t)$ of period T. Certain restrictions have to be placed upon the $f(t)$, but fortunately almost all time functions encountered in practical problems fulfill these restrictions. Two of the restrictions are: First, the function has to be bounded; this means that the function must not become infinitely large at any value of time t. Second, the function may have at most a finite number of finite jumps in a finite interval. Such finite jumps are shown at $t = a$ and at $t = b$ of Fig. 14-1-1.

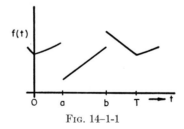

f(t)

O   a   b   T   t

Fig. 14-1-1

To determine the a's and b's formally, let

$$f(t) = \frac{a_0}{2} + \sum_{n=1}^{\infty} (a_n \cos n\omega t + b_n \sin n\omega t) \qquad (14\text{-}1\text{-}2)$$

344

Multiplying Eq. 14-1-2 by cos $m\omega t$ and integrating over one period T give

$$\int_{t_0}^{t_0+T} f(t) \cos m\omega t \, dt$$

$$= \int_{t_0}^{t_0+T} \frac{a_0}{2} \cos m\omega t \, dt + \int_{t_0}^{t_0+T} \cos m\omega t \left[\sum_{n=1}^{\infty} a_n \cos n\omega t + b_n \sin n\omega t \right] dt$$

$$= \int_{t_0}^{t_0+T} \frac{a_0}{2} \cos m\omega t \, dt$$

$$+ \sum_{n=1}^{\infty} \left[a_n \int_{t_0}^{t_0+T} \cos m\omega t \cos n\omega t \, dt + b_n \int_{t_0}^{t_0+T} \cos m\omega t \sin n\omega t \, dt \right]$$

$$= a_m \frac{T}{2} \qquad (14\text{-}1\text{-}3)$$

since

$$\int_{t_0}^{t_0+T} \cos m\omega t \cos n\omega t \, dt = \begin{cases} 0 \text{ if } m \neq n \\ T/2 \text{ if } m = n \end{cases}$$

$$\int_{t_0}^{t_0+T} \cos m\omega t \sin n\omega t \, dt = 0$$

Hence

$$a_m = \frac{2}{T} \int_{t_0}^{t_0+T} f(t) \cos m\omega t \, dt \qquad (14\text{-}1\text{-}4)$$

where t_0 is any value of time. In a similar fashion it is possible to show that

$$b_m = \frac{2}{T} \int_{t_0}^{t_0+T} f(t) \sin m\omega t \, dt \qquad (14\text{-}1\text{-}5)$$

The actual evaluation of Eqs. 14-1-4 and 14-1-5 may be made more simply in many cases by using the symmetry present in the problems. One form of this symmetry is the even-function type of symmetry which applies to functions $f(t)$ such that $f(t) = f(-t)$. In this case all of the b's are zero and the a's need be taken only over a half period instead of the whole period. Hence

$$a_m = \frac{4}{T} \int_0^{T/2} f(t) \cos m\omega t \, dt \qquad (14\text{-}1\text{-}6)$$

As an example let the a's be found for the square pulse in Fig. 14-1-2.

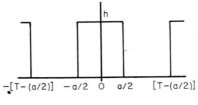

FIG. 14-1-2

Then

$$a_m = \frac{4}{T} \int_0^{a/2} h \cos m\omega t \, dt = \frac{4h}{Tm\omega} \sin m\omega t \Big|_0^{a/2}$$
$$= \frac{2h}{m\pi} \sin \frac{m\omega a}{2} \tag{14-1-7}$$

From Eqs. 14-1-1 and 14-1-7,

$$\frac{ha}{T} + \sum_{n=1}^{\infty} \left(\frac{2h}{n\pi} \sin \frac{n\omega a}{2} \cos n\omega t \right) \tag{14-1-8}$$

The series of Eq. 14-1-8 thus should represent the time function of Fig. 14-1-2. It is possible to show that the sum of the series is actually the time function except at the points of discontinuity such as the finite jump at $t = a/2$. At these points the sum of the series is one-half of the way along the finite jump, that is,

$$\tfrac{1}{2}[f(t+0) + f(t-0)] \tag{14-1-9}$$

Thus at $t = a/2$ the sum of the series is

$$\frac{1}{2}[0 + h] = \frac{h}{2} \tag{14-1-10}$$

14–2. Finite Series. Because in actual use the series must be terminated at some point and a finite number of terms of the series is then used, some idea of what happens in this case is important. If, in the example of Art. 14–1, a is put equal to $T/2$, so that the symmetrical square wave results, the series becomes

$$\frac{h}{2} + \frac{2h}{\pi} \sum_{m=1}^{\infty} (-1)^{m+1} \frac{\cos (2m-1)\omega t}{(2m-1)} \tag{14-2-1}$$

Suppose now that only the first term of the series is plotted as the solid line of Fig. 14–2-1a at a height $h/2$ while the square wave has the amplitude h. Two terms produce the solid curve of Fig. 14–2-1b, while three terms result in that of Fig. 14–2-1c. The result of adding four terms is shown in Fig. 14–2-1d. The more terms used, the more closely the sum of the finite series approaches that of the original square wave. It should be noted also that, at the points of discontinuity such as at $t = a/2$, the finite series always has the sum $h/2$, which seems to indicate that the sum of the infinite series is also $h/2$ as predicted by Eq. 14–1-9. Another interesting result is that the peak value of the sum always is slightly more than the peak value h of the original square wave. This peak value occurs closer and closer to the point of discontinuity $t = a/2$ as the number of terms in the finite series increases. This phenomenon is sometimes called the phe-

nomenon of Gibbs, after an American physicist who did a great deal of
work in the theory of heat.

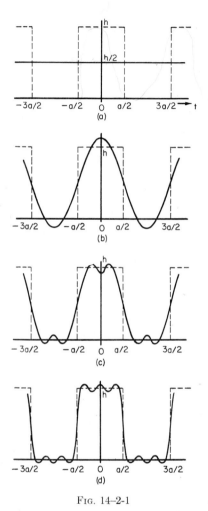

Fig. 14-2-1

14-3. Other Symmetries. There is another type of symmetry which
might be called the odd function symmetry, and it applies to periodic waves
in which $f(t) = -f(-t)$. If this is true, all the a's of Eq. 14-1-2 are zero, and

$$f(t) = \sum_{n=1}^{\infty} b_n \sin n\omega t \tag{14-3-1}$$

where

$$b_n = \frac{4}{T} \int_0^{T/2} f(t) \sin n\omega t \, dt \tag{14-3-2}$$

If $f(t) = -f(t + T/2)$, the even harmonics are zero and

$$f(t) = \sum_{n = 1, 3, 5, 7, \cdots}^{\infty} (a_n \cos n\omega t + b_n \sin n\omega t) \qquad (14\text{-}3\text{-}3)$$

where

$$a_n = \frac{4}{T} \int_0^{T/2} f(t) \cos n\omega t \, dt \qquad (14\text{-}3\text{-}4)$$

and

$$b_n = \frac{4}{T} \int_0^{T/2} f(t) \sin n\omega t \, dt \qquad (14\text{-}3\text{-}5)$$

The awareness that symmetry exists in a given wave decreases the amount of work necessary to evaluate the series. Other symmetries exist, but the three given so far cover most of those encountered in problems.

14–4. The Fourier Series of an Arbitrary Curve. In many practical problems a curve or a series of discrete points may represent the time function $f(t)$ whose Fourier series is desired. An integral such as that of Eq. 14-1-4 may be evaluated in several ways, each of which involves some numerical approximations. One way is to fit a known time function to the given curve by some method such as that of least squares and then evaluate the required integrals for a_n and b_n.

The method to be demonstrated is that in which the integrals for a_n and b_n are evaluated directly from the series of points, some approximation method being used for evaluating the integrals. The method is the trapezoid method, which is also one of the simplest. This method is shown in Fig. 14-4-1, where the curve $y = f(x)$ is plotted and the object is to approx-

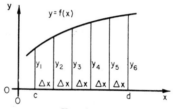

Fig. 14-4-1

imate to the area under the curve from $x = c$ to $x = d$. The interval $(d-c)$ is divided into a number of equal parts Δx as shown in the figure. The curve then is approximated by a series of straight lines. The area under the curve in each interval Δx can be approximated by a trapezoid. For example, the first trapezoid at the left of Fig. 14-4-1 has an altitude of Δx and bases of y_1 and y_2 and thus has an area of

$$\tfrac{1}{2} \Delta x (y_1 + y_2)$$

The total area then is

$$\tfrac{1}{2} \Delta x (y_1 + y_2) + \tfrac{1}{2} \Delta x (y_2 + y_3) + \tfrac{1}{2} \Delta x (y_3 + y_4) + \tfrac{1}{2} \Delta x (y_4 + y_5)$$
$$+ \tfrac{1}{2} \Delta x (y_5 + y_6) = \Delta x \left[\frac{y_1}{2} + y_2 + y_3 + y_4 + y_5 + \frac{y_6}{2} \right]$$

The example showing the method is presented in Table 14-4. It is assumed for this example that there is symmetry about the angle of 90 degrees, that

TABLE 14-4

ωt (degrees)	$f(t)$ (volts)	$f(t) \sin \omega t$
0	510	0.0
10	395	68.7
20	220	75.2
30	130	65
40	185	118.7
50	275	211
60	320	277
70	340	319
80	350	344
90	335	335

$f(t)$ is an odd function of time, and that the quantity $f(t)$ to be analyzed is in volts. From the symmetry, then, all the a's are zero and all the even b's are zero. An approximate value of b_1 is obtained by the following procedure, using $\theta = \omega t$ and Table 14-4:

$$b_1 = \frac{2}{T} \int_0^T f(t) \sin \omega t \, dt = \frac{8}{T} \int_0^{T/4} f(t) \sin \omega t \, dt = \frac{4}{\pi} \int_0^{\pi/2} f\left(\frac{\theta}{\omega}\right) \sin \theta \, d\theta$$

$$\approx \frac{4}{\pi} \left\{ \left(\frac{\pi}{18}\right)\frac{1}{2}(0.0 + 68.7) + \left(\frac{\pi}{18}\right)\frac{1}{2}(68.7 + 75.2) + \left(\frac{\pi}{18}\right)\frac{1}{2}(75.2 + 65) \right.$$

$$+ \left(\frac{\pi}{18}\right)\frac{1}{2}(65 + 118.7) + \left(\frac{\pi}{18}\right)\frac{1}{2}(118.7 + 211) + \left(\frac{\pi}{18}\right)\frac{1}{2}(211 + 277)$$

$$+ \left.\left(\frac{\pi}{18}\right)\frac{1}{2}(277 + 319) + \left(\frac{\pi}{18}\right)\frac{1}{2}(319 + 344) + \left(\frac{\pi}{18}\right)\frac{1}{2}(344 + 335) \right\}$$

$$\approx \left(\frac{4}{\pi}\right)\left(\frac{\pi}{18}\right)\left\{ \frac{0.0}{2} + 68.7 + 75.2 + 65 + 118.7 + 211 + 277 + 319 + 344 + \frac{335}{2} \right\}$$

$$\approx 365.8 \qquad (14\text{-}4\text{-}1)$$

Amplitudes of higher harmonics such as b_3 and b_5 are found similarly.

14-5. Steady-State Response of Circuits. Suppose that the input voltage to the circuit shown in Fig. 14-5-1 is

$$e_i = 100 + 200 \sin 100\,t - 100 \cos 200\,t + 50 \sin 300\,t \qquad (14\text{-}5\text{-}1)$$

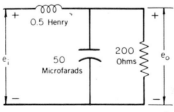

FIG. 14-5-1

Through the use of the superposition theorem the steady-state output voltage of the circuit is

$$e_o = 100 + 252.8 \sin (100\,t - 16.67°) - 200 \cos (200\,t - 90°)$$
$$+ 34.3 \sin (300\,t - 120.9°) \qquad (14\text{–}5\text{–}2)$$

To illustrate how e_o is calculated, the second term in the series is obtained. For this term $\omega = 100$ and the impedances are shown in Fig. 14–5-2. Then for the phasor $E_i = 200\underline{/0°}$ volts,

$$E_o = \cfrac{200\underline{/0°}}{j\,50 + \cfrac{200(-j\,200)}{200 - j\,200}} \times \frac{200(-j\,200)}{200 - j\,200} = 252.8\underline{/- 16.67°} \text{ volts} \quad (14\text{–}5\text{–}3)$$

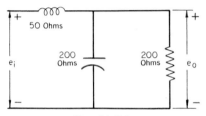

Fig. 14–5-2

The phasor value of $252.8\underline{/- 16.67°}$ volts becomes an instantaneous value of $252.8 \sin (100\,t - 16.67°)$ as indicated in Eq. 14–5-2.

14–6. Other Forms of Fourier Series. There are other forms of the Fourier series which are more useful in certain problems than the series of Eq. 14–1-1. For example, the a_n and b_n terms of Eq. 14–1-1 may be combined to give $c_n \cos (n\omega t + \phi_n)$, and the Fourier series then becomes

$$\frac{a_o}{2} + \sum_{n=1}^{\infty} c_n \cos (n\omega t + \phi_n) \qquad (14\text{–}6\text{–}1)$$

where

$$c_n = \sqrt{a_n{}^2 + b_n{}^2}$$

$$\cos \phi_n = \frac{a_n}{c_n} \qquad \sin \phi_n = \frac{b_n}{c_n}$$

Then c_n would be the maximum value of the harmonic voltage or current, and ϕ_n would be the phase angle of the harmonic voltage or current.

Another important form of the series is the exponential form:

$$\sum_{n=-\infty}^{+\infty} d_n \epsilon^{jn\omega t} \qquad (14\text{–}6\text{–}2)$$

where

$$d_n = \frac{a_n - jb_n}{2} = \frac{1}{T} \int_{t_0}^{t_0 + T} \epsilon^{-jn\omega t} f(t)\, dt$$

It should be noted that

$$d_{-n} = \frac{a_n + jb_n}{2} \quad \text{and} \quad d_o = \frac{a_o}{2}$$

These values of d are necessary because the series of Eq. 14–6-2 is summed over all integral values of n, including the zero and negative ones as well as the positive ones. This does not mean that the idea of negative frequencies is being used. The constant ω is still a positive constant, but to obtain the terms for a given harmonic of frequency $n\omega$ both the positive n and the negative n terms must be combined.

14–7. Transients Using Fourier Series. There are several ways in which Fourier series may be used to solve for the transients in a given circuit. One way is to use differential equations and solve for the steady-state and transient parts. As an example of this procedure, let the square-wave voltage of Fig. 14–7-1a be suddenly applied to the circuit of Fig. 14–7-1b by

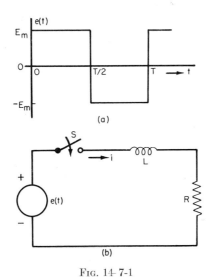

(a)

(b)

FIG. 14-7-1

closing the switch S at time $t = 0$. The Fourier series for this voltage may be shown to be

$$e(t) = \frac{4\,E_m}{\pi} \sum_{n=1}^{\infty} \frac{\sin\,(2\,n-1)\omega t}{(2\,n-1)} \tag{14-7-1}$$

From Fig. 14–7-1b,

$$L\frac{di}{dt} + Ri = e(t) \tag{14-7-2}$$

The steady-state current i_{ss} is

$$i_{ss} = \frac{4\,E_m}{\pi} \sum_{n=1}^{\infty} \frac{\sin\,[(2\,n-1)\omega t - \theta_n]}{Z_n(2\,n-1)} \tag{14-7-3}$$

where

$$Z_n = \sqrt{R^2 + (n\omega L)^2} \qquad \tan\theta_n = \frac{n\omega L}{R}$$

Since the time constant of the circuit is (L/R), the transient current i_{tr} is

$$i_{tr} = A\epsilon^{-Rt/L} \qquad (14\text{--}7\text{--}4)$$

The total current i is

$$i = i_{ss} + i_{tr} = \frac{4\,E_m}{\pi}\sum_{n=1}^{\infty}\frac{\sin\left[(2\,n-1)\omega t - \theta_n\right]}{Z_n(2\,n-1)} + A\epsilon^{-Rt/L} \qquad (14\text{--}7\text{--}5)$$

When the switch S is closed, the current initially is zero, so

$$0 = -\frac{4\,E_m}{\pi}\sum_{n=1}^{\infty}\frac{\sin\theta_n}{Z_n(2\,n-1)} + A$$

or

$$A = \frac{4\,E_m}{\pi}\sum_{n=1}^{\infty}\frac{\sin\theta_n}{Z_n(2\,n-1)} \qquad (14\text{--}7\text{--}6)$$

Hence the total current is

$$i = \frac{4\,E_m}{\pi}\sum_{n=1}^{\infty}\frac{1}{Z_n(2\,n-1)}\left\{\sin\left[(2\,n-1)\omega t - \theta_n\right] + (\sin\theta_n)\epsilon^{-Rt/L}\right\} \qquad (14\text{--}7\text{--}7)$$

Another way of obtaining the same result as in Eq. 14–7-7 would be to use the superposition theorem and consider each harmonic voltage as applied separately to the circuit. Each harmonic current is calculated, and their sum is the total current. The result should agree with that of Eq. 14–7-7.

A second method uses Laplace transforms. From Eq. 14–7-1, the Laplace transform of $e(t)$ is

$$\mathcal{L}[e(t)] = \frac{4\,E_m}{\pi}\sum_{n=1}^{\infty}\frac{\omega}{s^2 + (2\,n-1)^2\omega^2} \qquad (14\text{--}7\text{--}8)$$

The poles of the voltage are $s = \pm j(2\,n-1)\omega$ and are spaced on the imaginary axis of the s-plane as shown in Fig. 14–7-2. Another way of obtaining

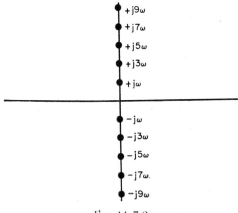

$+j9\omega$

$+j7\omega$

$+j5\omega$

$+j3\omega$

$+j\omega$

$-j\omega$

$-j3\omega$

$-j5\omega$

$-j7\omega$

$-j9\omega$

Fig. 14–7-2

the same information is to use the exponential form of the series of Eq. 14–6-2. From Eq. 14–7-1,

$$e(t) = \frac{2\,E_m}{\pi j} \sum_{n=1}^{\infty} \frac{\epsilon^{j(2n-1)\omega t}}{(2\,n-1)} - \frac{2\,E_m}{\pi j} \sum_{n=-1}^{-\infty} \frac{\epsilon^{j(2n+1)\omega t}}{(2\,n-1)} \qquad (14\text{–}7\text{–}9)$$

and the Laplace transform is

$$\mathcal{L}[e(t)] = \frac{2\,E_m}{\pi j} \sum_{n=1}^{\infty} \frac{1}{[s - j(2\,n-1)\omega](2\,n-1)} \\ - \frac{2\,E_m}{\pi j} \sum_{n=-1}^{-\infty} \frac{1}{[s - j(2\,n+1)\omega](2\,n+1)} \qquad (14\text{–}7\text{–}10)$$

The poles of Eq. 14–7-10 are the same as those of Eq. 14–7-8 and Fig. 14–7-2. The transform of Eq. 14–7-2 is

$$Ls\mathcal{L}(i) + R\mathcal{L}(i) = \mathcal{L}[e(t)]$$

or
$$\mathcal{L}(i) = \frac{1}{Ls + R}\,\mathcal{L}[e(t)] \qquad (14\text{–}7\text{–}11)$$

This assumes that the initial current is zero. From Eqs. 14–7-8 and 14–7-11,

$$\mathcal{L}(i) = \frac{4\,E_m}{\pi(Ls+R)} \sum_{n=1}^{\infty} \frac{\omega}{s^2 + (2\,n-1)^2\omega^2} \qquad (14\text{–}7\text{–}12)$$

The circuit adds an extra pole at $s = -\,(R/L)$ to each of the terms of the series. The result of evaluating Eq. 14–7-12 in terms of time function is that given by Eq. 14–7-7.

Still another method uses the sum function of the series of Eqs. 14–7-8 and 14–7-10. This sum function may be obtained by summing the series for the transforms of the steps of Fig. 14–7-1a:

$$\mathcal{L}[e(t)] = \frac{E_m}{s} - \frac{2\,E_m}{s}\,\epsilon^{-sT/2} + \frac{2\,E_m}{s}\,\epsilon^{-sT} - \frac{2\,E_m}{s}\,\epsilon^{-s3T/2} + \cdots \\ = \frac{E_m}{s}\left(\frac{1-\epsilon^{-sT/2}}{1+\epsilon^{-sT/2}}\right) = \frac{E_m}{s}\,\tanh\frac{sT}{4} \qquad (14\text{–}7\text{–}13)$$

The summation may be done by noticing that the series is a geometric series. Hence by comparing Eqs. 14–7-8 and 14–7-13,

$$\mathcal{L}[e(t)] = \frac{E_m}{s}\left(\frac{1-\epsilon^{-sT/2}}{1+\epsilon^{-sT/2}}\right) = \frac{4\,E_m}{\pi} \sum_{n=1}^{\infty} \frac{\omega}{s^2 + (2\,n-1)^2\omega^2} \qquad (14\text{–}7\text{–}14)$$

The poles may be obtained by putting $1 + \epsilon^{-sT/2} = 0$. Then $-sT/2 = \pm j(2\,n-1)\pi$, where n is a positive integer. The poles are then

$$s = \pm j(2\,n-1)\omega$$

again the same as those given in Fig. 14–7-2. The transform of the current is

$$\mathcal{L}(i) = \frac{E_m}{s(R+Ls)}\left(\frac{1-\epsilon^{-sT/2}}{1+\epsilon^{-sT/2}}\right) \qquad (14\text{–}7\text{–}15)$$

From the poles $s = \pm j(2n-1)\omega$, Eq. 14-7-3 is rewritten for convenience:

$$i_{ss} = \frac{4E_m}{\pi} \sum_{n=1}^{\infty} \frac{\sin\left[(2n-1)\omega t - \theta_n\right]}{Z_n(2n-1)} \tag{14-7-16}$$

From the pole $s = -(R/L)$,

$$i_{tr} = \frac{E_m}{L(-R/L)}\left(\frac{1 - \epsilon^{RT/2L}}{1 + \epsilon^{RT/2L}}\right)\epsilon^{-Rt/L}$$

$$= \frac{E_m}{R}\left(\frac{\epsilon^{RT/2L} - 1}{\epsilon^{RT/2L} + 1}\right)\epsilon^{-Rt/L} = \frac{E_m}{R}\left(\tanh\frac{RT}{4L}\right)\epsilon^{-Rt/L} \tag{14-7-17}$$

It is possible to show that Eq. 14-7-17 is the sum function of the series

$$i_{tr} = \frac{4E_m}{\pi}\epsilon^{-Rt/L}\sum_{n=1}^{\infty}\frac{\sin\theta_n}{Z_n(2n-1)} \tag{14-7-18}$$

PROBLEMS

14-1. (a) Choose the time origin so that the sawtooth wave of Fig. 14-P-1 is an even function. Then obtain the Fourier series of the wave.

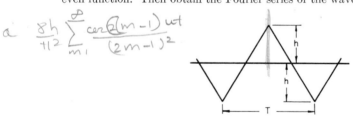

$$a \quad \frac{8h}{\pi^2}\sum_{m=1}^{\infty}\frac{\cos 2(m-1)\omega t}{(2m-1)^2}$$

FIG. 14-P-1

(b) Sketch figures like those of Fig. 14-2-1 for the first terms of the series.

14-2. Repeat Prob. 14-1 with the time origin chosen so that the wave of Fig. 14-P-1 is an odd function.

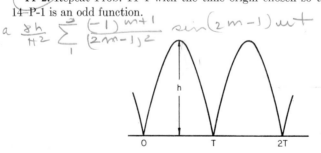

$$a \quad \frac{8h}{\pi^2}\sum_{1}^{\infty}\frac{(-1)^{m+1}}{(2m-1)^2}\sin(2m-1)\omega t$$

FIG. 14-P-2

14-3. The wave of Fig. 14-P-2 is composed of a series of half-sine loops. Obtain the Fourier series of this function.

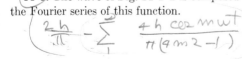

$$\frac{2h}{\pi} - \sum_{1}^{\infty}\frac{4h\cos m\omega t}{\pi(4m^2 - 1)}$$

But

14–4. Obtain the amplitudes b_3 and b_5 for the example in Art. 14–4.

14–5. A current i has the following values at the indicated angles:

θ (degrees)	i (amperes)	θ (degrees)	i (amperes)
0	+ 20.4	180	− 17.7
10	17.3	190	− 13.6
20	12.3	200	− 7.0
30	7.7	210	+ 2.8
40	3.8	220	7.6
50	4.3	230	13.2
60	6.5	240	17.1
70	10.2	250	19.9
80	15.9	260	20.6
90	14.4	270	18.4
100	11.8	280	16.2
110	8.1	290	13.5
120	+ 3.6	300	8.3
130	− 0.4	310	4.8
140	− 7.7	320	3.6
150	− 10.6	330	7.8
160	− 15.0	340	10.3
170	− 18.8	350	15.7

Obtain a_0, a_1, b_1, a_2, b_2, a_3, b_3.

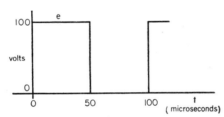

FIG. 14–P-3

14–6. The square wave of Fig. 14–P-3 is applied to the circuit of Fig. 14–P-4.
Find the Fourier series for the current i.

use $e = \begin{cases} +100 & 0 < t < 50 \text{ usec} \\ -100 & 50 \text{ usec} < t < 100 \text{ usec} \end{cases}$ find current for each independently

FIG. 14–P-4

$i = 4.17 \sin(188,500t - 52.37°) + 1.10 \sin(565,500t + 39.50°)$
$+ 1.14 \sin(942,500t + 63.15°)$

14–7. Determine the steady-state and transient voltages across the 300-μf capacitor of Fig. 14–P-5. Assume that the capacitor is initially uncharged.

$e = 125(1 - e^{-66.7t}) + \sum \frac{50000}{\sqrt{4 + 9\pi^2 n^2}} \left[\frac{-3e^{-66.7t}}{\sqrt{4 + 9\pi^2 n^2}} + \frac{1}{n\pi} \sin\left(100\pi n t - \tan^{-1} \frac{3\pi n}{2}\right) \right]$

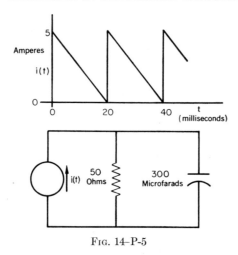

Fig. 14–P-5

14–8. Assume for Prob. 14–1 that h is 300 volts and T is 1 msec and that the voltage of Fig. 14–P-1 is applied to a series R-L with R equal to 150 ohms and L equal to 20 mh. Determine the steady-state and transient currents flowing in the circuit, assuming that the circuit switch is closed when the voltage is at its peak value.

CHAPTER 15

FOURIER INTEGRALS

15–1. Introduction. In the preceding chapter the solution of problems involving periodic functions was accomplished by the use of Fourier series. The method used was to determine the a's and b's from the given periodic function of time which might be a voltage. The a's and b's represent the amplitudes of the fundamental and harmonic components of the voltage and are similar to the concept of a line spectrum in optics. The voltage might then be applied to a circuit, and the problem is to determine the resulting current flow. The amplitudes and phases of the harmonics are modified as dictated by the circuit, and the resulting Fourier series is the required solution.

When single pulses are to be used in the problem, there no longer is any periodicity evident and the solution has to be modified. In doing this, Fourier integrals and transforms appear and the spectra become continuous.

15–2. Derivation of Fourier Integrals. In Fig. 15–2-1a is shown a square wave of voltage plotted against time, and in Fig. 15–2-1b are plotted the amplitudes of the fundamentals and harmonics making up the Fourier series of the square wave as a function of frequency. For clarity the time

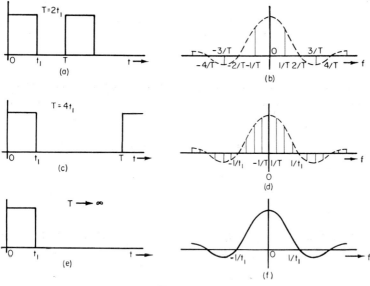

Fig. 15–2-1

origin has been placed at the beginning of the pulse, whereas actually the origin should be in the middle of the pulse. The exponential form of the Fourier series has been used, so negative as well as positive frequencies are present. The fundamentals and harmonics appear at frequencies of $1/T$, $3/T, 5/T, \cdots$. If the discrete amplitudes are connected by a broken line as shown, the broken line might be called the envelope of the frequency spectrum. The envelope has zeros at $\pm 2/T = \pm 1/t_1, \pm 2/t_1, \pm 3/t_1, \cdots$.

Now suppose that the length t_1 of the pulses is kept the same but the period T is doubled to $T = 4\,t_1$. The time and frequency curves are changed as shown in Figs. 15–2-1c and 15–2-1d. The fundamental frequency is one-half of the wave of Fig. 15–2-1a, but the envelope has exactly the same shape and zeros as that of Fig. 15–2-1b. If T were made larger, the fundamental frequency would approach zero but the zeros of the envelope function would not change. The density of the frequencies present between zero frequency and $f = 1/t_1$ would increase.

When the period T becomes infinitely large, the frequency distribution of the single pulse of Fig. 15–2-1e becomes the continuous distribution of Fig. 15–2-1f. The zeros of the envelope are at the same points as those of Figs. 15–2-1b and 15–2-1d. The Fourier series, however, must be replaced by its limit, which is an integral.

The transition from the Fourier series to the Fourier integral may be described in the following manner. Let the Fourier series have the exponential form

$$f(t) = \sum_{n=-\infty}^{+\infty} a_n \epsilon^{jn\omega_0 t} \tag{15–2-1}$$

where

$$a_n = \frac{1}{T} \int_{-T/2}^{+T/2} f(t)\epsilon^{-jn\omega_0 t}\, dt \tag{15–2-2}$$

$$\omega_0 = \frac{2\pi}{T}$$

and n is an integer, either positive or negative. The fundamental frequency of the series is $\omega_0/2\pi = 1/T$. Now let $n\omega_0 = \omega$, $\Delta n\omega_0 = \Delta\omega$, and $\Delta n = 1$. Then

$$f(t) = \sum_{n=-\infty}^{+\infty} \frac{a_n}{\omega_0} \epsilon^{jn\omega_0 t}\, (\Delta n\omega_0) \tag{15–2-3}$$

and

$$g(\omega) = \frac{a_n}{\omega_0} = \frac{1}{2\pi} \int_{-T/2}^{+T/2} f(t)\epsilon^{-jn\omega_0 t}\, dt \tag{15–2-4}$$

As the period T becomes very large, the fundamental frequency $\omega_0/2\pi$ approaches zero, $\Delta n\omega_0$ approaches $d\omega$, and $n\omega_0$ becomes ω. Hence the spacing between harmonics approaches zero, and the function $g(\omega)$ becomes a continuous function of the frequency $\omega/2\pi$ instead of a function defined only at the discrete frequencies spaced $\omega_0/2\pi$ apart. The Fourier series of Eq. 15–2–3 then becomes the Fourier integral.

$$f(t) = \int_{-\infty}^{+\infty} g(\omega)\epsilon^{j\omega t}\, d\omega \qquad (15\text{–}2\text{–}5)$$

where

$$g(\omega) = \frac{1}{2\pi} \int_{-\infty}^{+\infty} f(t)\epsilon^{-j\omega t}\, dt \qquad (15\text{–}2\text{–}6)$$

Eqs. 15–2–5 and 15–2–6 are the complex number form of the Fourier integrals, and they indicate that by use of Eq. 15–2–6 any pulse function $f(t)$ may be changed into its corresponding frequency spectrum $g(\omega)$. Similarly by the use of Eq. 15–2–5 any given frequency spectrum $g(\omega)$ may be changed into the corresponding time function $f(t)$. Of course, several restrictions somewhat similar to those needed when Fourier series are employed are necessary here. To ensure the convergence of Eq. 15–2–6 the integral $\int_{-\infty}^{+\infty} |f(t)|\, dt$ must be finite. Also, $f(t)$ may have only a finite number of maxima and minima and a finite number of points of discontinuity in any finite time interval. At a discontinuity Eq. 15–2–5 will give

$$\tfrac{1}{2}[f(t+0) + f(t-0)] \qquad (15\text{–}2\text{–}7)$$

as in the Fourier series.

These restrictions seem to rule out the use of direct currents and alternating currents in problems. It should be remembered, however, that any current has to be started at some time and will eventually be turned off. Therefore the above conditions are fulfilled and the integrals of Eqs. 15–2–5 and 15–2–6 may be used.

15–3. Example of the Use of the Fourier Integrals. As an example assume that a direct voltage E_0 is started at time $t = -\tfrac{1}{2}t_0$ and stops at time $t = +\tfrac{1}{2}t_0$, as shown in Fig. 15–3–1a. From Eq. 15–2–6 the frequency spectrum

$$g(\omega) = \frac{1}{2\pi} \int_{-t_0/2}^{+t_0/2} E_0\epsilon^{-j\omega t}\, dt = \frac{E_0 t_0}{2\pi} \left| \frac{\sin\dfrac{\omega t_0}{2}}{\dfrac{\omega t_0}{2}} \right| \qquad (15\text{–}3\text{–}1)$$

The spectrum $g(\omega)$ is proportional to the area ($E_0 t_0$) of the direct voltage and varies as the function $(\sin x)/x$, where $x = \omega t_0/2$. The resulting spectrum is plotted in Fig. 15–3–1b. Most of the energy of the voltage is concentrated between $f = -1/t_0$ and $f = +1/t_0$. For positive frequencies this means a frequency band from zero frequency to $f = +1/t_0$ or a band width of $1/t_0$ cycles per second. It is interesting to notice that a voltage of very long time duration requires a very narrow band width, whereas a short-pulse voltage requires a very wide band width to pass most of its energy.

If now the result for $g(\omega)$ given in Eq. 15-2-7 is placed in Eq. 15-2-5, the result should be the time function corresponding to the frequency spectrum of Fig. 15-3-1. Thus

$$\int_{-\infty}^{\infty} g(\omega)\epsilon^{j\omega t}\,d\omega = \int_{-\infty}^{\infty} \left(\frac{E_0 t_0}{2\pi}\right) \left| \frac{\sin\dfrac{\omega t_0}{2}}{\dfrac{\omega t_0}{2}} \right| \epsilon^{j\omega t}\,d\omega$$

$$= \frac{E_0}{\pi} \int_{-\infty}^{+\infty} \frac{\left(\sin\dfrac{\omega t_0}{2}\right)\cos\omega t\,d\omega}{\omega} + j\frac{E_0}{\pi} \int_{-\infty}^{+\infty} \frac{\left(\sin\dfrac{\omega t_0}{2}\right)\sin\omega t\,d\omega}{\omega} \qquad (15\text{-}3\text{-}2)$$

The second integral in the last portion of Eq. 15-3-2 has an integrand which is an odd function of ω, and thus the integral is zero for all values of t.

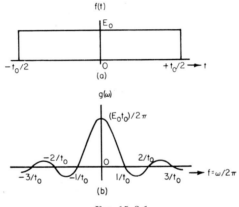

Fig. 15-3-1

The first integral, however, has an integrand which is an even function of ω, and hence the range of integration only need be zero to infinity. The following definite integral with an infinite upper limit will be useful now:

$$\int_0^\infty \frac{\sin au}{u}\,du = \begin{cases} \pi/2 \text{ if } a > 0 \\ 0 \text{ if } a = 0 \\ -\pi/2 \text{ if } a < 0 \end{cases} \qquad (15\text{-}3\text{-}3)$$

From Eqs. 15-3-2 and 15-3-3,

$$\int_{-\infty}^{+\infty} g(\omega)\epsilon^{j\omega t}\,d\omega = \frac{2E_0}{\pi} \int_0^\infty \frac{\left(\sin\dfrac{\omega t_0}{2}\right)\cos\omega t\,d\omega}{\omega}$$

$$= \frac{E_0}{\pi} \int_0^\infty \frac{\left[\sin\left(t+\dfrac{t_0}{2}\right)\omega\right]}{\omega}\,d\omega - \frac{E_0}{\pi} \int_0^\infty \frac{\sin\left[\left(t-\dfrac{t_0}{2}\right)\omega\right]}{\omega}\,d\omega \qquad (15\text{-}3\text{-}4)$$

The first integral of Eq. 15-3-4 is equal to $-E_0/2$ when $t < -t_0/2$ and equal to $+E_0/2$ when $t > -t_0/2$. Similarly the second integral is equal to $-E_0/2$ when $t < +t_0/2$ and equal to $+E_0/2$ when $t > +t_0/2$. Hence the time function given by Eq. 15-3-4 is exactly that of Fig. 15-3-1a except for the points of discontinuity. At these two points Eq. 15-3-4 gives $E_0/2$, which would also be the value predicted by Eq. 15-2-7. In theory, then, it appears as if the frequency spectrum $g(\omega)$ may be obtained for almost any time function $f(t)$ and conversely that the time function $f(t)$ may be obtained for any frequency spectrum $g(\omega)$ by the use of Eqs. 15-2-5 and 15-2-6. In practice, though, it is only the simpler cases that can be evaluated readily by the use of the integrals. In many cases electronic computers are useful in the evaluation of the integrals.

15-4. Response of an Ideal Filter to a Pulse Input. The effects of circuits are generally to change the amplitude and phase shift of the frequency spectrum of the input pulse. Again the more idealized these changes in amplitude and phase shift are, the easier are the evaluations of the integrals encountered. These idealized circuits are usually not realizable physically, and hence they produce results which cannot actually be obtained in practice. They are a great help, though, in indicating what would happen in a practical case.

As an example let it be assumed that the ideal filter is to have an input pulse similar to that of Fig. 15-3-1a impressed upon it. The resulting input frequency spectrum is given in Eq. 15-3-1 and is shown in Fig. 15-3-1b. Now let it be assumed that the ideal filter is a low-pass filter with a cutoff frequency $f_c = \omega_c/2\pi$, and that the gain in the pass band is a constant A while the gain outside the pass band is zero. Also, at the frequency f in the pass band the output wave lags the input wave by an angle $2\pi f t_d = \omega t_d$, where t_d is a constant which indicates by how much time the output wave is delayed with respect to the input wave. The output voltage of the filter is then obtained by taking the spectrum $g(\omega)$ of the input pulse as given by Eq. 15-3-1, modifying the spectrum according to the cutoff frequency, gain, and phase shift of the filter, and then using Eq. 15-2-5 to obtain the output pulse wave. Thus the input frequency spectrum

$$g_i(\omega) = \left(\frac{E_0 t_0}{2\pi}\right)\left| \frac{\sin \dfrac{\omega t_0}{2}}{\dfrac{\omega t_0}{2}}\right| \tag{15-4-1}$$

is modified by the filter to give the output frequency spectrum in the pass band:

$$g_o(\omega) = \left(\frac{A E_0 t_0}{2\pi}\right)\left| \frac{\sin \dfrac{\omega t_0}{2}}{\dfrac{\omega t_0}{2}}\right| \epsilon^{-j\omega t_d} \tag{15-4-2}$$

and outside the pass band $g_0(\omega) = 0$. Then, from Eqs. 15–4-1 and 15–2-5, the output voltage

$$
e_o(t) = \int_{-\omega_c}^{+\omega_c} \left(\frac{AE_0 t_0}{2\,\pi}\right) \left|\frac{\sin\dfrac{\omega t_0}{2}}{\dfrac{\omega t_0}{2}}\right| \epsilon^{-j\omega t_d}\,\epsilon^{j\omega t}\,d\omega
$$

$$
= \frac{AE_0}{\pi} \int_{-\omega_c}^{+\omega_c} \frac{\left(\sin\dfrac{\omega t_0}{2}\right)\cos\omega(t - t_d)\,d\omega}{\omega}
$$

$$
+ j\frac{AE_0}{\pi} \int_{-\omega_c}^{+\omega_c} \frac{\left(\sin\dfrac{\omega t_0}{2}\right)\sin\omega(t - t_d)\,d\omega}{\omega}
$$

$$
= \frac{AE_0}{\pi} \int_0^{\omega_c} \left[\sin\omega\!\left(t - t_d + \frac{t_0}{2}\right) - \sin\omega\!\left(t - t_d - \frac{t_0}{2}\right)\right]\frac{d\omega}{\omega} \qquad (15\text{–}4\text{–}3)
$$

The integrals of Eq. 15–4-3 cannot be evaluated directly in terms of the usual elementary functions. Since they are encountered frequently in various physical problems, the integrals have been calculated and tabulated.* One widely used definition of the integral involving a sine function is

$$
Si(x) = \int_0^x \frac{\sin u}{u}\,du \qquad (15\text{–}4\text{–}4)
$$

and this might be read "the sine integral of x." Using this definition in Eq. 15–4-3,

$$
e_0(t) = \frac{AE_0}{\pi}\left\{Si\left[\omega_c\!\left(t - t_d + \frac{t_0}{2}\right)\right] - Si\left[\omega_0\!\left(t - t_d - \frac{t_0}{2}\right)\right]\right\} \qquad (15\text{–}4\text{–}5)
$$

First of all, in Eq. 15–4-5 the time delay constant t_d subtracts directly from the time t, so the effect of increasing t_d is to move the output pulse to the right along the time axis without changing the shape. Hence t_d represents a true time delay.

Let the time delay t_d be assumed zero in Eq. 15–4-5, $A = 1$, and $\omega_c t_0 = 2\,\pi$. The resulting output pulse wave form is shown as the solid curve of Fig. 15–4-1a, while the input pulse is shown as a dotted line. The finite band width of the filter seems to distort the shape of the pulse and round its corners. If the band width of the filter is doubled so that $\omega_c t_0 = 4\,\pi$, the resulting output wave is that of Fig. 15–4-1b, while another doubling of the band width so that $\omega_c t_0 = 8\,\pi$ gives Fig. 15–4-1c. The wider the band width of the filter, the more nearly faithful is the reproduction of the input pulse. Also, the greater the band width, the faster is the rate of rise of the leading and trailing edges of the output pulse. The Gibbs phenomenon is also present in that the overshoot of the output pulse above the height E_0

Tables of Exponential, Sine, and Cosine Integrals, National Bureau of Standards, Washington, D.C., Vols. I and II.

of the input pulse appears to be practically independent of the band width as long as the band width is more than approximately $1/t_0$ cycles per second.

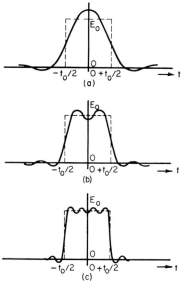

Fig. 15-4-1

It is interesting to notice that, at the points $t = -t_0/2$ and $t = +t_0/2$, the output pulse has approximately the value $E_0/2$, no matter what the band width is as long as it is $1/t_0$ or more.

One disturbing point about Fig. 15-4-1 is that it seems to indicate that there is some output voltage before the input pulse has started. The reason for this is that no physically realizable filter can be constructed having the characteristics of the ideal filter assumed. Hence one way of expressing the physical realizability of the filter would be to insist that the output should be zero until $t = -t_0/2$, when the input pulse starts. Actually this would be a necessary but not a sufficient condition for physical realizability of the filter.

15-5. Other Forms of the Fourier Integral. From Eq. 15-2-6, let

$$g(\omega) = \tfrac{1}{2}[a(\omega) - jb(\omega)] = \frac{1}{2\pi} \int_{-\infty}^{+\infty} f(t) \, (\cos \omega t - j \sin \omega t) \, dt \qquad (15\text{-}5\text{-}1)$$

where

$$a(\omega) = \frac{1}{\pi} \int_{-\infty}^{+\infty} f(t) \cos \omega t \, dt \qquad (15\text{-}5\text{-}2)$$

$$b(\omega) = \frac{1}{\pi} \int_{-\infty}^{+\infty} f(t) \sin \omega t \, dt \qquad (15\text{-}5\text{-}3)$$

It should be noticed that $a(\omega)$ is an even function of ω and hence is the even function part of $g(\omega)$. Similarly $b(\omega)$ is the odd-function part of $g(\omega)$. Now, from Eqs. 15–2–5 and 15–5–1,

$$f(t) = \int_{-\infty}^{+\infty} g(\omega)\epsilon^{j\omega t}\, d\omega = \tfrac{1}{2}\int_{-\infty}^{+\infty} [a(\omega) - jb(\omega)]\,(\cos \omega t + j \sin \omega t)\, d\omega$$

$$(15\text{–}5\text{–}4)$$

The real part of the integrand of Eq. 15–5–4 is an even function of frequency, while the imaginary part is an odd function. Hence the imaginary part of the integral is zero, and

$$f(t) = \int_{0}^{+\infty} [a(\omega) \cos \omega t + b(\omega) \sin \omega t]\, d\omega \qquad (15\text{–}5\text{–}5)$$

The real forms of the Fourier integral are given in Eqs. 15–5–2, 15–5–3, and 15–5–5 and correspond closely to the real form of the Fourier series.

Another important form is that displaying the amplitude function $c(\omega)$ and the phase shift function $\theta(\omega)$. These are defined as

$$c(\omega) = \sqrt{[a(\omega)]^2 + [b(\omega)]^2} \qquad (15\text{–}5\text{–}6)$$

and

$$\sin \theta = -\frac{b(\omega)}{c(\omega)} \qquad \cos \theta = \frac{a(\omega)}{c(\omega)} \qquad (15\text{–}5\text{–}7)$$

Then

$$f(t) = \int_{0}^{\infty} c(\omega) \cos (\omega t + \theta)\, d\omega \qquad (15\text{–}5\text{–}8)$$

Again these correspond closely to similar forms for the Fourier series. The amplitude function $c(\omega)$ is an even function of the frequency, while $\theta(\omega)$ is an odd function. It is possible to show that

$$g(\omega) = \tfrac{1}{2}\, c(\omega)\epsilon^{j\theta(\omega)} \qquad (15\text{–}5\text{–}9)$$

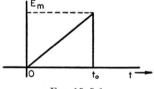

FIG. 15–5–1

As an example let the pulse have the triangular shape shown in Fig. 15–5–1. Then, from Eqs. 15–5–2 and 15–5–3,

$$a(\omega) = \frac{1}{\pi}\int_{-\infty}^{+\infty} f(t) \cos \omega t\, dt = \frac{1}{\pi}\int_{0}^{t_0} \frac{E_m t}{t_0} \cos \omega t\, dt$$

$$= \frac{E_m}{\pi t_0}\left(\frac{\cos \omega t_0}{\omega^2} - \frac{1}{\omega^2} + \frac{t_0 \sin \omega t_0}{\omega}\right) \qquad (15\text{–}5\text{–}10)$$

and
$$b(\omega) = \frac{1}{\pi} \int_{-\infty}^{+\infty} f(t) \sin \omega t \, dt = \frac{1}{\pi} \int_{0}^{t_0} \frac{E_m t}{t_0} \sin \omega t \, dt$$

$$= \frac{E_m}{\pi t_0} \left(\frac{\sin \omega t_0}{\omega^2} - \frac{t_0 \cos \omega t_0}{\omega} \right) \tag{15-5-11}$$

From Eqs. 15–5–6, 15–5–7, 15–5–10, and 15–5–11,

$$c(\omega) = \frac{E_m}{\pi t_0} \left[\frac{2(1 - \cos \omega t_0)}{\omega^4} - \frac{2 t_0 \sin \omega t_0}{\omega^3} + \frac{t_0^2}{\omega^2} \right]^{\frac{1}{2}} \tag{15-5-12}$$

$$\sin \theta = \frac{\left(t_0 \cos \omega t_0 - \dfrac{\sin \omega t_0}{\omega} \right)}{\left[\dfrac{2(1 - \cos \omega t_0)}{\omega^2} - \dfrac{2 t_0 \sin \omega t_0}{\omega} + t_0^2 \right]^{\frac{1}{2}}} \tag{15-5-13}$$

$$\cos \theta = \frac{\left[\dfrac{(\cos \omega t_0 - 1)}{\omega} + t_0 \sin \omega t_0 \right]}{\left[\dfrac{2(1 - \cos \omega t_0)}{\omega^2} - \dfrac{2 t_0 \sin \omega t_0}{\omega} + t_0^2 \right]^{\frac{1}{2}}} \tag{15-5-14}$$

Still other forms of the integrals may be obtained as follows. From Eq. 15–2–6,

$$g(\omega) = \frac{1}{2\pi} \int_{-\infty}^{+\infty} f(t) \epsilon^{-j\omega t} \, dt$$

$$g(-\omega) = \frac{1}{2\pi} \int_{-\infty}^{+\infty} f(t) \epsilon^{+j\omega t} \, dt$$

Adding
$$g(\omega) + g(-\omega) = \frac{1}{\pi} \int_{-\infty}^{+\infty} f(t) \cos \omega t \, dt$$

$$= \frac{1}{\pi} \int_{0}^{\infty} f(t) \cos \omega t \, dt + \frac{1}{\pi} \int_{-\infty}^{0} f(t) \cos \omega t \, dt$$

$$= \frac{1}{\pi} \int_{0}^{\infty} [f(t) + f(-t)] \cos \omega t \, dt$$

Let
$$F_1(t) = f(t) + f(-t) \qquad G_1(\omega) = g(\omega) + g(-\omega)$$

$$G_1(\omega) = \frac{1}{\pi} \int_{0}^{\infty} F_1(t) \cos \omega t \, dt \tag{15-5-15}$$

From Eq. 15–2–5,
$$F_1(t) = 2 \int_{0}^{\infty} G_1(\omega) \cos \omega t \, d\omega \tag{15-5-16}$$

Let
$$F_2(t) = f(t) - f(-t)$$
$$G_2(\omega) = j[g(\omega) - g(-\omega)]$$

Then, from Eqs. 15–2–5 and 15–2–6,

$$G_2(\omega) = \frac{1}{\pi} \int_{0}^{\infty} F_2(t) \sin \omega t \, dt \tag{15-5-17}$$

$$F_2(t) = 2 \int_{0}^{\infty} G_2(\omega) \sin \omega t \, d\omega \tag{15-5-18}$$

The forms of Eqs. 15–5–15 through 15–5–18 are real-function forms of the Fourier integrals. It is to be noticed that Eqs. 15–5–15 and 15–5–16 are even functions, while Eqs. 15–5–17 and 15–5–18 are odd functions.

15–6. Fourier Transforms. It is probably apparent that the integrals of Eqs. 15–2–5 and 15–2–6 bear a close resemblance to those of the Laplace transforms. Thus, from Eq. 15–2–6,

$$g(\omega) = \frac{1}{2\pi} \int_{-\infty}^{+\infty} f(t)\epsilon^{-j\omega t}\, dt \tag{15–2–6}$$

and the direct Laplace transform

$$F(s) = \int_{0}^{\infty} f(t)\epsilon^{-st}\, dt \tag{15–6–1}$$

are so similar that $g(\omega)$ is often called the direct Fourier transform of $f(t)$. Some differences are apparent; one is the $1/2\pi$ factor in the front of Eq. 15–2–6. This factor could have been included in $g(\omega)$, and therefore it is not of much importance. A second difference is the use of the complex number s in the Laplace transform, whereas the pure imaginary number $j\omega$ is used in the Fourier transform. The Laplace transform may range over the whole complex plane, while normally the Fourier transform is considered to remain on the pure imaginary frequency axis. Another important difference is that the Laplace transform is a single-ended integral, that is, the limits go from zero to infinity, while the Fourier transform is a double-ended integral.

From this, many Laplace transforms may be used as Fourier transforms and vice versa. As an example, the Laplace transform of ϵ^{-at} $(a > 0)$ is

$$\mathcal{L}[\epsilon^{-at}] = \frac{1}{s+a} \tag{15–6–2}$$

Similarly the Fourier transform of $\epsilon^{-at}u_{-1}(t)$ is

$$\mathcal{L}[\epsilon^{-at}u_{-1}(t)] = \frac{1}{2\pi} \int_{-\infty}^{+\infty} \epsilon^{-at}u_{-1}(t)\epsilon^{-j\omega t}\, dt = \frac{1}{(j\omega+a)2\pi} \tag{15–6–3}$$

where $u_{-1}(t)$ is the unit jump function of Chapter 9 and starts at $t = 0$. There are, however, Laplace transforms which have no corresponding Fourier transform. An example is the unit jump function $u_{-1}(t)$ whose Laplace transform is

$$\mathcal{L}[u_{-1}(t)] = \frac{1}{s} \tag{15–6–4}$$

Since in this case the integral $\int_{-\infty}^{+\infty} |f(t)|\, dt$ does not converge, the Fourier transform does not exist. A near approach to the Fourier transform of the unit jump function $u_{-1}(t)$ is that of Eq. 15–6–3 with a made very small.

Also there are Fourier transforms for which there are no corresponding Laplace transforms. As one example take the exponential type of pulse

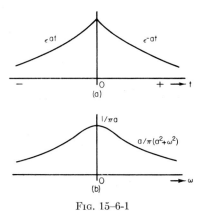

Fig. 15–6-1

shown in Fig. 15–6-1a. Its Fourier transform is

$$\mathscr{F}[f(t)] = \frac{1}{2\pi} \int_{-\infty}^{0} \epsilon^{at}\epsilon^{-j\omega t}\, dt + \frac{1}{2\pi} \int_{0}^{\infty} \epsilon^{-at}\epsilon^{-j\omega t}\, dt = \frac{a}{\pi(a^2 + \omega^2)} \quad (15\text{–}6\text{-}5)$$

The corresponding frequency spectrum is sketched in Fig. 15–6-1b. The situation concerning Fourier and Laplace transforms may be likened to two circles which intersect one another but have different centers. The common area represents the transforms which have the same form for both. The area remaining in the Fourier transform circle then represents the transforms peculiar to the Fourier transform alone. The same holds for the Laplace transform circle. A table of Fourier transforms* is very useful in solving Laplace transform problems, although not all of the transforms are usable as Laplace transforms. Exactly the same situation arises in the use of Laplace transform tables in the solution of Fourier transform problems.

To the inverse Laplace transform

$$\mathscr{L}^{-1}[F(s)] = f(t) = \frac{1}{2\pi j} \int_{c-j\omega}^{c+j\omega} \epsilon^{st} F(s)\, ds \quad (15\text{–}6\text{-}6)$$

corresponds to the inverse Fourier transform

$$\mathscr{F}^{-1}[g(\omega)] = f(t) = \int_{-\infty}^{+\infty} \epsilon^{j\omega t} g(\omega)\, d\omega \quad (15\text{–}2\text{-}5)$$

In many cases the Fourier transforms are called Fourier pairs. A short table of such pairs is given in the Appendix.

*R. M. Foster and G. A. Campbell, *Fourier Integrals for Practical Applications*, D. Van Nostrand Co., Princeton, N. J., 1940.

PROBLEMS

15–1. Obtain the frequency spectrum $g(\omega)$ for the time function composed of two pulses as shown in Fig. 15–P-1. Then obtain the time function resulting from the frequency function $g(\omega)$.

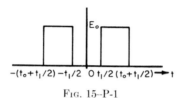

FIG. 15–P-1

15–2. A sinusoidal pulse as shown in Fig. 15–P-2 has the equation $E_m \cos \omega t$ when

$$\frac{-(2n-1)\pi}{2\omega} < t < \frac{(2n-1)\pi}{2\omega}$$

and is zero for all values of t outside this range. The integer n has any positive value. Obtain $g(\omega)$ and sketch the magnitude of $g(\omega)$ for $n = 1$, 2, and 3.

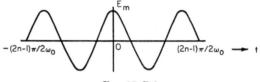

FIG. 15–P-2

15–3. The pulse of Fig. 15–3-1a is applied to an ideal band-pass filter without phase shift and with a gain of A in the pass band. The cutoff frequencies are $\frac{1}{2t_0}$ and $2/t_0$. Find the equation for the output pulse and plot the output wave.

15–4. The double pulse of Fig. 15–P-1 is applied to the input of the ideal low-pass filter of Art. 15–4 with cutoff frequency $\omega_c = 2/t_0$. Plot the output wave for (a) $t_1 = 2t_0$ and (b) $t_1 = t_0/2 = \frac{1}{2}t_0$.

15–5. Prove Eq. 15–5-9 and show that it holds for the example of Art. 15–5.

15–6. For the pulse of Fig. 15–P-3, obtain the expressions for $a(\omega)$, $b(\omega)$, $c(\omega)$, $\theta(\omega)$.

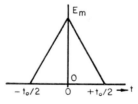

FIG. 15–P-3

15–7. Obtain the direct Fourier transform of the pulse whose equation for all t's is $\epsilon^{-a^2 t^2}$. Why does this pulse not have a Laplace transform?

CHAPTER 16

APPLICATIONS OF THE FOURIER INTEGRALS

16–1. The Unit Step Function. In work with transients in electric circuits the unit step function of Chapter 10 is very useful. It was pointed out in Chapter 15 that the direct Fourier transform did not converge for this particular function but that it could be approached by the use of an exponentially decaying time function. Such a function is shown in Fig. 16–1–1a, and its direct Fourier transform is, from Eq. 15–2–6,

$$g(\omega) = \frac{1}{2\pi} \int_{-\infty}^{0} (-\tfrac{1}{2}\,\epsilon^{at})\epsilon^{-j\omega t}\,dt + \frac{1}{2\pi} \int_{0}^{\infty} (\tfrac{1}{2}\,\epsilon^{-at})\epsilon^{-j\omega t}\,dt = \frac{\omega}{2\,\pi j(a^2 + \omega^2)}$$

$$(16\text{–}1\text{–}1)$$

When a is allowed to approach zero, the frequency spectrum $g(\omega)$ approaches

$$g(\omega) = \frac{1}{2\,\pi j\omega} \tag{16–1–2}$$

and the resulting step wave is shown in Fig. 16–1–1b. A plot of the amplitude of the frequency spectrum is shown in Fig. 16–1–1c; it indicates that the larger energies are concentrated toward the lower frequencies, although every frequency band would receive some energy no matter where it was

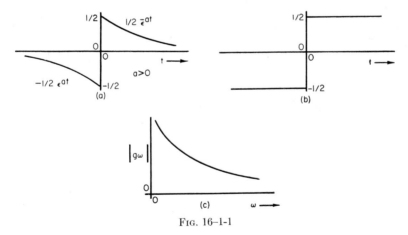

Fig. 16–1–1

located. This indicates why the closing or opening of a switch, as in a lamp, is often heard as a click in a radio receiver or seen as a disturbance on the screen of a television receiver.

To make the usual unit step voltage $u_{-1}(t)$ which is zero when time $t < 0$

and unity when $t > 0$, a $\frac{1}{2}$-volt direct voltage must be added also. A $\frac{1}{2}$-volt direct voltage must be added separately because it does not fulfill the condition of absolute integrability over the whole frequency range. Another reason why this $\frac{1}{2}$ volt has to be added separately is that it would represent a pole on the frequency axis, in particular at the origin or zero frequency. The Fourier integral is limited to poles lying off the frequency axis. Hence, from Eqs. 15–2-5 and 16–1-2,

$$u_{-1}(t) = \tfrac{1}{2} + \int_{-\infty}^{+\infty} \left(\frac{1}{2\,\pi j \omega}\right) \epsilon^{j \omega t}\, d\omega \qquad (16\text{–}1\text{-}3)$$

A real integral for $u_{-1}(t)$ may be obtained as follows:

$$u_{-1}(t) = \frac{1}{2} - \frac{j}{2\,\pi} \int_{-\infty}^{+\infty} \frac{(\cos \omega t)\, d\omega}{\omega} + \frac{1}{2\,\pi} \int_{-\infty}^{+\infty} \frac{(\sin \omega t)\, d\omega}{\omega}$$

Since the function $(1/\omega)(\cos \omega t)$ is an odd function of ω, and $(1/\omega)(\sin \omega t)$ is even,

$$u_{-1}(t) = \frac{1}{2} + \frac{1}{2\,\pi} \int_{-\infty}^{+\infty} \frac{(\sin \omega t)\, d\omega}{\omega}$$

$$= \frac{1}{2} + \frac{1}{\pi} \int_{0}^{\infty} \frac{(\sin \omega t)\, d\omega}{\omega} \qquad (16\text{–}1\text{-}4)$$

As a check, the integral

$$\int_{0}^{\infty} \frac{(\sin \omega t)\, d\omega}{\omega} = \begin{cases} \pi/2 \text{ when } t > 0 \\ 0 \text{ when } t = 0 \\ -\pi/2 \text{ when } t < 0 \end{cases} \qquad (16\text{–}1\text{-}5)$$

Thus Eq. 16–1-4 is equal to zero when $t < 0$, to $1/2$ when $t = 0$, and to 1 when $t > 0$.

The result of Eq. 16–1-4 may be obtained by the use of other pulse shapes than that of Fig. 16–1-1a. An example would be a flat-topped pulse of finite width starting at time $t = 0$ whose width is allowed to approach infinity.

16–2. The R-L Series Circuit. A series resistance-inductance circuit is shown in Fig. 16–2-1 with a voltage E applied through the switch S assumed to close at time $t = 0$. The frequency spectrum expression for the current

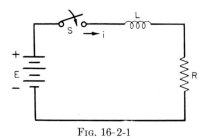

Fɪɢ. 16-2-1

flowing should be obtained by multiplying the voltage in the form of a frequency spectrum by the admittance of the circuit, also in the form of a frequency spectrum. Then, using the inverse Fourier transform, the current may be obtained as a time function. The frequency spectrum of the applied voltage may be obtained from Eq. 16–1–3, and the frequency spectrum of the circuit admittance $Y(\omega)$ is

$$Y(\omega) = \frac{1}{R + j\omega L} = \frac{R}{R^2 + \omega^2 L^2} - j\frac{\omega L}{R^2 + \omega^2 L^2} \tag{16–2–1}$$

The current $i(t)$ as a time function may then be found by using Eq. 15–2–5.

$$
\begin{aligned}
i(t) &= \frac{E}{2R} + \frac{E}{2\pi} \int_{-\infty}^{+\infty} \frac{\epsilon^{j\omega t}}{j\omega} \left(\frac{R}{R^2 + \omega^2 L^2} - j\frac{\omega L}{R^2 + \omega^2 L^2}\right) d\omega \\
&= \frac{E}{2R} + \frac{E}{2\pi} \int_{-\infty}^{+\infty} \frac{(R\cos\omega t + \omega L\sin\omega t) + j(R\sin\omega t - \omega L\cos\omega t)}{j\omega(R^2 + \omega^2 L^2)} d\omega \\
&= \frac{E}{2R} + \frac{E}{2\pi} \int_{-\infty}^{+\infty} \frac{(R\sin\omega t - \omega L\cos\omega t)}{\omega(R^2 + \omega^2 L^2)} d\omega \\
&= \frac{E}{2R} + \frac{E}{\pi} \int_{0}^{\infty} \frac{R\sin\omega t - \omega L\cos\omega t}{\omega(R^2 + \omega^2 L^2)} d\omega \tag{16–2–2}
\end{aligned}
$$

Two infinite integrals useful in evaluating Eq. 16–2–2 are*

$$\int_0^\infty \frac{(\sin ax)\,dx}{x(x^2 + b^2)} = \frac{\pi}{2b^2}(1 - \epsilon^{-ab})$$

$$\int_0^\infty \frac{(\cos ax)\,dx}{(x^2 + b^2)} = \frac{\pi}{2b}\epsilon^{-ab} \tag{16–2–3}$$

From Eqs. 16-2-2 and 16-2-3, the current $i(t)$ is, for $t > 0$,

$$
\begin{aligned}
i(t) &= \frac{E}{2R} + \frac{ER}{\pi L^2} \int_0^\infty \frac{\sin\omega t\,d\omega}{\omega(\omega^2 + R^2/L^2)} - \frac{E}{\pi L} \int_0^\infty \frac{\cos\omega t}{\omega^2 + R^2/L^2} d\omega \\
&= \frac{E}{2R} + \frac{E}{2R}(1 - \epsilon^{-Rt/L}) - \frac{E}{2R}\epsilon^{-Rt/L} \\
&= \frac{E}{R}(1 - \epsilon^{-Rt/L}) \tag{16–2–4}
\end{aligned}
$$

To obtain $i(t)$ for $t < 0$ let $t' = -t$, and then $t' > 0$. From Eqs. 16–2–2 and 16–2–3,

$$
\begin{aligned}
i(t) &= \frac{E}{2R} - \frac{ER}{\pi L^2} \int_0^\infty \frac{\sin\omega t'}{\omega(\omega^2 + R^2/L^2)} d\omega - \frac{E}{\pi L} \int_0^\infty \frac{\cos\omega t'}{\omega^2 + R^2/L^2} d\omega \\
&= \frac{E}{2R} - \frac{E}{2R}(1 - \epsilon^{-Rt'/L}) - \frac{E}{2R}\epsilon^{-Rt'/L} \\
&= 0 \tag{16–2–5}
\end{aligned}
$$

At time $t = 0$,

$$
\begin{aligned}
i(t) &= \frac{E}{2R} - \frac{E}{\pi L} \int_0^\infty \frac{d\omega}{\omega^2 + R^2/L^2} \\
&= \frac{E}{2R} - \frac{E}{2R} = 0 \tag{16–2–6}
\end{aligned}
$$

*D. Bierens de Haan, *Nouvelles Tables d'Intégrales Définies*, G. E. Stechert & Co., New York, 1939; W. Gröbner and N. Hofreiter, *Integraltafel*, Vol. I, Indefinite Integrals; Vol. II, Definite Integrals, Springer-Verlag, Vienna, 1949–50.

Thus, from Eqs. 16–2-4, 16–2-5, and 16–2-6,

$$i(t) = \frac{E}{R} (1 - \epsilon^{-Rt/L}) u_{-1}(t)$$

which is the well-known result.

16–3. General Response of a Circuit. The procedure of Art. 16–2 may be generalized by using the general sinusoidal response of a circuit. By response is meant the voltage, current, charge, or other variable which results at a given point in a circuit when a sinusoidal generator of angular frequency ω is applied at some other point in the circuit. The frequency is considered to be anywhere in the range from zero to infinity.

Let the response be given by

$$Y(\omega) = G(\omega) + jB(\omega) \qquad (16\text{–}3\text{-}1)$$

$G(\omega)$ is an even function of ω, $B(\omega)$ an odd function. By use of Eqs. 16–1-3 and 16–3-1, the transient response $A(t)$ to a unit step voltage is

$$A(t) = \frac{1}{2} G(0) + \frac{1}{2\pi} \int_{-\infty}^{+\infty} [G(\omega) + jB(\omega)] \frac{\epsilon^{j\omega t}}{j\omega} d\omega$$

$$= \frac{1}{2} G(0)$$

$$+ \frac{1}{2\pi} \int_{-\infty}^{+\infty} \frac{[G(\omega) \cos \omega t - B(\omega) \sin \omega t] + j[G(\omega) \sin \omega t + B(\omega) \cos \omega t]}{j\omega} d\omega$$

$$= \frac{1}{2} G(0) + \frac{1}{2\pi} \int_{-\infty}^{+\infty} \frac{G(\omega) \sin \omega t + B(\omega) \cos \omega t}{\omega} d\omega$$

$$= \frac{1}{2} G(0) + \frac{1}{\pi} \int_{0}^{\infty} \frac{G(\omega) \sin \omega t}{\omega} d\omega + \frac{1}{\pi} \int_{0}^{\infty} \frac{B(\omega) \cos \omega t}{\omega} d\omega \qquad (16\text{–}3\text{-}2)$$

Eq. 16–3-2 indicates that, if the response of a circuit is known at every frequency, the transient response $A(t)$ to a unit step voltage should be known and can be obtained by integrating this equation. Once $A(t)$ is found, the output response $e_o(t)$ may be expressed in terms of the input driving function $e_i(t)$ by use of one of the forms of the superposition theorem:

$$e_o(t) = \frac{d}{dt} \int_0^t A(t - \tau) e_i(\tau) \, d\tau$$

$$= \frac{d}{dt} \int_0^t A(\tau) e_i(t - \tau) \, d\tau$$

$$= A(0) e_i(t) + \int_0^t A'(t - \tau) e_i(\tau) \, d\tau$$

$$= A(t) e_i(0) + \int_0^t A(\tau) e_i'(t - \tau) \, d\tau$$

$$= A(0) e_i(t) + \int_0^t A'(\tau) e_i(t - \tau) \, d\tau$$

$$= A(t) e_i(0) + \int_0^t A(t - \tau) e_i'(\tau) \, d\tau \qquad (16\text{–}3\text{-}3)$$

The primes indicate derivatives with respect to time t.

16–4. Physical Realizability. If the response of Eq. 16–3-2 is to be physically realizable, it is necessary that $A(t)$ be zero for all values of time t less than zero. Let $t = -t'$ in Eq. 16–3-2.

$$0 = \frac{1}{2} G(0) - \frac{1}{\pi} \int_0^\infty \frac{G(\omega) \sin \omega t'}{\omega} d\omega + \frac{1}{\pi} \int_0^\infty \frac{B(\omega) \cos \omega t'}{\omega} d\omega \quad (16\text{–}4\text{-}1)$$

If now the primes are dropped and Eq. 16–4-1 is added to Eq. 16–3-2,

$$A(t) = G(0) + \frac{2}{\pi} \int_0^\infty \frac{B(\omega) \cos \omega t}{\omega} d\omega \quad (16\text{–}4\text{-}2)$$

Similarly, if Eq. 16–4-1 is subtracted from Eq. 16–3-2,

$$A(t) = \frac{2}{\pi} \int_0^\infty \frac{G(\omega) \sin \omega t}{\omega} d\omega \quad (16\text{–}4\text{-}3)$$

The two equations 16–4-2 and 16–4-3 indicate that the real and imaginary parts of Eq. 16–3-1 are not independent if the restriction of physical realizability is placed upon the circuit. Hence, if the real part $G(\omega)$ is known, it should be possible to determine $B(\omega)$ and vice versa. It should be noticed that Eqs. 16–4-2 and 16–4-3 hold only when the time $t > 0$. Actually Eq. 16–4-2 gives an $A(t)$ which is an even function of time, while Eq. 16–4-3 gives $A(t)$ as an odd function of t.

If $A(t)$ is known as a function of time, $G(\omega)$ may be obtained from $A(t)$ by inverting the integral of Eq. 16–4-3. This is done as follows:

$$\begin{aligned} A(t) &= \frac{2}{\pi} \int_0^\infty \frac{G(\omega) \sin \omega t}{\omega} d\omega \\ &= \frac{2}{\pi} \int_0^\infty \frac{G(\omega) \epsilon^{j\omega t}}{2j\omega} d\omega - \frac{2}{\pi} \int_0^\infty \frac{G(\omega) \epsilon^{-j\omega t}}{2j\omega} d\omega \\ &= \frac{1}{j\pi} \int_{-\infty}^{+\infty} \frac{G(\omega) \epsilon^{j\omega t}}{\omega} d\omega \end{aligned} \quad (16\text{–}4\text{-}4)$$

From Eqs. 15–2-5 and 15–2-6,

$$\begin{aligned} \frac{G(\omega)}{\omega} &= \frac{1}{2\pi} \int_{-\infty}^{+\infty} j\pi A(t) \epsilon^{-j\omega t} dt = \frac{j}{2} \int_{-\infty}^{+\infty} A(t) \epsilon^{-j\omega t} dt \\ &= \frac{j}{2} \int_0^\infty A(t) \epsilon^{-j\omega t} dt - \frac{j}{2} \int_\infty^0 A(-t') \epsilon^{j\omega t'} dt' \end{aligned}$$

or $\qquad\qquad \dfrac{G(\omega)}{\omega} = \displaystyle\int_0^\infty A(t) \sin \omega t \, dt \qquad\qquad\qquad (16\text{–}4\text{-}5)$

In a similar fashion, from Eq 16–4-2,

$$A(t) = \frac{2}{\pi} \int_0^\infty \frac{B(\omega) \cos \omega t}{\omega} d\omega$$

or $\qquad A(t) = \dfrac{2}{\pi} \displaystyle\int_0^\infty \frac{B(\omega) \epsilon^{j\omega t}}{2\omega} d\omega + \frac{2}{\pi} \int_0^\infty \frac{B(\omega) \epsilon^{-j\omega t}}{2\omega} d\omega$

$$\qquad\qquad = \frac{2}{\pi} \int_{-\infty}^{+\infty} \frac{B(\omega) \epsilon^{j\omega t}}{2\omega} d\omega \qquad\qquad\qquad (16\text{–}4\text{-}6)$$

$G(0)$ is assumed to be zero here so that inversion of the Fourier integral is possible. A constant term such as $G(0)$ will prevent inversion because the function is not integrable absolutely. Again from Eqs. 15-2-5 and 15-2-6,

$$\frac{B(\omega)}{\omega} = \frac{1}{2\pi} \int_{-\infty}^{+\infty} \pi[A(t)]\epsilon^{-j\omega t} \, dt$$

$$= \frac{1}{2} \int_{0}^{\infty} [A(t)]\epsilon^{-j\omega t} \, dt + \frac{1}{2} \int_{-\infty}^{0} [A(t)]\epsilon^{-j\omega t} \, dt$$

or

$$\frac{B(\omega)}{\omega} = \int_{0}^{\infty} [A(t)] \cos \omega t \, dt \tag{16-4-7}$$

From Eqs. 16-4-5 and 16-4-7, then, both the real $G(\omega)$ and the imaginary $B(\omega)$ parts of the response function $Y(\omega)$ of Eq. 16-3-1 may be obtained. Eqs. 16-4-5 and 16-4-7 may also be obtained by using the steady-state part of Eq. 16-3-3 and putting $e_i(t) = \sin \omega t$. Thus the response to a sinusoidal voltage is

$$\int_{0}^{t} A(\tau) \, \omega \cos \omega(t - \tau) \, d\tau$$

$$= \omega \cos \omega t \int_{0}^{t} A(\tau) \cos \omega \tau \, d\tau + \omega \sin \omega t \int_{0}^{t} A(\tau) \sin \omega \tau \, d\tau \tag{16-4-8}$$

Both the steady-state and transient parts of the response are included in Eq. 16-4-8, and they may be separated by rewriting it:

$$\omega \cos \omega t \int_{0}^{\infty} A(\tau) \cos \omega \tau \, d\tau + \omega \sin \omega t \int_{0}^{\infty} A(\tau) \sin \omega \tau \, d\tau$$

$$- \omega \cos \omega t \int_{t}^{\infty} A(\tau) \cos \omega \tau \, d\tau - \omega \sin \omega t \int_{t}^{\infty} A(\tau) \sin \omega \tau \, d\tau \tag{16-4-9}$$

where

$$\omega \cos \omega t \int_{0}^{\infty} A(\tau) \cos \omega \tau \, d\tau + \omega \sin \omega t \int_{0}^{\infty} A(\tau) \sin \omega \tau \, d\tau \tag{16-4-10}$$

is the steady-state part of the response.

From Eq. 16-3-1 the response to a sinusoidal voltage is the imaginary part of $[G(\omega) + jB(\omega)]\epsilon^{j\omega t}$ or

$$\text{Im} \{[G(\omega) + jB(\omega)]\epsilon^{j\omega t}\} = B(\omega) \cos \omega t + G(\omega) \sin \omega t \tag{16-4-11}$$

When Eqs. 16-4-10 and 16-4-11 are compared, Eqs. 16-4-5 and 16-4-7 are seen to result.

As an example let the response $A(t)$ to a unit step voltage be

$$A(t) = C\epsilon^{-t/t_0} \tag{16-4-12}$$

where t_0 is the time constant of the response. Then, from Eq. 16-4-5,

$$\frac{G(\omega)}{\omega} = \int_{0}^{\infty} A(t) \sin \omega t \, dt = \int_{0}^{\infty} C\epsilon^{-t/t_0} \sin \omega t \, dt = \frac{C\omega}{1/t_0^2 + \omega^2}$$

or

$$G(\omega) = \frac{C\omega^2}{\omega^2 + 1/t_0^2} \tag{16-4-13}$$

Also from Eq. 16–4–7,

$$\frac{B(\omega)}{\omega} = \int_0^\infty A(t) \cos \omega t \, dt = \int_0^\infty C\epsilon^{-t/t_0} \sin \omega t \, dt = \frac{C(1/t_0)}{1/t_0{}^2 + \omega^2}$$

or

$$B(\omega) = \frac{C(\omega/t_0)}{1/t_0{}^2 + \omega^2} \tag{16–4–14}$$

The admittance $Y(\omega)$ is then, from Eqs. 16–4–13 and 16–4–14,

$$Y(\omega) = G(\omega) + jB(\omega)$$

$$= \frac{C\omega^2}{\omega^2 + 1/t_0{}^2} + j\frac{(C\omega/t_0)}{\omega^2 + 1/t_0{}^2} = \frac{C\omega(\omega + j/t_0)}{(\omega + j/t_0)(\omega - j/t_0)}$$

$$= \frac{C\omega}{\omega - j/t_0} \tag{16–4–15}$$

The impedance $Z(\omega)$ is

$$Z(\omega) = \frac{1}{Y(\omega)} = \frac{1}{C} - j\frac{1}{\omega C t_0} = R_0 - j\frac{1}{\omega C_0} \tag{16–4–16}$$

where $R_0 = 1/C$ and $C_0 = Ct_0$. The impedance producing the exponentially decaying response of Eq. 16–4–12 when a unit voltage was applied is a series resistance-capacitance circuit with a time constant

$$t_0 = R_0 C_0 \tag{16–4–17}$$

If either $G(\omega)$ or $B(\omega)$ were known, the other function of ω could be obtained from it along with $A(t)$. Thus, in the above example, suppose that $B(\omega)$ was known:

$$B(\omega) = \frac{(C\omega/t_0)}{\omega^2 + 1/t_0{}^2} \tag{16–4–14}$$

Then, from Eqs. 16–4–2 and 16–2–3,

$$A(t) = \frac{2}{\pi} \int_0^\infty \frac{(C/t_0) \cos \omega t}{\omega^2 + 1/t_0{}^2} \, d\omega = C\epsilon^{-t/t_0} \tag{16–4–18}$$

and, from Eqs. 16–4–5 and 16–4–13,

$$G(\omega) = \frac{C\omega^2}{\omega^2 + 1/t_0{}^2} \tag{16–4–13}$$

The above example indicates that, if either $A(t)$, or $G(\omega)$, or $B(\omega)$ is known and fulfills the conditions of a physically realizable network, it is possible to construct the network. Also in $G(\omega) + jB(\omega)$, if $\omega = -js$ and s is used as a complex variable, the poles and zeros of the network may be determined. This function of s is very useful in network theory.

16–5. Some Fourier Pairs. The time function $f(t)$ and the frequency function $g(\omega)$ of Eqs. 15–2–5 and 15–2–6 constitute a Fourier pair. Several of these pairs have been developed so far, such as the unit step voltage of Fig. 16–5–1a and the corresponding hyperbolic frequency distribution $g(\omega)$.

Because in several parts of Fig. 16–5-1 $g(\omega)$ is complex, the magnitude $|g(\omega)|$ is plotted. When the band width is restricted by an idealized low-

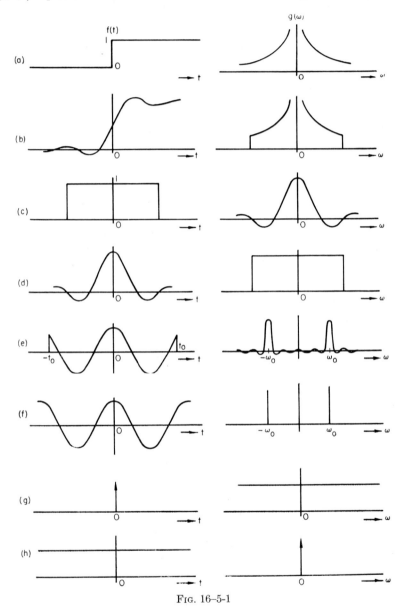

Fig. 16–5-1

pass filter, the time function has a definite rise time and overshoot as shown in Fig. 16–5-1b. A square pulse in time has the attenuated sinusoidal loop frequency response of Fig. 16–5-1c. Similarly, an attenuated sinusoidal loop time wave has the rectangular frequency response of Fig. 16–5–1d. The similarity between Figs. 16–5–1c and 16–5–1d is a consequence of the symmetry of Eqs. 15–2–5 and 15–2–6.

A cosine wave stretching from $(-t_0)$ to $(+t_0)$ has the frequency spectrum

$$g(\omega) = \frac{1}{2\pi} \int_{-\infty}^{+\infty} \epsilon^{-j\omega t} f(t)\, dt$$

$$= \frac{1}{2\pi} \int_{-t_0}^{+t_0} \epsilon^{-j\omega t} \cos \omega_0 t\, dt$$

$$= \frac{\sin (\omega_0 - \omega)t_0}{2\pi(\omega_0 - \omega)} + \frac{\sin (\omega_0 + \omega)t_0}{2\pi(\omega_0 + \omega)} \qquad (16\text{–}5\text{–}1)$$

This spectrum is shown in Fig. 16–5–1e and indicates that the energy is concentrated about the frequency $f_0 = (\omega_0/2\pi)$. As the time t_0 is made larger, the energy is concentrated more and more closely about f_0 until in the limit as t_0 becomes very large the frequency spectrum becomes two discrete lines at the frequencies $(\pm f_0)$ as shown in Fig. 16–5–1f.

If a pulse of unit area such as that of Fig. 16–5–2a is put in Eq. 15–2–6, the frequency spectrum is

$$g(\omega) = \frac{1}{2\pi} \int_{-\infty}^{+\infty} f(t)\epsilon^{-j\omega t}\, dt$$

$$= \frac{1}{2\pi} \int_{-\Delta t/2}^{+\Delta t/2} \frac{1}{\Delta t} \epsilon^{-j\omega t}\, dt = \frac{\epsilon^{-j\omega t}}{2\pi \Delta t(-j\omega)} \bigg|_{-\Delta t/2}^{+\Delta t/2}$$

$$= \frac{1}{2\pi(\Delta t\omega/2)} \sin \left(\frac{\omega \Delta t}{2}\right) \qquad (16\text{–}5\text{–}2)$$

This frequency spectrum is that shown in Fig. 16–5–1c. If, however, Δt is allowed to approach zero in Eq. 16–5–2, the pulse of Fig. 16–5–2a approaches the unit impulse $u_0(t)$ of Chapter 9 whose height becomes very large but its area is still unity. The frequency spectrum $g(\omega)$ of Eq. 16–5–2 approaches

$$g(\omega) = \frac{1}{2\pi} \qquad (16\text{–}5\text{–}3)$$

as shown in Fig. 16–5–1g. Corresponding to this is a direct voltage of Fig. 16–5–1h whose frequency spectrum is one discrete line at zero frequency. Notice the comparison between Figs. 16–5–1g and 16–5–1h. The unit impulse function is the same as the Dirac delta function $\delta(t)$, which is usually defined as the integral

$$\int_{-A}^{B} f(t)\, \delta(t)\, dt = f(0) \qquad (16\text{–}5\text{–}4)$$

where both A and B are greater than zero and $f(t)$ is a continuous function of time. When $f(t) = 1$, the area under the delta function is unity.

An impulse of the second order $u_1(t)$, or doublet impulse, is the result of allowing Δt to approach zero in the double pulse of Fig. 16–5-2b. The

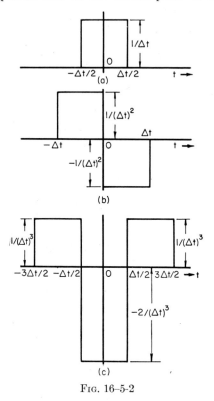

FIG. 16–5-2

frequency spectrum of the double pulse is

$$g(\omega) = \frac{1}{2\,\pi} \int_{-\infty}^{+\infty} f(t)\epsilon^{-j\omega t}\, dt$$

$$= \frac{1}{2\,\pi} \int_{-\Delta t}^{0} \left(\frac{1}{\Delta t}\right)^2 \epsilon^{-j\omega t}\, dt - \frac{1}{2\,\pi} \int_{0}^{\Delta t} \left(\frac{1}{\Delta t}\right)^2 \epsilon^{-j\omega t}\, dt$$

$$= \frac{j\omega}{2\,\pi} \left(\frac{\sin\dfrac{\omega\Delta t}{2}}{\dfrac{\omega\Delta t}{2}}\right)^2 \tag{16–5-5}$$

When Δt is allowed to approach zero,

$$g(\omega) = \frac{j\omega}{2\,\pi} \tag{16–5-6}$$

Hence the frequency spectrum of a second-order impulse has an amplitude which increases directly with frequency. This second-order impulse corresponds to the derivative of the Dirac delta function. A pulse which will lead to the third-order impulse $u_2(t)$ is shown in Fig. 16–5-2c.

Another interesting pulse is the Gaussian error function pulse, which has the time function

$$f(t) = \epsilon^{-\sigma^2 t^2/2} \qquad (16\text{-}5\text{-}7)$$

where σ is a constant. The corresponding frequency spectrum $g(\omega)$ is

$$g(\omega) = \frac{1}{\sigma\sqrt{2\pi}}\, \epsilon^{-\omega^2/2\sigma^2} \qquad (16\text{-}5\text{-}8)$$

When σ is small, the time function for the pulse is relatively slow whereas the frequency spectrum drops off very quickly, as may be seen in Fig. 16-5-3a. This indicates that a long pulse requires a relatively narrow band

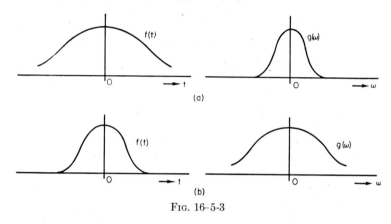

(a)

(b)

FIG. 16-5-3

of frequencies. When σ is large, as shown in Fig. 16-5-3b, a short pulse leads to a wide frequency spectrum. One of the interesting facts about these pulses is that the frequency spectrum has the same shape as the time function. This type of pulse is very useful in that it exhibits no overshoot or ringing. Both of these effects, for example, are present in the wave form of Fig. 16-5-1b.

16-6. Energy Expressions. Let it be assumed that the Fourier transform of $f_1(t)$ is $g_1(\omega)$, and similarly for $f_2(t)$ and $g_2(\omega)$. Then form the integral

$$\int_{-\infty}^{+\infty} f_1(t)f_2(t)\,dt = \int_{-\infty}^{+\infty}\left[\int_{-\infty}^{+\infty} g_1(\omega)\epsilon^{j\omega t}\,d\omega\right] f_2(t)\,dt$$

$$= \int_{-\infty}^{+\infty}\left[\int_{-\infty}^{+\infty} f_2(t)\epsilon^{j\omega t}\,dt\right] g_1(\omega)\,d\omega$$

$$= 2\pi \int_{-\infty}^{+\infty} g_1(\omega)g_2(-\omega)\,d\omega \qquad (16\text{-}6\text{-}1)$$

The above assumes that $f_1(t)$ and $g_1(\omega)$, $f_2(t)$ and $g_2(\omega)$ are Fourier pairs and satisfy Eqs. 15-2-5 and 15-2-6. In addition the integrals of Eq. 16-6-1 are assumed to converge and the functions are such that the order of integration may be reversed without trouble.

Now let
$$g_1(\omega) = A_1(\omega)\epsilon^{j\phi\,(\omega)} \qquad\qquad (16\text{-}6\text{-}2)$$
$$g_2(\omega) = A_2(\omega)\epsilon^{j\phi_2(\omega)}$$

where the A's are even functions of ω and the ϕ's are odd functions of ω. Then

$$2\pi\int_{-\infty}^{+\infty} g_1(\omega)g_2(-\omega)\,d\omega = 2\pi\int_{-\infty}^{+\infty} A_1(\omega)A_2(\omega)\epsilon^{j[\phi_1(\omega)-\phi_2(\omega)]}\,d\omega$$

$$= 2\pi\int_{-\infty}^{+\infty} A_1(\omega)A_2(\omega)\cos[\phi_1(\omega)-\phi_2(\omega)]\,d\omega$$

$$+\,j\,2\pi\int_{-\infty}^{+\infty} A_1(\omega)A_2(\omega)\sin[\phi_1(\omega)-\phi_2(\omega)]\,d\omega \quad (16\text{-}6\text{-}3)$$

Now the first integrand is an even function, and the second is an odd function of ω. Then

$$2\pi\int_{-\infty}^{+\infty} g_1(\omega)g_2(-\omega)\,d\omega = 4\pi\int_{0}^{\infty} A_1(\omega)A_2(\omega)\cos[\phi_1(\omega)-\phi_2(\omega)]\,d\omega$$
$$(16\text{-}6\text{-}4)$$

If $f_1(t) = f_2(t)$, then, from Eqs. 16-6-1 and 16-6-4,

$$\int_{-\infty}^{+\infty} [f(t)]^2\,dt = 4\pi\int_{0}^{\infty} [A(\omega)]^2\,d\omega \qquad\qquad (16\text{-}6\text{-}5)$$

This is the Fourier integral energy theorem. The left side of Eq. 16-6-5 could represent the integral of the square of the voltage or the current, and would be proportional to the total power. The right side would then also be proportional to the total power. The total energy of the pulse is equal to the integral of its frequency components. The cross product of one frequency with another frequency does not contribute to the power. Only components of the same frequency are multiplied together to produce the increment of power at each frequency.

16-7. Summary. The Fourier transforms may be used to solve circuit problems in much the same way that Laplace transforms are used. The Laplace transforms have an advantage in that poles on the imaginary axis and to the right of the imaginary axis may be used, and the Fourier transforms have the advantage that the whole time axis from minus infinity to plus infinity may be used. When all poles are to the left of the imaginary axis and the time is greater than zero, both methods are equally applicable and the choice seems to rest with the user. Certain problems, however, such as that of Art. 15-4 seem to be much easier to solve with Fourier transforms than with Laplace transforms. Both Fourier and Laplace transforms probably solve the linear problems faster than the classical methods, particularly when a good table of transforms is available. In nonlinear problems, however, resort must be had for the most part to the classical method of solution.

PROBLEMS

16-1. Obtain the result of Eq. 16-1-4 by using the pulse shown in Fig. 16-P-1. Allow t_0 to approach infinity.

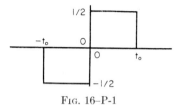

Fig. 16-P-1

16-2. If the switch S were closed at time $t = 0$, using Fourier integrals obtain the expression for the current $i(t)$ in the circuit shown in Fig. 16-P-2. Assume that the capacitor is initially uncharged.

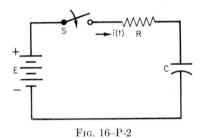

Fig. 16-P-2

16-3. In the circuit of Fig. 16-P-3 the switch S is opened at time $t = 0$. The current I is assumed constant, and the inductor and capacitor are assumed initially to have zero energy stored. Using Fourier integrals, find the voltage $e(t)$.

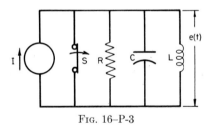

Fig. 16-P-3

16-4. Obtain the circuit whose current response to a unit applied voltage is $(A\epsilon^{-at} \sin bt)u_{-1}(t)$, where A, a, and b are constants.

16-5. A certain circuit has

$$G(\omega) = \frac{A\omega^2}{(\omega^2 + a^2)^2}$$

where A and a are constants. Find the circuit and its current response to a unit applied voltage.

16–6. Find and sketch the frequency spectrum corresponding to the portion of the sinusoidal wave shown in Fig. 16–P-4.

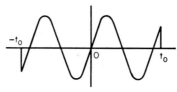

Fig. 16–P-4

16–7. Obtain the frequency spectrum corresponding to a third-order impulse by the use of Fig. 16–5-2c.

16–8. Show that Eq. 16–5-8 follows from Eq. 16–5-7.

16–9. Assume that a current impulse of strength I is passed through a parallel resistance-capacitance circuit. Use the Fourier integral to obtain the voltage across the circuit.

16–10. A voltage has the form $e^{-b^2 t^2}$. Obtain the total power in a 1-ohm resistor by using: (a) the time integral of Eq. 16–6-5; and (b) the frequency integral of Eq. 16–6-5.

APPENDIX

APPENDIX

FOURIER PAIRS

	$f(t) = \int_{-\infty}^{+\infty} \epsilon^{j\omega t} g(\omega)\, d\omega$	$g(\omega) = \int_{-\infty}^{+\infty} \epsilon^{-j\omega t} f(t)\, dt$
1	$1,\ \|t\| < \dfrac{t_0}{2}$ $0,\ \|t\| > \dfrac{t_0}{2}$	$\dfrac{2}{\omega} \sin \dfrac{\omega t_0}{2}$
2	$1,\ t_1 < t < t_2,\ \text{and}\ t < t_1$ $0,\ t > t_2$	$\dfrac{2}{\omega} \epsilon^{-j\omega\left(\frac{t_1+t_2}{2}\right)} \sin \dfrac{\omega}{2}(t_2 - t_1)$
3	$\epsilon^{-t/t_0},\ t > 0,\ t_0 > 0$ $0,\ t < 0$	$\dfrac{t_0}{1 + j\omega t_0}$
4	$\epsilon^{-t/t_0},\ t < 0,\ t_0 > 0$ $0,\ t > 0$	$\dfrac{t_0}{1 - j\omega t_0}$
5	$\epsilon^{-\|t\|/t_0},\ t_0 > 0$	$\dfrac{2 t_0}{1 + \omega^2 t_0^2}$
6	$t\epsilon^{-t/t_0},\ t > 0,\ t_0 > 0$ $0,\ t < 0$	$\dfrac{t_0^2}{(1 + j\omega t_0)^2}$
7	$t\epsilon^{t/t_0},\ t < 0,\ t_0 > 0$ $0,\ t > 0$	$-\dfrac{t_0^2}{(1 - j\omega t_0)^2}$

8	$t\epsilon^{-|t|/t_0},\ t_0 > 0$	$-\dfrac{4\,j\omega t_0^3}{(1+\omega^2 t_0^2)^2}$
9	$|t|\,\epsilon^{-|t|/t_0},\ t_0 > 0$	$\dfrac{2\,t_0^2(1-\omega^2 t_0^2)}{(1+\omega^2 t_0^2)^2}$
10	$\epsilon^{-t/t_0}\sin(\beta t + \theta),\ t > 0,\ t_0 > 0$ $0,\ t < 0$	$\dfrac{t_0[(1+j\omega t_0)\sin\theta + \beta t_0\cos\theta]}{(1+j\omega t_0)^2 + \beta^2 t_0^2}$
11	$\epsilon^{t/t_0}\sin(\beta t + \theta),\ t < 0,\ t_0 > 0$ $0,\ t > 0$	$\dfrac{t_0[(1-j\omega t_0)\sin\theta - \beta t_0\cos\theta]}{(1-j\omega t_0)^2 + \beta^2 t_0^2}$
12	$\epsilon^{-|t|/t_0}\sin(\beta t + \theta),\ t_0 > 0$	$\dfrac{2\,t_0\sin\theta\,(1+\omega^2 t_0^2 + \beta^2 t_0^2) - 4\,j\omega\beta t_0^3\cos\theta}{(1+\omega^2 t_0^2)^2 + 2\,\beta^2 t_0^2(1-\omega^2 t_0^2) + \beta^4 t_0^4}$
13	$\sin(\beta t + \theta),\ |t| < \dfrac{t_0}{2}$ $0,\ |t| > \dfrac{t_0}{2}$	$\dfrac{2(\beta\sin\theta - j\omega\cos\theta)\sin\dfrac{\beta t_0}{2}\cos\dfrac{\omega t_0}{2} + 2\,j\,(\beta\cos\theta + j\omega\sin\theta)\cos\dfrac{\beta t_0}{2}\sin\dfrac{\omega t_0}{2}}{(\beta^2 - \omega^2)}$
14	$\epsilon^{-(t/t_0)^2}$	$t_0\sqrt{\pi}\,\epsilon^{-(\omega t_0/2)^2}$

LAPLACE TRANSFORM FORMULAS

	$F(s)$	$f(t)$	
1	$\dfrac{1}{s}$	$u_{-1}(t)$	
2	$\dfrac{1}{s^n}$, n is a positive integer	$\dfrac{t^{n-1}}{(n-1)!}$	
3	$\dfrac{1}{s+a}$	ϵ^{-at}	
4	$\dfrac{1}{(s+a)^n}$, n is a positive integer	$\dfrac{t^{n-1}\epsilon^{-at}}{(n-1)!}$	
5	$\dfrac{\omega}{s^2+\omega^2}$	$\sin \omega t$	
6	$\dfrac{s}{s^2+\omega^2}$	$\cos \omega t$	
7	$\dfrac{b}{s^2-b^2}$	$\sinh bt$	
8	$\dfrac{s}{s^2-b^2}$	$\cosh bt$	
9	$\dfrac{\omega}{(s+a)^2+\omega^2}$	$\epsilon^{-at}\sin \omega t$	
10	$\dfrac{s+a}{(s+a)^2+\omega^2}$	$\epsilon^{-at}\cos \omega t$	
11	$\dfrac{b}{(s+a)^2-b^2}$	$\epsilon^{-at}\sinh bt$	

12	$\dfrac{s+a}{(s+a)^2 - b^2}$	$\epsilon^{-at}\cosh bt$
13	$\dfrac{a_1 s + a_0}{(s+a)^2 + \omega^2}$	$A\epsilon^{-at}\sin(\omega t + \alpha)$ where $A\,\underline{/\alpha} = \left[\dfrac{a_0 - a_1(a - j\omega)}{\omega}\right]$
14	$\dfrac{a_1 s + a_0}{(s+a)(s+b)}$	$\left(\dfrac{a_0 - a_1 a}{b - a}\right)\epsilon^{-at} + \left(\dfrac{a_0 - b a_1}{a - b}\right)\epsilon^{-bt}$
15	$\dfrac{a_1 s + a_0}{(s+a)^2}$	$[a_1 + (a_0 - a_1 a)t]\epsilon^{-at}$
16	$\dfrac{a_2 s^2 + a_1 s + a_0}{(s+a)(s+b)(s+c)}$	$\dfrac{a_2 a^2 - a_1 a + a_0}{(b - a)(c - a)}\,\epsilon^{-at} + \dfrac{a_2 b^2 - a_1 b + a_0}{(a - b)(c - b)}\,\epsilon^{-bt} + \dfrac{a_2 c^2 - a_1 c + a_0}{(a - c)(b - c)}\,\epsilon^{-ct}$
17	$\dfrac{a_2 s^2 + a_1 s + a_0}{(s+a)^2(s+b)}$	$\left[\dfrac{b(a_1 - 2 a_2 a) + a_2 a^2 - a_0}{(b - a)^2}\right]\epsilon^{-at} + \left(\dfrac{a_2 a^2 - a_1 a + a_0}{b - a}\right)t\epsilon^{-at} + \left[\dfrac{a_2 b^2 - a_1 b + a_0}{(b - a)^2}\right]\epsilon^{-bt}$
18	$\dfrac{a_2 s^2 + a_1 s + a_0}{(s+a)^3}$	$a_2\epsilon^{-at} + (a_1 - 2\,a_2 a)t\epsilon^{-at} + \tfrac{1}{2}(a_2 a^2 - a_1 a + a_0)t^2\epsilon^{-at}$
19	$\dfrac{a_2 s^2 + a_1 s + a_0}{[(s+a)^2 + \omega^2](s+b)}$	$A\epsilon^{-at}\sin(\omega t + \alpha) + \dfrac{a_0 - a_1 b + a_2 b^2}{(a - b)^2 + \omega^2}\,\epsilon^{-bt}$ where $A\,\underline{/\alpha} = \dfrac{a_0 - a_1(a - j\omega) + a_2(a - j\omega)^2}{\omega(b - a + j\omega)}$
20	$\dfrac{a_3 s^3 + a_2 s^2 + a_1 s + a_0}{(s+a)(s+b)(s+c)(s+d)}$	$\dfrac{a_0 - a_1 a + a_2 a^2 - a_3 a^3}{(b - a)(c - a)(d - a)}\,\epsilon^{-at} + \dfrac{a_0 - a_1 b + a_2 b^2 - a_3 b^3}{(a - b)(c - b)(d - b)}\,\epsilon^{-bt}$ $+ \dfrac{a_0 - a_1 c + a_2 c^2 - a_3 c^3}{(a - c)(b - c)(d - c)}\,\epsilon^{-ct} + \dfrac{a_0 - a_1 d + a_2 d^2 - a_3 d^3}{(a - d)(b - d)(c - d)}\,\epsilon^{-dt}$

LAPLACE TRANSFORM FORMULAS (Continued)

	$F(s)$	$f(t)$
21	$\dfrac{a_3 s^3 + a_2 s^2 + a_1 s + a_0}{(s+a)^2(s+b)(s+c)}$	$\dfrac{a_0 - a_1 a + a_2 a^2 - a_3 a^3}{(b-a)(c-a)} t\epsilon^{-at} + \left[\dfrac{a_1 - 2 a_2 a + 3 a_3 a^2}{(b-a)(c-a)} - \dfrac{(a_0 - a_1 a + a_2 a^2 - a_3 a^3)(b+c-2a)}{(b-a)^2(c-a)^2}\right]\epsilon^{-at}$ $+ \dfrac{a_0 - a_1 b + a_2 b^2 - a_3 b^3}{(a-b)^2(c-b)}\epsilon^{-bt} + \dfrac{a_0 - a_1 c + a_2 c^2 - a_3 c^3}{(a-c)^2(b-c)}\epsilon^{-ct}$
22	$\dfrac{a_3 s^3 + a_2 s^2 + a_1 s + a_0}{(s+a)^2(s+b)^2}$	$\dfrac{(a_0 - a_1 a + a_2 a^2 - a_3 a^3)}{(b-a)^2} t\epsilon^{-at} + \dfrac{(a_0 - a_1 b + a_2 b^2 - a_3 b^3)}{(a-b)^2} t\epsilon^{-bt}$ $+ \left\{\dfrac{a_1 - 2 a_2 a + 3 a_3 a^3}{(b-a)^2} - \dfrac{2(a_0 - a_1 a + a_2 a^2 - a_3 a^3)}{(b-a)^3}\right\}\epsilon^{-at}$ $+ \left\{\dfrac{a_1 - 2 a_2 b + 3 a_3 b^2}{(a-b)^2} - \dfrac{2(a_0 - a_1 b + a_2 b^2 - a_3 b^3)}{(a-b)^3}\right\}\epsilon^{-bt}$
23	$\dfrac{a_3 s^3 + a_2 s^2 + a_1 s + a_0}{(s+a)^3(s+b)}$	$\dfrac{a_0 - a_1 a + a_2 a^2 - a_3 a^3}{2(b-a)} t^2\epsilon^{-at} + \dfrac{a_0 - a_1 b + a_2 b^2 - a_3 b^3}{(a-b)^3}\epsilon^{-bt}$ $+ \left[\dfrac{a_1 - 2 a_2 a + 3 a_3 a^2}{b-a} - \dfrac{a_0 - a_1 a + a_2 a^2 - a_3 a^3}{(b-a)^2}\right] t\epsilon^{-at}$ $+ \left[\dfrac{a_2 - 3 a_3 a}{b-a} - \dfrac{a_1 - 2 a_2 a + 3 a_3 a^2}{(b-a)^2} + \dfrac{a_0 - a_1 a + a_2 a^2 - a_3 a^3}{2(b-a)^3}\right]\epsilon^{-at}$
24	$\dfrac{a_3 s^3 + a_2 s^2 + a_1 s + a_0}{(s+a)^4}$	$\tfrac{1}{6}(a_0 - a_1 a + a_2 a^2 - a_3 a^3)t^3\epsilon^{-at} + \tfrac{1}{2}(a_1 - 2 a_2 a + 3 a_3 a^2)t^2\epsilon^{-at} + (a_2 - 3 a_3 a)t\epsilon^{-at} + a_3\epsilon^{-at}$
25	$\dfrac{a_3 s^3 + a_2 s^2 + a_1 s + a_0}{[(s+a)^2 + \omega^2](s+b)(s+c)}$	$A\epsilon^{-at}\sin(\omega t + \alpha) + \dfrac{a_0 - a_1 b + a_2 b^2 - a_3 b^3}{[(a-b)^2 + \omega^2](c-b)}\epsilon^{-bt} + \dfrac{a_0 - a_1 c + a_2 c^2 - a_3 c^3}{[(a-c)^2 + \omega^2](b-c)}\epsilon^{-ct}$ where $A\underline{/\alpha} = \dfrac{a_0 - a_1(a - j\omega) + a_2(a - j\omega)^2 - a_3(a - j\omega)^3}{\omega(b - a + j\omega)(c - a + j\omega)}$

#	Transform	Inverse
26	$\dfrac{a_3 s^3 + a_2 s^2 + a_1 s + a_0}{[(s+a)^2 + \omega^2](s+b)^2}$	$A\epsilon^{-at}\sin(\omega t + \alpha) + \dfrac{a_0 - a_1 b + a_2 b^2 - a_3 b^3}{[(a-b)^2 + \omega^2]}\, t\epsilon^{-bt}$ $+\left\{\dfrac{a_1 - 2a_2 b + 3a_3 b^2}{[(a-b)^2 + \omega^2]} - 2\,\dfrac{(a_0 - a_1 b + a_2 b^2 - a_3 b^3)(a - b)}{[(a-b)^2 + \omega^2]^2}\right\}$ where $A\underline{/\alpha} = \dfrac{a_0 - a_1(a - j\omega) + a_2(a - j\omega)^2 - a_3(a - j\omega)^3}{\omega(b - a + j\omega)^2}$
27	$\dfrac{a_3 s^3 + a_2 s^2 + a_1 s + a_0}{[(s+a)^2 + \omega^2][(s+b)^2 + \sigma^2]}$	$A\epsilon^{-at}\sin(\omega t + \alpha) + B\epsilon^{-bt}\sin(\sigma t + \beta)$ where $A\underline{/\alpha} = \dfrac{a_0 - a_1(a - j\omega) + a_2(a - j\omega)^2 - a_3(a - j\omega)^3}{\omega[(b - a + j\omega)^2 + \sigma^2]}$ $B\underline{/\beta} = \dfrac{a_0 - a_1(b - j\sigma) + a_2(b - j\sigma)^2 - a_3(b - j\sigma)^3}{\sigma[(a - b + j\sigma)^2 + \omega^2]}$
28	$\dfrac{a_3 s^3 + a_2 s^2 + a_1 s + a_0}{[(s+a)^2 + \omega^2]^2}$	$-\dfrac{At\epsilon^{-at}}{2\,\omega^2}\cos(\omega t + \alpha) + 2\,B\,\epsilon^{-at}\cos(\omega t + \beta)$ where $A\underline{/\alpha} = a_0 - a_1(a - j\omega) + a_2(a - j\omega)^2 + a_3(a - j\omega)^3$ $B\underline{/\beta} = \dfrac{a_1 - 2a_2(a - j\omega) + 3a_3(a - j\omega)^2}{(2j\omega)^2} - \dfrac{2[a_0 - a_1(a - j\omega) + a_2(a - j\omega)^2 - a_3(a - j\omega)^3]}{(2j\omega)^3}$
29	$\dfrac{a_4 s^4 + a_3 s^3 + a_2 s^2 + a_1 s + a_0}{(s^2+\omega^2)(s+a)(s+b)(s+c)}$	$\dfrac{a_0 - a_1 a + a_2 a^2 - a_3 a^3 + a_4 a^4}{(a^2+\omega^2)(b-a)(c-a)}\,\epsilon^{-at} + \dfrac{a_0 - a_1 b + a_2 b^2 - a_3 b^3 + a_4 b^4}{(b^2+\omega^2)(a-b)(c-b)}\,\epsilon^{-bt}$ $+\dfrac{a_0 - a_1 c + a_2 c^2 - a_3 c^3 + a_4 c^4}{(c^2+\omega^2)(a-c)(b-c)}\,\epsilon^{-ct} + A\sin(\omega t + \alpha)$ where $A\underline{/\alpha} = \dfrac{a_0 + a_1(j\omega) + a_2(j\omega)^2 + a_3(j\omega)^3 + a_4(j\omega)^4}{\omega(j\omega + a)(j\omega + b)(j\omega + c)}$
30	$\dfrac{a_4 s^4 + a_3 s^3 + a_2 s^2 + a_1 s + a_0}{(s^2+\omega^2)(s+a)^2(s+b)}$	$\dfrac{a_0 - a_1 a + a_2 a^2 - a_3 a^3 + a_4 a^4}{(a^2+\omega^2)(b-a)}\,t\epsilon^{-at} + \dfrac{a_0 - a_1 b + a_2 b^2 - a_3 b^3 + a_4 b^4}{(b^2+\omega^2)(a-b)^2}\,\epsilon^{-bt}$ $+\left[\dfrac{a_1 - 2a_2 a + 3a_3 a^2 - 4a_4 a^3}{(a^2+\omega^2)(b-a)} - \dfrac{(a_0 - a_1 a + a_2 a^2 - a_3 a^3 + a_4 a^4)(\omega^2 - 2ab + 3a^2)}{(a^2+\omega^2)^2(b-a)^2}\right]\epsilon^{-at}$ $+ A\sin(\omega t + \alpha)$ where $A\underline{/\alpha} = \dfrac{a_0 + a_1(j\omega) + a_2(j\omega)^2 + a_3(j\omega)^3 + a_4(j\omega)^4}{\omega(j\omega + a)^2(j\omega + b)}$

LAPLACE TRANSFORM FORMULAS (Continued)

	$F(s)$	$f(t)$
31	$$\dfrac{a_4 s^4 + a_3 s^3 + a_2 s^2 + a_1 s + a_0}{(s^2 + \omega^2)(s + a)^3}$$	$A \sin(\omega t + \alpha) + \dfrac{a_0 - a_1 a + a_2 a^2 - a_3 a^3 + a_4 a^4}{2(a^2 + \omega^2)} t^2 \epsilon^{-at}$ $+ \left[\dfrac{a_1 - 2 a_2 a + 3 a_3 a^2 - 4 a_4 a^3}{a^2 + \omega^2} + \dfrac{2 a(a_0 - a_1 a + a_2 a^2 - a_3 a^3 + a_4 a^4)}{(a^2 + \omega^2)^2} \right] t \epsilon^{-at}$ $+ \left[\dfrac{2 a_2 - 6 a_3 a + 12 a_4 a^2}{a^2 + \omega^2} + \dfrac{4 a(a_1 - 2 a_2 a + 3 a_3 a^2 - 4 a_4 a^3)}{(a^2 + \omega^2)^2} \right.$ $\left. + \dfrac{(6 a^2 - 2 \omega^2)(a_0 - a_1 a + a_2 a^2 - a_3 a^3 + a_4 a^4)}{(a^2 + \omega^2)^3} \right] \epsilon^{-at}$ where $\quad A\underline{/\alpha} = \dfrac{a_0 + a_1(j\omega) + a_2(j\omega)^2 + a_3(j\omega)^3 + a_4(j\omega)^4}{\omega(j\omega + a)^3}$
32	$$\dfrac{a_4 s^4 + a_3 s^3 + a_2 s^2 + a_1 s + a_0}{(s^2 + \omega^2)[(s + a)^2 + \sigma^2](s + b)}$$	$A \sin(\omega t + \alpha) + B \epsilon^{-at} \sin(\sigma t + \beta) + \dfrac{a_0 - a_1 b + a_2 b^2 - a_3 b^3 + a_4 b^4}{(b^2 + \omega^2)[(a - b)^2 + \sigma^2]} \epsilon^{-bt}$ where $A\underline{/\alpha} = \dfrac{a_0 + a_1(j\omega) + a_2(j\omega)^2 + a_3(j\omega)^3 + a_4(j\omega)^4}{\omega[(j\omega + a)^2 + \sigma^2](j\omega + b)}$ $B\underline{/\beta} = \dfrac{a_0 - a_1(a - j\sigma) + a_2(a - j\sigma)^2 - a_3(a - j\sigma)^3 + a_4(a - j\sigma)^4}{\sigma[(a - j\sigma)^2 + \omega^2](b - a + j\sigma)}$

INDEX